5-19-60

EVOLUTION AND CHRISTIAN THOUGHT TODAY

THE EDITOR

RUSSELL L. MIXTER received the B.A. degree from Wheaton College, the M.S. degree from Michigan State University, and the Ph.D. degree from the University of Illinois. He has been very active in the affairs of the American Scientific Affiliation, having served that organization as president and as author of the A.S.A. monograph on *Creation and Evolution*. He is Professor of Zoology at Wheaton College.

EVOLUTION and CHRISTIAN THOUGHT TODAY

V. ELVING ANDERSON
CORDELIA ERDMAN BARBER
WILBUR L. BULLOCK
JAMES O. BUSWELL III
J. FRANK CASSEL
WALTER R. HEARN

RICHARD A. HENDRY
CARL F. H. HENRY
THOMAS D. S. KEY
IRVING W. KNOBLOCH
DONALD S. ROBERTSON
GEORGE K. SCHWEITZER

JOHN C. SINCLAIR

EDITED BY

RUSSELL L. MIXTER

PROFESSOR OF ZOOLOGY
WHEATON COLLEGE

WM. B. EERDMANS PUBLISHING COMPANY
GRAND RAPIDS, MICHIGAN

PRINTED IN THE UNITED STATES OF AMERICA

EDITOR'S PREFACE

Seldom has one voyage made so much impact on men's thinking. The voyage of the *H.M.S. Beagle*, with Charles Darwin aboard, resulted in the publication of a book which has been as significant in scientific circles as the finding of the Americas.

That book is *The Origin of Species*, first published in November of 1859. Its subject is evolution, and Darwin's great contribution to that subject was twofold: he presented new facts, collected on his voyage, to show that species are mutable; and he argued persuasively that the theory of natural selection made these mutations intelligible. As Dr. Henry says in the concluding essay of this book, "It was Darwin's researches and writings that catapulted evolution to recognition as the prevailing scientific conception of nature."

On this centennial of Darwin's monumental work, it is wise to compare the present status of the theory of evolution with the tenets of the Christian faith. The intervening one hundred years have seen arduous work by scientists to refine and establish the theory of evolution, while a far from unanimous reaction has come from the ranks of orthodox Christianity. To establish the exact import of the theory of evolution; to weigh the claims made by its proponents in the light of contemporary research; to re-examine the scriptural data relevant to the questions of origin and organic development — these are the tasks to which the authors of the present symposium have addressed themselves.

This book had its initial stimulus from a local gathering of Christian men of science in California about ten years ago. These men sent a recommendation to the officers of the American Scientific Affiliation, a group of over eight hundred evangelical Christians professionally trained and active in scientific work. As a result of this recommendation, the present editor was appointed at the Affiliation's Colorado Springs annual meeting in 1955. He chose members of the symposium deemed especially qualified to deal with evolution, and asked these men to present papers before a subsequent annual meeting of the Affiliation. Criticisms of the ideas were used in the revised writings, then duplicated copies of each author's work were sent to all the other members of the symposium. After exchange of comments and a minimum amount of revision by the editor, third and final drafts were prepared and sent to the publisher. The publisher's science editor lent further aid in clarifying and emphasizing the basic facts and implications of the evolutionary hypothesis.

Briefly, the pattern of approach in this book is as follows. Chapter 1 is a survey of the influence of Darwinian thought on the various fields of biology, with brief indications of how workers in these fields have reacted to the new doctrine. Views held by Bible scholars are included to show how they attempted to defend the idea of creation. Chapters 2 and 3 deal with origins; the former explains the basis of contemporary theories about the origin of stars, sun, moon, and planets, particularly our earth, on which there were created the biological beings so intimately hemmed in with us in an environment of sunshine, air, and water. The following chapter explains the processes by which these living organisms may have arisen.

As a third major topic, this symposium discusses in Chapter 4 how evolution could have occurred, stressing both the successes and the limitations of hereditary processes. A study of the past suggests change, and genetics seeks to answer how this change could begin and has continued.

The next major topic, discussed in Chapters 5 through 9, is concerned with the areas of thinking which led modern science to accept almost completely the "fact" of evolution. Crossing one kind of animal with another gives a clue to ancestries; fossils hint at the parade of the past; classifying living things suggests a relationship between them; collections of organisms from the continents and islands effectively emphasize the derivation of some species from common sources; and perhaps most convincing of all, the study of comparative anatomy has convinced speculative scientists that the many observed similarities signify kinship.

Naturally most people are concerned about the origin of mankind. Hence, in Chapter 10, an anthropologist peers at the bones and artifacts of early man, presents the varied views about them, and compares scriptural and scientific conclusions.

To conclude this series of searchings into the meaning of evolution, and to climax them, is the chapter on "Theology and Evolution." From the wisdom of the centuries, the eternal doctrines of a changeless God are applied to the implications of evolutionary ideas which have reigned for the comparatively short time of a hundred years.

The reader may or may not agree with the conclusions urged by these authors. This is his privilege, and the respective authors ask only that their presentations be judged without prejudice. Each of them is committed to the evangelical Christian doctrine that the world and its living members are the result of the activity of God as declared in the Holy Scriptures. They do not hold that their views are the only possible ones, but they do maintain that the information they submit is accurate, and that their interpretations are fair to both Christian and scientific principles. These principles, rather than any particular doctrine held by Christians of the past, have been their criteria of judgment.

Considerable credit is due the publishers of this volume, the Wm. B. Eerdmans Publishing Company, for their suggestions and co-operation. And to the many books of many publishers from which our facts have been taken goes our gratitude, for without their works this symposium would not have been possible.

— RUSSELL L. MIXTER

CONTENTS

Editor's Preface   5

List of Illustrations   10

1   THE INFLUENCE OF DARWIN ON BIOLOGY   11
        by Thomas D. S. Key

2   THE ORIGIN OF THE UNIVERSE   33
        by George K. Schweitzer

3   THE ORIGIN OF LIFE   53
        by Walter R. Hearn and Richard A. Hendry

4   GENETICS   71
        by Donald S. Robertson and John C. Sinclair

5   THE ROLE OF HYBRIDIZATION IN EVOLUTION   92
        by Irving W. Knobloch

6   SYSTEMATICS AND SPECIATION   107
        by Wilbur L. Bullock

7   THE DISTRIBUTION OF ANIMALS   123
        by V. Elving Anderson

8   FOSSILS AND THEIR OCCURRENCE   136
        by Cordelia Erdman Barber

9   SIMILARITIES — THE IMPORTANCE OF THE OBVIOUS   154
        by J. Frank Cassel

10 A CREATIONIST INTERPRETATION OF PREHISTORIC MAN   165
        by James O. Buswell, III

11 THEOLOGY AND EVOLUTION   190
        by Carl F. H. Henry

Index   222

List of Contributors   223

LIST OF ILLUSTRATIONS

All illustrations appear at the end of the book, following page 224.

1. Short segment of a helical arrangement of a protein chain.

2. Model of DNA.

3. Tobacco mosaic virus.

4. Tomato bushy stunt virus

5. Bacterial virus of the T-4 strain

6. Behavior of the chromosomes during mitosis

7. Behavior of the chromosomes during meiosis

8. Logarithmic growth curve of a bacterial culture

9. Fertile mule and one of her offspring

10. Fertile genus hybrid

11. Effect of polyploidy on hybridization

12. Adaptive radiation of Darwin's finches

13. Evolution of a group of Mississippian zaphrenthids

14. Homology and adaptation in bones of the left fore limb in land vertebrates

15. Analogy between wings of insects and of vertebrates

16. Series of vertebrate embryos in three successive and comparable stages of development

17. Oceanic vertebrates, showing adaptive convergence for swimming

18. Skulls of Sinanthropus pekinensis and modern northern Chinese: lateral view

19. Two skulls of Figure 18 in front view

20. Two skulls of Figure 18 in occipital view

21. Skull of Australopithecus

22. Australopithecine tooth pattern

10

Chapter One

THE INFLUENCE OF DARWIN ON BIOLOGY

By Thomas D. S. Key

Charles Darwin has had a profound effect upon modern biology. It is the purpose of this chapter to determine some of the effect his concepts have had on modern biology, not primarily to give a moral evaluation of his views. The honest mind will readily recognize that in some cases Darwinism stimulated research in much needed areas. Some of this research was done with the purpose of refuting the concepts he presented, while other research was done to provide confirmation of those concepts. In either event man's knowledge of the world of life was considerably increased. Darwin, it will be seen, helped to break the shackles of superstition in many cases. He also contributed much to biology which had no relation to his evolutionary concept. For example, he revealed to us the value of earthworms to the fertility of the soil, and the origin of atolls.

On the negative side, however, it must be pointed out that regardless of his intentions to the contrary, his evolutionary concepts brought about many dire results. As we shall see, in some cases these concepts acted as a brake against further research. In many instances they resulted in contradictory and incorrect conclusions. Even more serious consequences are to be found in the social, moral, and theological realms, in which man's responsibility to a personal God was seriously questioned.

In surveying the influence of Darwin on biology, we shall look briefly at various branches of biology, at some evolutionary theories, and at several theories of creationism.

DARWIN'S INFLUENCE ON VARIOUS BRANCHES OF BIOLOGY

Influence on Comparative Anatomy and Physiology.

For some time prior to Darwin's *The Origin of Species* (1859) treatises on anatomy were characterized either by descriptions of anatomy interspersed with praises to the Creator for his wisdom, or were purely descriptive. A typical example of the former is Sir Charles Bell's *The Hand*, a classic of comparative anatomy which contains hymns and poems in the midst of its descriptions.

Although Darwin tried to remain aloof from the traditional vitalistic interpretation and its growing struggle with mechanism, the effect of his theory, by its very nature, definitely favored mechanism and helped quickly and effectively to drive the supernatural out of the bulk of biological literature. So effective was the victory of mechanism over vitalism that it has been only in recent years that we have begun to see a revival of vitalism in biological literature, examples of which are such recent works as Lecomte Du Noüy's *Human Destiny* and A. Cressy Morrison's *Man Does Not Stand Alone*.

The concept of homologies was introduced by the eminent British anatomist, Richard Owen, a contemporary of Charles Darwin and one who was strongly opposed to Darwin's theory of natural selection. Homologous organs are those which have the same origin and function in different animals, though they may differ radically in appearance. Examples are the hand of a man, the hand of a monkey, the flipper of a whale, and the forelimb of a bat. The concept of homologies, however, was adopted by the evolutionists themselves as an argument of their own, and has continued to be held by them to the present time. This concept that similarity of organs proves kinship is perhaps Darwin's best known influence on comparative anatomy and physiology. Owen considered homologous organs to exemplify a type or pattern followed by the Creator, while they have been accepted by evolutionists as evidence of the evolutionary kinship of animals. Modern creationists not only accept Owen's view that similarity indicates a common Creator, but they also consider structural similarity to be more or less necessary in similar environments. Thus, lions, monkeys, and men all have lungs because they all live in and breathe the same air.

Prior to the time of Darwin there appears to have been little interest in the so-called "vestigial" or "rudimentary" organs as proof of evolutionary concepts. This is largely attributable to scant knowledge of the functions of any of our organs, and widespread acceptance of creationist views.

The wildfire acceptance of Darwinism produced a skyrocketing interest in biological research in an attempt to defend the newer opinions against the attacks of the theologians. It was this mushrooming interest in anatomy which introduced the concept that our bodies are living museums filled with useless relics of our evolutionary history. In pre-Darwinian times, however, if the use of an organ was unknown, either the organ was ignored, or it was assigned some function more or less arbitrarily (just as Descartes reasoned that the pineal body is the seat of the soul), or it was assumed to have some use not understood at that time, and thus was regarded as deserving of further study. Among scientists today there is more sympathy with the latter point of view. Another view, one which resulted in stagnating research, was that of the more radical followers of Darwin, viz., that organs whose functions were unknown simply had no use, and thus could not have been created by an intelligent Creator. They were merely "leftovers" from our animal ancestors.

A typical case in point is the vermiform appendix of man. We find it mentioned only rarely before Darwin's time, because it was not known to have any use and because it was not considered to be closely related to natural theology. The greatly increased post-Darwinian research sparked interest in those organs whose uses were not known, but unfortunately this research too often ended in labeling those organs "useless." The result was detrimental to biological knowledge. "Useless" organs were commonly considered open and shut cases. It was one thing to discover an unknown organ, but quite another thing to find a use for it, as that was tantamount to doubting the truth of evolution. Thus Darwinism acted as a brake to biological advance.

Fortunately, at the present time research tends to be more objective, so that the list of over 180 vestigial organs compiled by Wedersheim, including such "useless" organs as the pituitary and adrenal glands, has been reduced to only a few whose functions are not known.

With regard to the appendix, in recent years there have appeared with increasing frequency such statements as the following by Sir Arthur Keith from his brochure on the appendix:

> ...an organ which increases in length until the twentieth year, or even until the fiftieth does not merit the name "vestigial."

And Sir Wilfred LeGros Clark of Oxford University says:

> The significance of the vermiform appendix is still obscure, but in view of its rich blood supply it is almost certainly correct to regard it as a specialized and not a degenerate organ.[1]

In a similar vein Professor William L. Straus, Jr., of Johns Hopkins University says:

> There is no longer any justification for regarding the vermiform appendix as a vestigial structure.[2]

Although we still find much in modern evolutionary literature regarding so-called vestigial organs, there is a striking, almost complete, absence of reference to the early Darwinian term "nascent organs" — organs that are evolving up to the state of usefulness. As the British zoologist Douglas Dewar says, "the theory of evolution requires for its proof, not vestigial, but nascent organs, because the

1. Sir Wilfred LeGros Clark, *Early Forerunners of Man* (London: Balliere, 1934), p. 205.
2. William L. Straus, Jr., *Quarterly Review of Biology*, 1947, p. 149.

existence of useless vestiges merely shows that animals may lose organs."[3] The concept of nascent organs is repulsive to much of modern neo-Darwinism as it would imply teleology or purposefulness.

Louis Pasteur rendered a great service to biology and medicine in his experiments showing that spontaneous generation is a concept without foundation in fact — a serious setback for mechanism as well as for those hyper-vitalists who believed that God creates maggots in rotting meat and tadpoles in water.

Darwin himself believed all organisms to be descended from a few common ancestors. There is no record of his insisting that these few common ancestors must have arisen by mere spontaneous generation. Herbert Spencer, however, carried Darwin's idea to its logical extreme, saying that the first life resulted from a "fortuitous concourse of atoms." Spencer's view has become widely accepted; many profess it, however, who seem not to have real faith in it. Thus, the late Professor Paul Lemoine, formerly director of the Museum of Natural History in Paris, spoke of "evolutionists who do not believe in evolution."[4] Professor S. J. Holmes of the University of California said that "Sir Arthur Keith has remarked that 'even our leading biologists and masters of history are evolutionists only from the lip outward.' "[5]

Though Lamarckism was expressed in mechanistic fashion, it was basically vitalistic, since it asserted that animals were innately capable "of modifying their structure, not by direct response to external stimuli but indirectly owing to 'needs' arising in the animal in a psychic way."[6]

Although Darwin was personally neutral in the question of vitalism versus mechanism, his works on natural selection were basic to the swing toward mechanism. His concepts opposed the vitalistic concept that the organic realm is distinct from the inorganic, that organisms have special qualities not derived from physical and chemical laws. In spite of this, Darwin appealed to vitalism for the special creation of original life (see conclusion of *The Origin of Species*) and for certain tendencies of animal behavior. Further, he refused to discuss the origin of the primary mental powers.[7]

The growth of animal (or comparative) psychology, a branch of

3. Dewar, *More Difficulties of the Evolution Theory* (London: Thynne, 1938), p. 51.

4. Lemoine, *Encyclopedie Francaise*, V (1939), 5.

5. Holmes, *Science*, Aug. 11, 1939, p. 117.

6. L. R. Wheeler, *Vitalism: Its History and Validity* (London: H. F. G. Witherby, 1939), p. 200.

7. Charles Darwin, *The Origin of Species by Means of Natural Selection*, with additions and corrections from the 6th and last English edition, two vols. in one (New York: Appleton, 1905), I, 319.

physiology, was sparked by the compiling of information to supply both sides of the controversy between the Darwin-inspired, mechanistic Thomas Huxley and his vitalistic opponents. For some time after the publication of Darwin's *The Origin of Species,* the heretofore neglected field of animal psychology became contaminated by much exaggerated material attempting to bridge the gap between the mind of man and that of the lower animals. Not only subsequent evolutionists, but also Darwin himself attempted such explanations.[8]

INFLUENCE ON EMBRYOLOGY.

In his *The Origin of Species* Darwin discusses the similarity between embryos of different animals, and agrees with Von Baer's suggestion that this indicates evolutionary relationship. From this discussion Ernst Haeckel derived his concept that developing animals actually repeat in condensed form the evolutionary sequence of their ancestors. This precept is known as the Biogenetic Principle or the Recapitulation Theory, commonly expressed by the statement, "ontogeny recapitulates phylogeny," or, "the development of the individual repeats the evolution of the race."

Unfortunately, Haeckel was so eager to convince the world of Darwinian evolution that he did not always adhere to the truth. As Nordenskiöld says of him,

> Haeckel was never a specialist in embryology and its points of detail were of no interest to him in themselves, but only in so far as they could serve as evidence to prove the descent of man. His ideas of embryology could in such circumstances only be one-sided and deficient; the professional embryologists offered serious objections to them, which he either affected to overlook or else answered with personal abuse. Complaints were made especially against his illustrations, which, contrary to usual practice, he hardly ever borrowed from monographs on the subject, but drew himself. Being designed exclusively to prove one single assertion, his illustrations were naturally extremely schematic and without a trace of scientific value, sometimes indeed so far divergent from the actual facts as to cause him to be accused of deliberate falsification — an accusation that a knowledge of his character would have at once refuted.[9]

Haeckel's influence popularized Darwinian evolution on the Continent, and shifted embryological investigation into evolutionary lines. Two dissenters, His (1831-1904) and Kleinenberg (1842-1897), who favored a more physiological approach, were not well accepted until the more recent mechanical theories came into vogue.[10]

Several pertinent quotations depict recent thinking: Sir Arthur Keith has said,

---

8. Washburn, *The Animal Mind* (New York: Macmillan, 1916), pp. 13-14.
9. Erik Nordenskiöld, *The History of Biology* (New York: Tudor, 1928), p. 517.
10. *Ibid.,* pp. 529-533.

It was expected that the embryo would recapitulate the features of its ancestors from the lowest to the highest forms in the animal kingdom. Now that the appearances of the embryo at all stages are known, the general feeling is one of disappointment; the human embryo at no stage is anthropoid in its appearance.[11]

Nordenskiöld says,

In fact, the entire "biogenetic principle" is nowadays severely challenged, even as a hypothesis; in the vegetable kingdom it has received no confirmation, which is indeed strange for a theory proposed to hold good as a general explanation of life, but even those zoologists who in general give any support at all to the recapitulation theory do so with considerable reservations, called for by the results of modern hereditary research and experimental biology.[12]

The leading embryology texts today either ignore the recapitulation theory altogether, or if they mention it, they do so only in a negative way.[13]

INFLUENCE ON PALEONTOLOGY.

During the Dark Ages the established Church fostered the notion that fossils were the result of any or several of the following causes:[14] (1) creations by the devil to fool mankind; (2) creations by God to test true believers; (3) creations by God to confirm unbelievers in their unbelief; (4) mineral deposits whose resemblance to living organisms were coincidental; and (5) results of spontaneous generation.

Some pre-Darwinians such as Cuvier, however, considered fossils to be genuine animal and plant remains, though a number of curious explanations were expressed as to *how* they became fossils. Several theories adopted some form of catastrophism, that is, the view that some disastrous event or series of events occurred that suddenly annihilated some or all of life. Although the concept that fossils were the actual remains of animals and plants of the past was held by some pre-Darwinians, Darwin served to confirm this concept more firmly than anyone prior to his time. This was certainly a valuable contribution to science.

Darwin's defeat of the traditional catastrophic interpretation of fossils by clearly demonstrated facts permitted development of a number of concepts which have since either died out or are losing influence at the present time. These include both Eimer's ortho-

11. Sir Arthur Keith, *The Human Body* (London: T. Butterworth, 1932), p. 92.
12. Nordenskiöld, *op. cit.,* p. 519.
13. For example: L. B. Arey, *Developmental Anatomy* (6th ed.; Philadelphia: Saunders, 1954); L. G. Barth, *Embryology* (New York: Dryden Press, 1949); W. Shumway and F. B. Adamstone, *Introduction* to Vertebrate Embryology (New York: Wiley, 1954).
14. Andrew D. White, *A History of the Warfare Between Science and Theology in Christendom* (New York: Braziller, 1955), I, 27, 28, 210-241.

genesis, which is accepted to some extent by a number of paleontologists today, and which asserts that organisms have an innate tendency forcing them to evolve along a straight, unvarying path; and Dollo's Law of Irreversibility of Evolution, which asserts that a specialized organism will never again return to the generalized condition, and that once an organ has been lost in evolution it can never be regained.

Darwinism greatly stimulated research for transitional forms or "missing links" (a term seldom used by present-day scientists) as evidences for the theory of evolution. A number of fossil links between modern man and his assumed animal forebears began to appear, some of which have since been rejected, for example, Nebraska Man, Palestine Man, and Piltdown Man, while others are still more or less accepted as valid. The exposure of Piltdown Man, especially, caused quite a stir when it was publicized in 1953 by Weiser, Oakley, and Clark as a deliberate hoax.[15]

In regard to the lack of really conclusive fossil evidence for the evolution of all organisms from a few common ancestors, that is, a fossil record showing all transitional stages, Darwin suggested questions and explanations which are still in vogue among modern defenders of evolution:

> Why . . . is not every geological formation and every stratum full of . . . intermediate links? . . . The explanation lies, as I believe, in the extreme imperfection of the geological record. . . . We continually overrate the perfection of the geological record, and falsely infer, because certain genera or families have not been found beneath a certain stage, that they did not exist before that stage."[16]

Darwin's views regarding paleontological evidence for evolution were based on two assumptions, that there had been many linking stages, and that the reason for these stages not being found was due to incompleteness of the fossil record.

It would be well for creationists to remember that modern evolutionists do not ordinarily assert that permanent, distinctive species changes are taking place visibly or have done so to any significant extent even during the whole of man's recorded history. Paleontologists point out that man's recorded history compares to the total existence of all life on the earth much as the thickness of a dime would compare to the height of the Empire State Building. Therefore

15. Weiner, Oakley, and Clark, "The Solution of the Piltdown Problem," *Bulletin of the British Museum of Natural History, Geology,* II, No. 3 (1953).

16. Darwin, *op. cit.,* II, 49, 77. See Dunbar, *Historical Geology* (New Haven: Yale University Press, 1956); Emmons, Thiel, Stauffer, Allison, *Geology* (New York: McGraw-Hill, 1955), p. 4; Moore, *Introduction to Historical Geology* (1949), see index; Von Engeln, *Geology* (1952), see index.

we can draw no conclusions from what we have seen after man's appearance on earth.

Modern creationists often point out that fossils indicate: (1) wide gaps between kinds (as between whales and land mammals) ; (2) sudden appearance of new and distinct forms (as with Cambrian Period) ; (3) fixity of type in many cases (as insects) ; (4) limited variation in many cases (as coiling in Gastropods, rib number in horses, etc.) . G. K. Hebbert, British entomologist, has said, "The evidence of fossils very definitely favors creation and not the evolution theory."[17]

INFLUENCE ON TAXONOMY.

Although the branch of modern biology dealing with classification was begun by the Swedish botanist Linnaeus (1707-1778) , a devout Lutheran who believed each species to be directly created by God, his system came to be used by the evolutionists as evidence of kinship, rather than of the orderliness of God. Linnaeus' system has undergone very little basic modification by the present evolutionary school of biology. The present system of classification is based on Linnaeus' work, but evolutionists altered it to the extent that the order in nature is no longer attributed to God but to progressive evolutionary divergence. Thus the term "cat family" (or family *Felidae*) no longer means merely a group of animals with certain "cat-like" features as conceived by Linnaeus, but now also implies a relationship of descent from a common ancestor, based primarily on structural similarity.

Mayr, in his *Systematics and the Origin of Species,* points out that today when there is a question about the classification of an organism on the basis of its characteristics, taxonomists try to discern the simplest and most reasonable evolutionary path required, and classify the organism on that basis. As this method of classification is based on theoretical paths which cannot be confirmed by observation, and as taxonomists differ widely in their ideas of the paths evolution has followed, this method is losing emphasis, particularly among botanists, in favor of what Mayr refers to as a more practical system based on the characteristics of organisms.

While evolutionists consider the fact that organisms can be classified in a logical, progressive order as evidence of evolution, creationists consider this pattern as evidence of the orderliness of our Creator, and point to the wide taxonomic gaps separating each phylum, etc., as necessitating special creation, and to the wide discrepancies between phylogenetic trees as evidence that taxonomy does not favor evolution.

17. G. K. Hebbert, *A Biologist's Views on Evolution* (Stoke, Hayling Island, England: The Evolution Protest Movement), p. 5.

INFLUENCE ON ECOLOGY.

The branch of biology dealing with organisms in their relation to their environment became a recognized and independent science partly as a result of Darwin's own studies of the environment. It was, however, left to Haeckel to name it. He called it "ecology" from the Greek *oikos*, meaning "home," and *logos*, meaning "a study."[18] Darwin and his contemporaries early developed for ecology some of its major avenues of study, namely, geographic distribution, transportation of seeds, barriers limiting the ranges of organisms, climatic influences, behavior of animals in reaction to their environment, parasitism, and so on.

One immediate effect of Darwinism was to stimulate investigation and research both by scientists who were sympathetic and those who were inimical to Darwin's views. Thus rapid growth of knowledge resulted in a progressive defeat for numerous animistic superstitions and related ideas about snakes being morally wicked and universally injurious, black cats signifying bad luck, ornithomancy or fortune-telling by the flight of birds, grossly exaggerated wisdom attributed to animals, and other such ideas. While it helped defeat superstition, Darwinism popularized the idea that all Nature is characterized by an almost constant, violent struggle for survival — an idea with serious economic and political consequences for this century.[19] This idea, once set forth by Darwin, has remained dominant ever since, though in the past few years, largely under the influence of W. C. Allee and his colleagues, the idea is being modified to the extent that today:

(a) In most cases "struggle" is not considered necessarily deliberate or violent, but passive or moderate competition, for example, where the food supply is less than the demand, or in the competition of plants for a given area; and

(b) Co-operation is regarded as a highly significant factor in Nature, being essential to forms which live in colonies, as well as in such commensalistic relationships as that between the remora fish and the shark. Particularly is co-operation essential in symbiosis, even to the extent of vital dependence of each species upon the other. For example, in lichens a fungus and an alga unite to form a colony of individuals absolutely dependent upon both species. This same mutual dependence occurs between the termite and its intestinal flagellates in which either would die without the other. Co-operation is also essential in such functions as parental care of young and in gathering together into packs or herds for hunting or for mutual protection.

18. Nordenskiöld, *op. cit.*, p. 514.
19. *Ibid.*, pp. 507ff.

Thus we see that modern biology has come to consider both competition and co-operation as keys to understanding Nature.

THE RISE AND FALL OF VARIOUS EVOLUTIONARY THEORIES

Contrary to popular assumption, there is not just one way of looking at organic evolution. It has been commonly said that there are almost as many variations of the evolutionary concept, the path it has followed, its causes, its relation to the supernatural, and even the specific definition of the term "evolution," as the number of scientists discussing it.

The idea of evolution itself has been evolving since long before Darwin's day, and is still changing to such an extent that all who are concerned with the subject must study considerable current literature to see what evolutionists are saying today. For creationists to judge modern ideas of evolution on the basis of what evolutionists said a generation or more ago would be about as valid as for one to evaluate modern brain or cardiovascular surgery by what he knew of it as practiced in 1918.

Among the more prominent evolutionary theories during the past century have been the following:

VIEWS CONCERNING THE RELATION OF EVOLUTION TO THE SUPERNATURAL.

Many biologists of our time appear to think it unscholarly to discuss publicly the possibility of the relation of evolution to supernatural guidance; yet upon examination of the problem it does seem apparent that there are several distinct concepts of the relationship:

Atheistic Evolution — the idea that there is no God and that natural laws thus necessarily originated by chance. This purely mechanistic outlook is frequently assumed and even frankly professed in textbooks, technical papers, and lectures on biology today. Atheism took immediate advantage of Darwin's explanation of the origin of species by purely natural means, and rose to the climax of its influence in the last part of the nineteenth century. In recent years we have been experiencing a revival of militant atheistic evolutionism. It appears to offer the advantage of explaining Nature apart from the necessity of requiring a God who expects the submission of human will. On the other hand, the view faces such difficulties as have been frequently summarized in the statements "design implies a Designer" and "a machine requires a Machinist."

Deistic Evolution — the belief that the evolutionary processes are more or less intermittently controlled by an impersonal Mind behind the universe — directed by one who is concerned only with events, not with individuals. One commonly encounters this belief in secular and some church-related educational institutions today about as frequently as it has been encountered in the past.

Deistic evolution takes the middle of the road and offers the advantage of avoiding the objections from design, mentioned above, as well as the inconsistencies of theistic evolution, discussed below. It has the advantage of not having to rely on references to God except to overcome serious difficulties of the origin of life, physiological and anatomical difficulties facing evolution, the present neutral and degenerative trend of mutations, and like problems. The theory faces some serious difficulties, however. It would be inconsistent for the Creator to expend the effort to produce this complex universe, and then fail to have a vital personal interest in it. Further, while it is true that the immensity of the stars dwarfs human beings to insignificance, it is also true that man dwarfs the microscopic world and stands in inverse relation to it as he stands to the astronomical world. Thus one might well say that "man is the mean between the microcosm and the macrocosm," or "man is approximately the average-sized object in the universe." If size is any criterion of the Creator's interest, it would seem that man is in the very center of his thoughts.

Theistic Evolution — the belief that God personally directs the evolutionary processes much as a chess player directs his chessmen. This view is growing rapidly today, and is taught largely in church-related schools as well as from many pulpits, and in many public schools in communities with a strong religious background. Various degrees of it are found in the writings of Robert Chambers and A. R. Wallace as well as in the writings of such thoroughly orthodox theologians as A. H. Strong and James Orr, and others who also consider the Bible and evolution to be mutually consistent. Many theistic evolutionists see no difficulty whatever between believing in both evolution and the Bible so long as evolution is considered a God-guided process.

Theistic evolution has the advantage of wearing the garb of Christianity or another theism, though some object to it on the ground that it makes God, as the director of evolution, seem just as interested in the mating of dogs and of grasshoppers as in the redemption of mankind. Theistic evolution also encounters difficulties in harmonizing its views with the literal creation of Adam (Gen. 2:7), the necessarily obvious literal creation of Eve from Adam's side (Gen. 2:21-22), the account of man's willful moral fall from an original state of innocence and perfection (Gen. 3), the numerous biblical implications that the human species descended from only a single pair of parents, the problem of human antiquity (i.e., can biblical history be stretched to permit man's origin over one million years ago?), the intelligence and accomplishments of Adam and his immediate descendants (Gen. 2:20; 3:23; 4:2; 4:17-22), and similar difficulties.

Some have objected to theistic evolution (sometimes known as Christian evolution) on the ground that "the truth shall make you free" (John 3:32), whereas belief in evolution often results in moral, spiritual, social, and political chaos. Any kind of ultimate truth should elevate man, whereas belief in evolution has resulted in such blights as Nazism, Communism, some of the "robber-baron" capitalists of the past century, and much of modern materialistic living. Dampier makes the following comment about the effects of Darwinism on mankind:

> And it was in Germany that Darwin's explanation of evolution by the principle of natural selection, when accepted by Haeckel and other biologists, went to build up a thoroughgoing *Darwinismus* and most strongly reinforced the materialist tendencies in both philosophy and political theory, the latter being used by some as a basis for the ideas of communism.[20]

Pantheistic Evolution — the concept that as Nature evolves, so God also evolves, because God is all and all is God. God and Nature are one and the same. Pantheism is more typical of Oriental thinking and therefore pantheistic evolution has never become commonly accepted in Western countries. While pantheistic evolution does seem to answer some theological questions regarding God's omnipresence, it faces the inconsistency — in the light of violence in nature — of making God the merciless killer as well as the helpless victim.

Agnostic Evolution — noncommittal in regard to the supernatural. We are told that "we cannot know of a certainty the part God plays in evolution, or even if there is a God. Some facts do seem to imply divine wisdom, and possibly even personal interest, while others seem to contradict this. The facts are not decisive enough to warrant dogmatism about the First Cause." Because of the uncertainty which characterizes this theory of evolution, it has not had as wide appeal as some of the other views. Its primary appeal is to intellectuals; its primary weakness is that, being noncommittal, it provides no real answer to the problem.

VIEWS CONCERNING THE MECHANICS OF EVOLUTION.

Inheritance of Acquired Characteristics (Lamarck) — the theory that environment-caused effects are passed on to offspring. For example, giraffes are said to have obtained long necks by constant stretching for the leaves of trees, and snakes are said to have lost their

20. Sir William Dampier, *A Shorter History of Science* (New York: Meridian, 1957), p. 126.

original legs by wearing them off while escaping from birds by running through knotholes. This idea was superseded in Western thinking by Darwin's work, although up through the middle of this century it has been held in high esteem by communist scientific circles. If inheritance of acquired characters were a sound principle, one would expect to find cocker spaniels born with short tails, as their naturally long tails have been customarily bobbed for years. One might expect some hereditary effect of the Jewish and Moslem custom of circumcision, which has been practiced for many centuries, yet it must be repeated in each generation. For centuries the Chinese had the custom of binding their women's feet, yet the custom has left no detectable hereditary effects on any of the succeeding generations.

Atrophy Through Disuse (Lamarck) — closely related in substance, and in weakness, to the Lamarckian principle discussed above is the idea that a trait possessed but not used by the immediate ancestors is not inherited by the offspring. Vestigial organs are sometimes taken as substantiation of this concept.

Natural Selection (Darwin) — overpopulation and consequent scarcity of food result in a struggle in which the fittest survive, this process bringing about progressive modification of the species. This is the theory for which Darwin is best known. Though it rapidly became widely accepted, it has since its introduction undergone modification in various directions, these modifications being known collectively as neo-Darwinism. Most modern Western biologists go beyond Darwin's understanding in an emphasis on heredity, while the Russian Communistic world stresses the environmental aspect. The principle of natural selection as put forth by Charles Darwin was greatly admired by such men as Hitler and Marx, and according to numerous of their own writings, was a significant factor in the forming of the Nazi and Communist philosophies.

According to natural selection, the strongest, most experienced animal gets the most prey. But, as summarized by Hugo de Vries, the Dutch botanist and originator of the mutation theory, the main weakness of natural selection is that "natural selection may explain the survival of the fittest, but it cannot explain the arrival of the fittest."

Sexual Selection (Darwin) — the theory which attempted to explain why males and females of some species are so different from each other by asserting that the fastest, most colorful, strongest, most fertile, most ornate, or most intelligent rivals for potential mates will be the ones to reproduce most frequently, and thus will be most likely to pass on their traits to future members of the species.

This theory failed to gain as wide acclaim as did natural selection, partly because the latter was of more basic and universal application while the former primarily dealt with secondary sex traits in some dimorphic species. Darwin himself considered that sexual selection played only a minor supplementary role. It seems evident that these factors were responsible for the rarity of references to the theory in current literature. The same difficulty found by de Vries in the theory of natural selection could apply equally to sexual selection. Thus sexual selection may explain the maintenance of sex differences, but it cannot offer an adequate explanation of how sex traits originated in the first place.

Pangenesis (Darwin) — the hypothesis proposed by Darwin to attempt a harmony between his own and Lamarck's views. Realizing that his two selection theories merely explained effects on traits already present and did not present a cause of needed traits, Darwin reasoned that he must rely on the old Lamarckian idea of the origin of structures by inheritance of acquired characters. Darwin conceived the notion that every part of the body produces tiny "gemmules." Inheritance of acquired characters is brought about when these gemmules become affected by the environment, and afterwards migrate to the reproductive organs. There they unite with the gemmules of one's mate, and thus determine the heredity of the offspring. Darwin believed that his pangenesis idea accounted for the fact that progeny resemble their ancestors, and that pangenesis filled in the serious gap left by natural selection — namely, how *new* organs originate in the first place. Darwin's theory of natural selection could at best only suggest how the organs might improve within narrow limits, not how they might have originated.

Pangenesis proved to be even less of a success than did sexual selection, for as a result of the findings of Mendel and his successors in genetics, gemmule had to give way to gene. Today, one hundred years after the publication of *The Origin of Species,* we rarely ever encounter even the mention of the theory of pangenesis. Modern Western evolutionists rely upon the much more sound concept that the traits to be selected originate, not by inheritance of acquired characters, but by mutation, and that they are carried by genes and chromosomes, not by any imaginary "gemmules."

Orthogenesis (Eimer) — a term which has become vague. Originally the term referred to a conceived tendency for organisms to evolve along a consistent, straight path. Thus, horses are believed to have lost toes in their descent from their unknown original ancestor with an assumed five on each foot, to *Eohippus* with four on the front feet and three on the hind feet, to *Mesohippus* with three on all feet, to *Protohippus* with three toes on all feet (the outer toes being reduced), to the modern *Equus* with only one toe on each foot plus two splints on a metacarpal and metatarsal. Other examples commonly cited are the tendency for longer trunks in the history of the elephant and the increase in coiling in gastropods (snails and their relatives).

The orthogenesis hypothesis spread rapidly among geologists and paleontologists especially during the last part of the last century. Though it came to be propounded by such notable biologists as Professor D. M. S. Watson, it never acquired the prominence of Darwin's natural selection. This was in spite of the fact that many scientists thought that natural selection was not adequate to stand alone.

Eimer's orthogenesis suffered a setback and eventual complete modification by the genetic discoveries in the first half of the twentieth century, but not the decisive defeat that Darwin's pangenesis suffered. Though some paleontologists today still cling to Eimer's original concept of an innate compelling tendency to evolve along a straight path, modern genetics finds no such hereditary tendency. Orthogenesis was further defeated by lack of sufficient decisive examples. True, the horse, the elephant, the snail, and a few others appeared to be examples, but such examples seemed to be the exception to the rule of indeterminate variation, or sheer coincidence. And upon further examination of these very examples it was seen that orthogenesis was inadequate to account for them, for while horses lost in numbers of toes from their ancestors to present-day horses, they varied back and forth in various structures such as rib number.[21]

In spite of the essential defeat of Eimer's original view, the term orthogenesis is perpetuated today primarily in reference to striking examples of a straight path followed for a short time by a given organ — not to an innate hereditary tendency forcing the direction of inheritance of the whole organism.

Mutationism (de Vries). As biologists became more aware of laws of heredity, it became progressively more evident that species must do more than simply "improve" by a mere selection of the fit. It was discovered that in order to acquire new organs a species must acquire new genes (hereditary determiners inside each cell). How could this happen in the light of the hereditary law that "like begets like"? Hugo de Vries, the Dutch botanist mentioned, noted what appeared to be rare but striking exceptions to the "like begets like" law. He noticed that some evening primroses did not look just like their parents; yet their progeny continued to produce the new traits. Although the behavior of his primroses has since been judged by the Swedish geneticist Heribert-Nilsson as exemplifying normal variation of traits originally existing in the species, de Vries thought that he

21. See G. G. Simpson, *The Meaning of Evolution* (New York: The American Library, 1951), pp. 30-34.

was seeing evolution in its normal action, and that evolution occurs, not gradually as Darwin believed, but visibly and suddenly in great jumps. Many genuine examples of hereditary changes have since been found on the gene level, and are known variously as saltations, mutations, mutants, sports, and "freaks."

In spite of the fact that de Vries' mutationism (announced in 1901) was closer to the crux of the problem than any preceding theory, dealing as it did with genetics and mutations, it never succeeded in becoming completely established. De Vries intended only to supplement natural selection, not to supplant it.

Although mutationists could rally such noteworthy examples as the Shetland pony, Kentucky wonder bean, change in eye color in the fruit fly (Drosophila), and others, they were faced with a growing number of insistent problems such as the following: (1) the number of original mutations of all kinds is extremely low; (2) beneficial mutations are far less common than neutral, harmful, or fatal ones; and (3) mutations have never been observed to produce new organs.[22]

Today de Vries' idea that species give rise suddenly in one generation to completely distinct species is essentially outmoded, being replaced with a kind of "neo-de Vriesian" view that mutations do occur suddenly, but that virtually all of them, except the fatal ones, are of such slight significance that it might take several hundreds of mutations to bring about transformation into a distinct species. Actually this new concept is combined today with natural selection to form the basis of much of modern neo-Darwinism, today's most commonly accepted theory. This view asserts that Nature selects the fittest few mutations to survive, and eliminates the mass of harmful ones for the evolution of one species into another. There has been offered, however, no sound explanation for new organs arising by mutations. The tendency is simply to assume that such radical and closely coordinated mutations have occurred.

Modern Synthetic Western View of Evolutionary Mechanics. Because of the tremendous number of scientific discoveries in the past century having a bearing on evolution, evolutionists have had to modify their positions considerably since the publication of Darwin's epochal works. One century after his most significant publication we find hardly any biologists relying entirely on even Darwin's best theory, natural selection, as *the* explanation of how evolution has come about — to say nothing of his theory of sexual selection and his

22. The same can be said of organ products. Cf. C. D. Turner, *General Endocrinology* (Philadelphia, Saunders, 1949), p. 10. "Pathologic endocrine tissues may produce excessive or deficient amounts of their respective hormones, but they are not known to produce chemically abnormal kinds of hormones."

grossly erroneous pangenesis theory. "Darwinism" is no longer an exact synonym of "evolution."

Because of an increasing feeling that no one theory of evolutionary mechanics can stand alone, there has been in recent years a growing tendency to attempt to combine the strong points of various theories and to eliminate the weaker ones.

Although this synthetic view is growing rapidly today, replacing others by incorporating their conceived virtues and reducing their faults, it is still too much in its early development to make a detailed description of it, or to give it an adequate and simple name, or to attribute its conception to any one man. We must remember that even Darwin tried to correlate his own and Lamarck's views in his pangenesis.

While Darwin's natural selection hypothesis can be summarized as overpopulation, struggle for existence, and survival of the fittest, in general it may be stated that modern Western biologists as a whole believe something like the following regarding the manner of evolution:

(1) Genetic recombination occurs whenever an egg is fertilized, shuffling traits already in existence.

(2) Random mutations arise spontaneously from time to time that add new hereditary traits to the species. Some of these are fatal, many are harmful, and many are merely neutral — that is, neither beneficial nor harmful — and a very few of all mutations are beneficial. Most are somewhat similar to the normal (or "wild type"), though some may be radical departures from the normal.

(3) Natural selection tends to eliminate those genetic recombinations and random mutations that do not adjust to environmental demands, and to favor reproduction of those which do fit environmental demands. Thus, in time a population shift will be brought about. Natural selection may not be limited to violent struggles between organisms, as supposed by many of Darwin's early disciples, but often includes adaptability to changing physical factors such as drought, cold weather, etc.

(4) Speciation occurs when the traits of a population shift so far from the original ones that reproduction can no longer take place between earlier and later varieties, or when anatomical and other differences are pronounced.

Most modern creationists would agree with each of the above factors, but would insist that while species can lose some traits and gain new ones, the fluctuations in any genus or family are extremely limited. A creationist can consider the foregoing four points as the Creator's means of giving to each organism a limited ability to adapt to changing environments.

It is interesting to note that evolutionists have failed to demonstrate satisfactorily in detail how there could possibly be functional stages between, for example, the flipper of a whale and the legs of its supposed land ancestor.

VIEWS CONCERNING THE PATH EVOLUTION IS BELIEVED TO HAVE TAKEN.

As these are far too numerous and relatively of much less significance to the purposes of this book than are the preceding and following topics, they will only be suggested here.

One pertinent change has been made during the past one hundred years in the traditional concept, "from ameba to man." Protozoologists no longer consider the ameba to be the simplest animal. For a number of pertinent reasons it has been replaced by the flagellate. Flagellate protozoa are considered to have come from flagellate bacteria, and they in turn from virus-like DNA (desoxyribonucleic acid) molecules, and these eventually from inorganic molecules.

Another concept, that of indeterminism, proposed for the physical sciences by Heisenberg, is rapidly making itself felt in the biological sciences, tending to replace orthogenetic and many theistic evolutionary concepts of innate upward tendencies with the concept of random variation in all directions.

Divergence is a similar concept, referring to a group of organisms giving rise to varied stocks. This is not a recent concept, being termed "embranchment" by Lamarck and "divergence" by Darwin. H. F. Osborn used the term "adaptive radiation" to describe the same thing, and was the first to state it clearly as a law.[23] The term as coined by Darwin is well established by this time.

The converse of divergence is the concept of convergence, or parallel evolution. This refers to examples of unrelated organisms which have become similar to each other. For example, cave animals are typically pale colored, have degenerate eyes, and have slender bodies. These features may be seen in such unrelated forms as cave insects, cave salamanders, and cave fish.

Darwin as well as his predecessors agreed that organisms might follow the downward path of degeneration. Notable examples of such degenerative evolution would be such parasitic forms as the tapeworm, hookworm, and pinworm, all of which are said to have lost their ancestral power of locomotion. Though the concept of retrogression has become well established in "orthodox" evolutionary thought, it is sometimes distasteful to some schools of theistic evolu-

---

23. See Osborn's "The Law of Adaptive Radiation," *American Naturalist*, XXXVI (1902), 353-363; Moon, Mann, Otto, *Modern Biology* (1956), see index for "ameba"; Winchester, *Biology* (1949), see index; Milne and Milne, *The Biotic World and Man* (1952), see index; Chandler, *Introduction to Parasitology* (9th ed.; 1955), see index.

tion (primarily clergymen) and is usually ignored by the adherents of orthogenesis (certain geologists). The notion typically held by the latter two groups, that organisms have an innate tendency to evolve upward, has by now been fairly well abandoned by biologists in general.

An array of specific theories has been proposed regarding the origin of birds, mammals, reptiles, fish, and all other classes of both plants and animals. It seems noteworthy that no one of the detailed phylogenetic schemes which has been suggested has become universally accepted. It is interesting to note in this connection that the subphylum *Vertebrata* has been theorized to have arisen from practically every one of the invertebrate phyla, with a number of evidences listed in support of each view. As we stand at present, most evolutionists consider that the detailed path evolution has taken probably will never be known, though future investigation should reveal more detail than we now know.

Creationists are not at all surprised by this complete perplexity of the evolutionists in trying to determine the path of evolution, as illustrated by the wide differences between the evolutionists' phylogenetic trees. Creationists consider this as a result of the fact that each class is an independent, orderly creation, distinct from all other classes of organisms.

A SURVEY OF THE INFLUENCE OF DARWINISM ON CREATIONIST CONCEPTS

Darwin's influence on evangelical Christian concepts of creation is worthy of attention at this point. It would be impractical to discuss here in any detail the several score of theories that have been proposed, attempting to harmonize the creation account of the Bible with scientific concepts. From among these we have selected several for brief examination.

Although some "new evangelicals" have come to embrace some degree of theistic evolution, the majority of conservatives, evangelicals, and fundamentalists still adhere to one or another of a number of theories of special creation. We shall not take time here to discuss some of the more naive theories of creation, as they can be encountered easily enough elsewhere. Here we shall concern ourselves with a few typical views held by some Bible-believing Christians who have an understanding of factual discoveries of science. Among these orthodox believers are included scientists, theologians, and laymen in both fields. Darwin's primary effect on these orthodox cosmologies was to rid them of naiveness, and to force evangelicals to search for intelligent, sound reasons for their beliefs (I Peter 3:15). Briefly stated, some principal views are these:

PROGRESSIVE CREATIVE CATASTROPHISM THEORY.

There is an implied gap of an indefinite but vast expanse of time between Genesis 1:1 and 1:2, during which time the geological ages occurred — the ages in which God created the dinosaurs and other prehistoric creatures in the progressive order indicated by the fossils and Scripture. At about the time of the commencement of the Ice Ages some sort of supernatural catastrophe occurred, resulting in sudden extinction of many organisms. The six literal days of creation (or more accurately of re-creation) of new forms occurred later.

DAY-AGE CATASTROPHISM THEORY.

The Hebrew word in Genesis translated "day" literally means "age" (as in Zephaniah 1:7, for example), so that God created things suddenly, but at various times during the geological ages. There was a supernatural catastrophe which had relatively minor or local results, that is, it possibly brought on the Ice Ages, but did not exterminate all species. The account from Genesis 1:3 onward refers to God's addition of new organisms.

PROGRESSIVE CREATIONISM THEORY.

This theory agrees with Day-Age Catastrophism that the Hebrew word in Genesis translated "day" literally means "age," so that God, in a continual process, created things suddenly at different times throughout the geologic ages. In contrast to both the catastrophic theories mentioned above, this view holds that to attempt to fit the ages between Genesis 1:1 and 1:2 would oppose the literal rendering of the original Hebrew manuscripts which imply no such gap at that point. Attempts to determine geological evidence for such a geological catastrophe present a difficulty to the catastrophic views that progressive creationism does not encounter.

ALTERNATE DAY-AGE THEORY.

The "days" of Genesis were actually twenty-four-hour days, but these days of special creation were separated by vast geological ages of development and adaptation. The adherents of this theory believe that God's command after each creation to "multiply and cover the earth" implies such a gap after each day.

EDEN-ONLY THEORY.

The creation account in Genesis is largely about God's special creation of the Garden of Eden a few thousand years ago, which was prepared in six literal days. The theory asserts also that the Genesis account has almost nothing to do with the rest of the earth and its life, which was created at spontaneous intervals throughout the millions of years before Eden's preparation.

CONCURRENT (OVERLAPPING) AGES THEORY.

The Creator is the God of eternity, and as the great *I AM* in Scripture, he is not concerned with time as is man. He could have used six literal days, or six seconds, or six minutes, or six billion years, as he chose. Time does not limit him. So the "days" of Genesis might well refer to creative acts that may be overlapping in occurrence without reference to time, rather than consecutive events. Though difficult for man to comprehend, this would seem to be consistent with God's nature as revealed in Scripture. Even the events recorded in the gospel accounts are not in consecutive order. Isaiah 65:24 tells us that God sometimes answers prayer before we even express ourselves. Another example of overlapping ages in our own time is the fact that we are said to be in the Iron Age, Jet Age, Machine Age, Atomic Age, Space Age, and the Age of Realism, all simultaneously.

SPLIT WEEK THEORY.

The infinite Creator is not limited to time, and certainly not to earth-time. He could use seconds, minutes, days, centuries, or eons, as he chooses. Thus he might have used seconds for some events and eons for others according to any purpose he might have. The Hebrew word translated "day" in Genesis refers to more than a mere twenty-four-hour period in Genesis 2:4 and elsewhere. We have no way of knowing its actual duration in the creation account. All we know is that each of the consecutive creative "days" was long enough for the Creator's purpose, and thus may have varied, perhaps a moment for the creation of light, and millions of years for the creation of animals and plants.

REVELATION DAY THEORY.

The days of Genesis are apparently literal days of twenty-four hours each, in which God revealed his creative acts. As "he that keepeth Israel shall neither slumber nor sleep" (Psalm 121:4), the expression "evening and morning" in Genesis 1 obviously does not pertain to God. He could create animals and plants at night as well as in the day. (Perhaps that was when nocturnal forms were created). As night and day are highly important to human beings, the expression "evening and morning" must refer to days in Moses' life in which he received God's revelation of the Creation.

SUMMARY.

It will be seen that these theories deal with the possible interpretations of the mechanics, but all are based on the underlying fact of biblical creation.

In order for any minority to maintain its existence successfully it must rely upon certain convictions of what it considers important and true. Creationists are in the minority today in publicized scientific thought. While Darwin's theories stimulated a sudden upsurge of investigation by some to refute his ideas and by others to confirm them, biology in many ways was aided, while in others it was handicapped.[24] The rapid growth of evolutionism forced creationists to branch out in their theories and to search both the Scriptures as the word of God and science as the work of God for views which were more sound than their pre-Darwinian creationary theories that had degenerated during the Dark Ages. Numerous creationary theories were proposed as alternatives to evolution. A few of those theories sought to combine evolution and creation, though most were a reaction against evolution.

It is not enough for one to raise objections to evolution, sound as they might be, but one must offer even more sound creationist possibilities to put in its place. The above creationist theories are offered as suggestions of possible solutions — and there are a number of additional possibilities. It is hoped that the reader will pursue the subject further until he is satisfied in both mind and conscience.

24. Nordenskiöld points out that some of Darwin's views have "in no small degree contributed towards retarding the development of biology into an exact science." *Op. cit.*, p. 471.

Chapter Two

THE ORIGIN OF THE UNIVERSE

By GEORGE K. SCHWEITZER

HISTORY

As far back as recorded history allows us to go, we find that men have always been interested in the nature and origin of the universe. The area of knowledge which deals with the nature of the universe is known as *cosmology* (from the Greek words *kosmos,* meaning world, and *logos,* meaning word, and denoting science) .[1] That sub-area within cosmology which deals with the origin of the universe is known as *cosmogony* (from the Greek word *kosmos,* and the root of the Greek word *gignesthai,* meaning to be born) .[2]

Historical and archaeological researchers have given us much information concerning the cosmogonic beliefs of numerous early peoples.[3] The early cosmogonies were mythological, assigning the creation of the world to animals, demigods, or gods, who used materials such as vapors, water, slime, or living creatures. Very few, if any, of the early creation myths convey the idea of creation without the use of previously existing materials.[4]

About six centuries before Christ, the Ionian philosophers questioned the ancient mythologies, and cosmogony passed from the realm of myth into the realm of philosophy. This group believed that the world came from some "simple stuff" which arose by natural

1. *Encyclopedia Britannica* (Chicago: Encyclopedia Britannica, Inc., 1954), VI, 503. *Webster's New International Dictionary* (Springfield, Mass.: Merriam, 1954), p. 601.

2. *Encyclopedia Britannica* (1954), VI, 498. *Webster's New International Dictionary* (1954), p. 601.

3. J. L. E. Dreyer, *A History of Astronomy* (New York: Dover, 1953), pp. 7-8. *Encyclopedia of Religion and Ethics,* ed. J. Hastings (New York: Scribner, 1913-1927), IV, 125-179, 226-231. *The Mythology of All Races,* ed. J. A. McMulloch (Boston: Archaeological Institute of America, 1932), XIII, 92-94. *The New Schaff-Herzog Encyclopedia of Religious Knowledge,* ed. S. H. Jackson (Grand Rapids: Baker, 1950), III, 296-304. A. Heidel, *The Babylonian Genesis* (Chicago: University of Chicago Press, 1951). G. A. Barton, *Archaeology and the Bible* (Philadelphia: American Sunday School Union, 1946), pp. 275-310. G. A. Barton, *Religions of the World* (Chicago: University of Chicago Press, 1937), pp. 148-149, 309-310. J. H. Thomas, *Hibbert Journal,* L (1951-2), 153.

4. A. H. Strong, *Systematic Theology* (Philadelphia: Judson, 1907), pp. 376-377.

causes and then separated into various parts.[5] From that time until about the end of the seventeenth century, philosophers set forth all sorts of ideas. Some believed that the universe was eternal; others believed that it had a beginning. Some believed that a supernatural agency was involved; others disputed this. Many mechanisms for the creation of the world were proposed. However, all of these ideas were simply speculations, for there was hardly any experimental evidence to support or refute them.

In 1692 an important advance in cosmogonic thought occurred, for it was the gateway through which cosmogony passed from the domain of philosophy into the domain of science. Newton stated that he believed the sun and stars to have originated by the grouping together, through the agency of gravity, of finely divided matter which had been evenly dispersed throughout an infinite space.[6] This idea, although modified in detail, was generally accepted during the eighteenth and nineteenth centuries.[7]

Since the early years of the present century, numerous observations have been made on the universe.[8] In addition, a multitude of discoveries in the sciences, particularly mathematics and physics, have been made.[9] All of this new information has necessitated some radical changes in our views on cosmogony. In the remainder of this chapter, we shall discuss these new observations and ideas, the two major interpretations of the facts, and scriptural statements bearing upon the facts and their interpretations.

THE CHRISTIAN VIEW

The source book of Christian belief with regard to ultimate questions is the Bible. By the very nature of this revelation of God to men, Christians do not expect to find in the Holy Scriptures a detailed account of *how* the universe came into being. The basic

5. F. S. Taylor, *Science, Past and Present* (London: Heinemann, 1945), pp. 16-17. S. F. Mason, *A History of the Sciences* (London: Routledge, Kegan Paul, 1953), p. 24.

6. G. J. Whitrow, *The Structure of the Universe* (London: Hutchinson, 1949), pp. 75-76. *Encyclopedia Britannica* (1954), VI, 498.

7. S. F. Mason, *op. cit.*, p. 239. W. C. Dampier, *A History of Science* (New York: Macmillan, 1949), p. 180.

8. D. ter Haar, *Review of Modern Physics*, XXII (1950), 119. P. Couderc, *The Expansion of the Universe* (London: Faber, 1952). Whitrow, *op. cit.* H. Shapley, *Galaxies* (London: Churchill, 1947). H. P. Robertson, *Scientific American*, CXCV (1956), 75-81.

9. D. Halliday, *Introductory Nuclear Physics* (New York: Wiley, 1955). G. Friedlander and J. W. Kennedy, *Nuclear and Radiochemistry* (New York: Wiley, 1955). K. Rankama, *Isotope Geology* (New York: McGraw, 1954). A. S. Eddington, *The Mathematical Theory of Relativity* (New York: Cambridge University Press, 1930).

purpose of the Bible with regard to creation is to tell us *who*. Briefly the Bible sets forth the following doctrine of creation. The Triune God, by a free act according to his sovereign will, and for his own glory, created the whole visible and invisible universe, without the use of pre-existing material; therefore, the universe is a thing completely distinct from God, and yet totally dependent upon him for its continued existence.[10]

The importance of the biblical doctrine of creation is difficult to overemphasize.[11] The Bible opens with answers to three important questions, one of which is the origin of the universe (the other two being the origin of life and the origin of man). Time after time in the Old Testament, God is appealed to and worshipped as the Creator of the heavens and the earth. In a similar fashion, the New Testament continues the emphasis, relating Christ Jesus indissolubly to God the Creator.

THE UNIVERSE   1120429

THE SOLAR SYSTEM[12]

The earth on which we live is an approximate sphere having a diameter of about 7900 miles. This planet has an average distance from the sun of roughly 93 million miles, and it revolves around the sun once a year in a slightly elliptical orbit. Our planet is one of the nine major planets moving around the sun. In their order, starting with the one nearest the sun, and with their average distances from the sun in millions of miles affixed, they are: Mercury (36), Venus (67), Earth (93), Mars (142), Jupiter (483), Saturn (886), Uranus (1783), Neptune (2796), and Pluto (3675). The sun and all these planets lie nearly in a plane, so that the whole solar system is a plate-like structure. Some of the planets have smaller bodies or satellites rotating around them, and there are many smaller chunks of matter traveling in orbits around the sun.

The luminous spherical body which acts as the focus of our solar system and which is known as the sun is in reality about an average star. Its diameter is about 866,000 miles and its mass is about 332,000 times that of the earth. The temperature of the sun is around 6000°C on its surface and much higher inside, with almost 90,000 calories leaving each square centimeter of its surface per minute.

10. W. M. Smith, *Therefore Stand* (Chicago: Moody, 1945), p. 277. Strong, *op. cit.*, p. 371. T. C. Hammond, *In Understanding Be Men* (Chicago: Inter-Varsity, 1951), pp. 58-64.

11. Smith, *op. cit.*, p. 276.

12. W. M. Smart, *The Origin of the Earth* (New York: Cambridge University Press, 1951). C. Payne-Gaposchkin, *Introduction to Astronomy* (New York: Prentice-Hall, 1954), pp. 250-254.

The sun consists of tiny amounts of heavier elements, small amounts of oxygen, nitrogen, and carbon, moderate amounts of helium, and the remainder is hydrogen. Nuclear reactions in which hydrogen is converted into helium account for the tremendous energies liberated by the sun and the ability of the sun to radiate for billions of years.

OUR GALAXY[13]

Our sun is one of about 100 billion stars which make up a giant community of stars known as a galaxy. In addition to the main body or spiral of stars, the galaxy contains smaller groups of stars known as clusters, clouds of gas and dust, and it has a very, very thin atmosphere chiefly of hydrogen. The galaxy is in the process of rotating, making one rotation about every 200 million years.

Since the size of the galaxy and the distances between its stars are so great, it is quite burdensome to use an ordinary measure of distance, because we would have to write so many zeros. Therefore, astronomical distances are usually expressed in terms of light-years, which is the distance that light travels in one year. This gives the light-year a value equivalent to 5,880,000,000,000 or 5.88 trillion miles. The main body of our galaxy is about 80,000 light-years in diameter (about 470,000,000,000,000,000 miles) and about 10,000 light-years thick at the center (about 58,800,000,000,000,000 miles). Our sun is situated about 26,000 light-years from the center of the galaxy in one of the spiral arms. It is believed that only an extremely small percent of the other stars in our galaxy have planetary systems similar to our solar system.

OTHER GALAXIES[14]

Our galaxy is a member of a small cluster of 19 galaxies. They occupy a region over 3 million light-years in diameter. Nearest in space to our cluster are a few other small galaxial clusters. The first large cluster is about 30 million light-years from us, and it contains over 1000 galaxies. On and on out into space in all directions cluster after cluster can be seen, as far out as telescopes can reach. Over a billion galaxies can now be observed. (This gives a total of 100,000,-000,000,000,000,000,000 or 100 sextillion stars.) The observed gal-

13. R. H. Baker, *Astronomy* (New York: Van Nostrand, 1955), pp. 463-483. W. S. Krogdahl, *The Astronomical Universe* (New York: Macmillan, 1952), pp. 437-486. Payne-Gaposchkin, *op. cit.*, pp. 436-443. W. T. Skilling and R. S. Richardson, *A Brief Text in Astronomy* (New York: Holt, 1954), pp. 261-262. P. van de Kamp, *Basic Astromony* (New York: Random House, 1952), pp. 296-304.

14. Baker, *op. cit.*, p. 484. Krogdahl, *op. cit.*, pp. 489-495. Payne-Gaposchkin, *op. cit.*, p. 420. Skilling and Richardson, *op. cit.*, pp. 274-285. Van de Kamp, *op. cit.*, pp. 362-364.

axies which are most distant are a little over 3 billion light-years away.

DISTANCE MEASUREMENTS[15]

Distances in astronomy range all the way from the distance to the moon (239,000 miles) to the distance out to the galaxies at the limit of our present telescopes (17,600,000,000,000,000,000,000 miles). Because of this large range, astronomers find it necessary to combine several techniques in order to make measurements.

The first technique, which can be applied to stars within a range of about 300 light-years, involves the use of trigonometric calculations coupled with the apparent movement of stars against the general star background. The principle of this method is essentially that used for surveying.

The second technique, which can be applied to stars within a range of about 20 million light-years, involves the brightness of the star. The farther a star is from us, the dimmer it appears to be. Thus, if an astronomer knows the actual brightness of a star, and the measured apparent brightness, he can calculate the distance. Several methods are available for ascertaining the actual brightnesses of stars; two of the better ones are as follows. (a) It is known that there are definite relationships between the brightnesses of certain types of stars and their colors. Thus if the color of such a star is measured, its actual brightness can be calculated. (b) Many different types of variable stars have been discovered. The brightnesses of these stars rise and fall regularly. The time required for such a star to change from minimum brightness to maximum brightness and then back to minimum brightness is called its period. Periods ranging from less than a day to hundreds of days have been observed. There is a relationship between the period of a star and its actual brightness, the brightness being greatest for long periods. Hence, if the period of a variable star is known, its actual brightness can be calculated.

The second technique can be used to evaluate the distances to about 100 galaxies, since these are close enough for individual stars to be visible. However, for obtaining the distances to all the other galaxies, a third technique must be employed. Unlike stars, the brightnesses of galaxies have a very small range of values. The average brightness of a galaxy is about equal to that of 400 million suns. Thus knowing the approximate actual brightness and the measured apparent brightness of a galaxy, its distance can be estimated.

15. Baker, *op. cit.*, pp. 300-306, 334-347. Krogdahl, *op. cit.*, pp. 308-312, 409-415. Payne-Gaposchkin, *op. cit.*, pp. 272-277, 363-369. Skilling and Richardson, *op. cit.*, pp. 205-211, 239-243. Van de Kamp, *op. cit.*, pp. 319-326.

VELOCITY MEASUREMENTS[16]

Each chemical element is capable of absorbing certain characteristic colors of light. Colors of light can be designated quite accurately by expressing them in terms of wave lengths. For example, a wave length of 4000 Angstroms represents violet light, 4600 blue, 5100 green, 5700 yellow, 6300 orange, and 7000 red. Intermediate colors are represented by numbers between these. Light may be readily separated into its various colors or wave lengths by use of an instrument called the spectrograph. Every visible star produces all colors of light; however, when the light passes through the outer layers of the star, certain colors are removed by the chemical elements there. For example, in the sun, hydrogen removes colors at wave lengths of 3889, 3970, 4102, 4861, and 6563 Angstroms; calcium removes colors at 3934 and 3969 Angstroms; and sodium removes colors at 5890 and 5896 Angstroms.

When the spectrograph is turned on galaxies out in space, an amazing thing is observed. Calcium, instead of removing the wave lengths of 3934 and 3969 Angstroms, seems to remove wave lengths at higher numbers. The light from a galaxy 26 million light-years away shows the colors at 3950 and 3985 Angstroms taken out (a shift of 16 Angstroms); the light from a galaxy 465 light-years away shows the colors at 4228 and 4265 Angstroms taken out (a shift of almost 300 Angstroms); and the light from a galaxy 1304 million light-years away shows the colors at 4838 and 4881 Angstroms taken out (a shift of over 900 Angstroms). It is generally held that this shift of the removed colors is due to the fact that the galaxies are going away or receding from us. The amount of shift is a measure of the velocity at which the various galaxies are leaving us; 750 miles per second for the first one, 13,400 miles per second for the second, and 38,000 miles per second for the third.

Many more measurements on other galaxies show us that all the clusters of galaxies are receding from us. At first glance, this appears to mean that we are at the center, but this is not necessarily so. Think of a growing watermelon; the seeds are all receding from each other, and none of them is at the exact center. Another important thing has been noted. The farther away a galaxy is, the faster it is moving away from us. In short, the universe is expanding.

The recognition that the universe is expanding has led to two important theories regarding its age and origin. These are known as the superdense state theory and the steady state theory. They will

---

16. Baker, *op. cit.*, pp. 89-90, 503-511. Krogdahl, *op. cit.*, pp. 257-258, 511-514. Payne-Gaposchkin, *op. cit.*, pp. 290, 458-461. Skilling and Richardson, *op. cit.*, pp. 131, 285-288. Van de Kamp, *op. cit.*, pp. 368-369.

be discussed in the second major section following, after we have discussed methods for dating the earth, our galaxy, and the universe.

AGE DETERMINATIONS

THE AGE OF THE EARTH

Several methods are available for estimating the ages of the earth, our galaxy, and the universe.[17] These vary widely in the degree to which they are to be trusted. An attempt has been made to pick out some of the more reliable methods. Among the better ones for approximating the age of the earth are these that follow.

(a) Cooling of the earth's crust. Assuming that the crust of the earth was once molten, an estimate of the time required for it to cool to its present temperature can be made. An answer of a few billion years is obtained.[18]

(b) Salinity of the ocean. The present amount of salt in the oceans and the rate at which salt has been carried to the oceans allows calculations which give an age for the oceans of the order of a billion years. Of course, the earth must be older.[19]

(c) Formation of sedimentary rocks. The rate at which igneous rocks (rocks crystallized from molten materials) have been changed into sedimentary rocks yields an estimated age for the earth of a few billion years.[20]

(d) The recession of the moon. The moon is gradually moving away from the earth. Studies of the rate of this movement coupled with the assumption that the moon started from a position very close to the earth yield a time of some few billions of years ago for the beginning of this process.[21]

(e) The presence of radioactive elements. The half-life of a radioactive substance is the time required for one-half of a given amount of it to change into some other substance. The following radioactive substances are found in considerable quantities in the crust of the earth: potassium-40 and uranium-235. Both of these have half-lives of about a billion years. This means that if the earth were more than 10 billion years old, only very, very slight traces would remain. But since there are more than traces present, the earth could not be over 10 billion years old.[22]

17. D. ter Haar, *Science Monthly*, LXXVII (1953), 173. J. T. Davies, *Research*, IX (1956), 119-123.

18. A. Holmes, *Endeavor*, VI (1947), 99. *Nature*, CLXIII (1949), 453. H. Jeffries, *Nature*, CLXIV (1949), 1046.

19. *Ibid.*

20. Ter Haar, *op. cit.*

21. H. Jeffries, *The Earth* (London: Cambridge University Press, 1952), chap. 8.

22. K. Rankama, *op. cit.*, pp. 109-117, 302-311, 411-418.

(f) Atom ratios. Two types of isotopes of the element uranium are found in the crust of the earth. One of them, uranium-235, changes into some other substance faster than does the other one, uranium-238. If one assumes that these two isotopes were present in equal quantities at the beginning of the earth, then the ratio of uranium-238 to uranium-235 will increase as time goes on, since uranium-235 disappears faster. The ratio of uranium-238 to uranium-235 today is 139. From a knowledge of the rates at which these substances turn into other substances and the value of this ratio, the age of the earth arrived at is from 3 to 6 billion years.[23]

(g) Radioactive decay products. Various radioactive substances in the crust of the earth decay (or turn) into other substances at known rates. For example, uranium-238 changes into lead-206 and helium-4, uranium-235 changes into lead-207 and helium-4, thorium-232 changes into lead-208 and helium-4, potassium-40 decays into argon-40 or calcium-40, and rubidium-87 turns into strontium-87. Consider a rock containing 1 ounce of uranium-238; after one billion years, it contains 0.12 ounces of lead-206, 0.02 ounces of helium-4, and 0.86 ounces of uranium-238; after 2 billion years, 0.23 ounces of lead-206, 0.03 ounces of helium-4, and 0.74 ounces of uranium-238; after 3 billion years, 0.31 ounces of lead-206, 0.05 ounces of helium-4, and 0.64 ounces of uranium-238; after 4 billion years, 0.39 ounces of lead-206, 0.06 ounces of helium-4, and 0.55 ounces of uranium-238; and so on. Thus the measurement of the amounts of lead-206 and uranium-238 (or helium-4 and uranium-238) in a rock should allow an estimate of the age of the rock. Similar techniques apply to the other decaying substances. A value of almost 5 billion years has been obtained for the oldest rocks.[24]

(h) Age of meteorites. An examination of the amounts of radioactive elements and their decay products in meteorites which fall to the earth gives an upper limit of about 5 billion years for the age of the meteorites. Ages of meteorites are probably closely related to the age of the solar system, since it is believed that meteorites are debris from the formation of the planets or fragments resulting from the breakup of a small planet.[25]

Thus the various methods set forth above give an estimate of from 3 to 5 billion years for the age of the earth.

23. *Ibid.*, pp. 415-418.
24. Holmes, *loc. cit. Nature*, CLVII (1946), 680. *Nature*, CLIX (1947), 127. Rankama, *op. cit.*, pp. 114, 301, 332, 336, 352, 374, 391, 395, 397, 400, 411.
25. J. W. Arrol *et al.*, *Nature*, CXXXXIX (1942), 235. B. J. Bok, *M.N.R.A.S.*, CVI (1946), 61. A. Z. Unsold, *Astrophysics*, XXIV (1948), 278. C. A. Bauer, *Physical Review*, LXXII (1947), 354. *Physical Review*, LXXIV (1948), 501. *Science Digest*, XXXVII (1955), 34.

THE AGE OF OUR GALAXY

Several methods which lead to an approximate age for our galaxy are also available.

(a) Distribution of stars among stellar classes. From the colors, sizes, and masses of stars, their compositions and something about their ages can be ascertained. The distribution of stars among various types allows an estimate of an upper limit for the age of the stars in our galaxy. An answer of 100 billion years is obtained. Since not all stars are taken into consideration, this method is quite uncertain.[26]

(b) Distribution of kinetic energy among stars. A study of the physical properties of stars and their motions within our galaxy reveals certain correlations which indicate a relationship between physical state and kinetic energy. On the basis of these somewhat meager data, the age of our galaxy is estimated to be a few billion years.[27]

(c) Separation of binary stars. There occur in our galaxy a number of paired stars, that is, stars that revolve around each other. Studies of their distances of separation, which property is thought to increase with time, point to an age for our galaxy of not more than 10 billion years.[28]

(d) Openness of star clusters. A typical open star cluster, as distinguished from a densely populated one, undergoes a development which leads to its random dispersion in about 2 or 3 billion years. A study of the number of such clusters and their present degrees of dispersion yields for the age of our galaxy a figure of from 4 to 7 billion years.[29]

Thus, the indications seem to be that the age of our galaxy is in the neighborhood of about 4 to 7 billion years.

THE AGE OF THE UNIVERSE

Not quite so many methods are available for attempting to date the universe. The best two of these are given following.

(a) Galaxial clusters. Galaxies are known to occur in clusters, as has been indicated previously. The density of population of the

26. Unsold, *loc. cit.* H. N. Russell, *Science Monthly*, LV (1942), 233. C. F. von Weizsacker, *Physik. Z.* XXXIX (1938), 633. H. A. Bethe, *Physical Review*, LV (1939), 434. P. Ledoux, *Astrophysics*, XI (1948), 174. F. Hoyle, *M.N.R.A.S.*, CVII (1947).

27. Bok, *loc. cit.* A. N. Vyssotsky, *Astrophysics*, LXXXXVII (1943), 38. A. N. Vyssotsky and E. T. R. Williams, *Astrophysics*, LXXXXVIII (1943), 187. F. Z. Gondolatsch, *Astrophysics*, XXIV (1948), 330.

28. S. Chandrasekhar, *Astrophysics*, LXXXXIX (1949), 54. G. P. Kuiper, *Astrophysics*, LXXXXV (1942), 212.

29. S. Chandrasekhar, *Principles of Stellar Dynamics* (Chicago: University of Chicago Press, 1942), chap. 5.

galaxies within a cluster is considered to be an indication of the age of the cluster. A study of these densities in several clusters leads to an estimated age of the universe of from 2 to 10 billion years.[30]

(b) Velocities of galaxial cluster recession. Since the clusters of galaxies are all receding from one another, and since the distances are proportional to the recessional velocities, it follows that as one goes back in time, the clusters were closer together. Calculating back, we find that all the clusters were packed into an extremely small volume about 6 billion years ago.[31]

Thus we can see that determinations of the ages of the earth, our galaxy, and the universe all show answers which are practically the same, that is, in the range of 4 to 7 billion years.

THEORIES OF ORIGIN

THE SUPERDENSE STATE THEORY[32]

Assuming that the total amount of matter plus energy in the universe has remained constant, the present expanding galaxial clusters can be traced back to the time when they were all packed together. This packed state, known as the superdense state, must have been the condition about 6 billion years ago.

According to the superdense state theory of the origin of the universe, it is proposed that 6 billion years ago all the matter and energy of the universe were compressed into a small, densely-packed conglomerate. This lump had a temperature that was extremely high, and underwent an explosion which hurled the matter and radiation outward. The matter, which was initially neutrons, interacted at the super-hot temperatures to produce atoms. As the expansion continued outward, the temperature decreased and the atoms cooled to form clouds of gas. Some of these clouds, under the action of local turbulence, then condensed to form the planets, stars, galaxies, and galaxial clusters. The galaxial clusters are still expanding from the force of the explosion.

By the very nature of the theory, no information regarding the time before the superdense state is available. Speculations and guesses may be made, but there are no scientific data to aid in their evaluations.

30. M. Tuberg, *Astrophysics*, LXXXXVIII (1943), 501. G. C. Omer, Jr., *Sky and Telescope*, VIII (1949), 123.

31. G. Gamow, *Scientific American*, CLXXXX (1954), 61.

32. G. Gamow, *The Creation of the Universe* (New York: Viking, 1952). G. Lemaitre, *The Primeval Atom* (New York: Van Nostrand, 1950). P. Couderc, *op. cit.* G. Gamow, *Scientific American*, CLXXXX (1954), 58. G. Gamow in *The New Astronomy* (New York: Simon & Schuster, 1956).

TESTS OF THE THEORY

The superdense state theory is one theory which explains in a fairly adequate way the things we know about the universe. It does not violate any presently-accepted physical law. It accounts for the recession of the galaxial clusters; it is fairly successful in predicting the abundances of the elements; and it provides a date for the universe which agrees with the ages of the earth, our galaxy, and the universe as determined by other methods.

In the years to come, several tests of this theory will probably be made. It says a number of things, some of which may lend themselves to experimental test: (a) all galaxies are younger than 6 billion years, (b) the universe is decreasing in average density as time goes on, (c) the rate of expansion has been constant since the time of the explosion, (d) the total amount of matter plus energy in the universe is a constant, and (e) the relative proportions of the heavy elements in the oldest stars may be different from those in the younger stars. Some objectors have claimed that one of the main weaknesses of the superdense state theory is that it puts its most important event in the distant past where it can never be subjected to direct experimental test.

THE STEADY STATE THEORY[33]

At the present, we can see no farther out into our universe than a little over 3 billion light-years. At this distance, then, there is a cosmic curtain beyond which no observations can now be made. Clusters of galaxies are constantly crossing this observational barrier and are thus being lost to our unit of the universe.

The steady state theory says that hydrogen atoms are being created out in space at the rate of 1 atom per year in a volume about the size of a skyscraper. This amounts to about 1,000,000,000,000,-000,000,000,000,000 tons per second in the observable universe. As this matter is created, it begins to form clouds; these then condense into planets, stars, galaxies, and galaxial clusters. The clusters recede from all other clusters and finally pass beyond the limit of observation.

Thus while clusters of galaxies are continually reaching the horizon of observation, other clusters are being created within the observational unit and starting to recede toward the horizon. It is stated that this process has been going on for an infinite time. This

33. F. Hoyle, *The Nature of the Universe* (New York: New American Library, 1950). *Frontiers of Astronomy* (New York: Harper, 1955). W. H. McCrea, *Endeavor*, IX (1950), 3. *Journal of the Transactions of the Victoria Institute*, LXXXIII (1951), 105. H. S. Jones, *Science Digest*, XXXII (1952), 52. *Science News*, XXXII (1954), 19.

means that the picture of the universe is the same, regardless of
when one observes it, 100 billion years ago, 10 billion years ago,
1 billion years ago, today, 1 billion years ahead, 10 billion years
ahead, or 100 billion years ahead. Hence, the name of steady state
theory is applied to this idea. Any individual galaxial cluster, galaxy,
star, or planet may be said to have had a discrete origin, but not
the universe.

TESTS OF THE THEORY

The steady state theory is not as widely accepted by scientists as
the superdense state theory. It is indeed unfortunate that the two
major ideas involved in the steady state theory do not at present
lend themselves to being tested. The proposed rate of creation is too
small to be observed. Also, in order to ascertain if the density of the
universe remains constant, as this theory asserts, a long time would
be required.

However, perhaps in the future some of the claims of the theory
will be subjected to tests. Following are the chief assertions that
need to be examined in the light of observational information:
(a) some galaxies are older than 6 billion years, (b) the density of
the universe remains constant as time passes, (c) matter is being
created in space, and (d) the relative proportion of heavy elements
in older and younger stars is the same. There is a general feeling
that the close agreement of the ages of the moon, the earth, the sun,
our galaxy, and the age of the universe as provided by the superdense
state theory is a strong argument against the steady state theory. The
steady state theory is not looked upon favorably also because it
would cause us to modify several of the basic principles of physics
for these reasons: (a) no process capable of building up matter
from nothing is recognized, (b) the disorder of the universe is
generally held to be increasing, but in this theory, it would remain
constant, (c) the law of conservation of matter and energy is vio-
lated. These ideas are not necessarily beyond examination, but it
does not seem proper that a theory which has no direct observational
foundations should be allowed to supersede three ideas well based
upon experimental evidences.

Strong philosophical arguments have been levelled against the
steady state theory.[34] Science has generally held that no statement
about nature should be made unless there is positive evidence for it.
The originators of the steady state theory have been accused of

---

34. H. Dingle, *The Scientific Adventure* (New York: Philosophical Library,
1953), pp. 151-169. *Nature*, CLXVI (1950), 82 and CLXXIII (1954), 574.
M.N.R.A.S., XIII (1953), 3. *Science*, CXX (1954), 513. *Observatory*, LXXIII (1953),
46. *Scientific American*, CLXXXXV (1956), 224. P. Couderc, *op. cit.*, p. 219.

operating on an opposite and unacceptable principle, namely, that any statement may be made which cannot immediately be refuted. Along with this accusation has come the claim that the theory of the steady state has no more basis than the fancy of a few mathematicians who have concluded what they wanted in a universe, and then have set out to fit mathematical relations to their preconceived ideas. Numerous reviewers warn readers against believing everything that one exponent of the steady state theory writes in his books.[35]

THE ORIGIN OF THE EARTH[36]

Many theories of the origin of the earth have been set forth. One group of theories postulates that the planets came into being as the result of another star almost colliding with the sun. As the star came close to our sun, huge tides were produced on the surface of the sun, and large quantities of gaseous material were torn from it. These gaseous clouds took up positions around the sun and ultimately condensed into planets.

Another theory states that there was once another star closely associated with our sun. This star exploded, and even though most of the material was blown far out into space, small amounts of gaseous matter remained in the gravitational field of the sun. These gaseous clouds of matter clumped up into the planets.

Of all the types of theory on the origin of the solar system, the one which describes the formation of the planets at the same time the sun coalesced out of a dust cloud seems to present the smallest number of difficulties. This theory says that about 5 or 6 billion years ago dust and gas out in the universe began to form huge clouds which would then start to contract due to gravitational attraction. The cloud from which our solar system came probably began to contract when it was around 6 trillion miles in diameter. As the contraction or shrinking proceeded, turbulence gave rise to one main cloud plus numerous sub-clouds within the original material. The main cloud would collapse to form the sun, the tremendous forces of gravity giving it great internal pressure and temperature. This rise in temperature would start the nuclear reactions which would cause it to begin radiating as a star. The sub-clouds would clump up into the planets, their interior temperatures rising to several thousand degrees, causing them to be semi-plastic or maybe molten. However,

35. K. F. Mather, *Science*, CXIII (1951), 427. *Christian Century*, LXVIII (1951), 1470. G. P. Thomson, *New Republic*, CXXIV (1951), 19. H. Dingle, *Nature*, CLXVI (1950), 82. C. Spielberger, *Nation*, CLXXII (1951), 570. H. Brown, *Saturday Review of Literature*, XXXIV (1951), 19. G. S. Spinks, *Hibbert Journal*, XXXXIX (1951), 192. D. S. Evans, *Discovery*, IX (1950), 305.

36. W. M. Smart, *op. cit.* F. Hoyle, *Frontiers of Astronomy* (New York: Harper, 1955), pp. 83-126.

since these temperatures are not nearly hot enough to start nuclear reactions, the planets would gradually cool off. The satellites of the planets, like our moon, formed in the sub-clouds in a manner similar to the formation of the planets around the sun.

A recent variation of this last theory has attracted some interest. This idea says that the spinning huge cloud of dust collapsed into the sun without forming sub-clouds. As the collapse proceeded, the spin became faster and faster, so that the sun was rotating at a tremendous speed when it took shape. During the latter stages of condensation, the speed of rotation caused a platelike disc of matter to grow out of the equator. Rotational momentum was transferred to the disc, slowing the sun down, and pushing the disc out. Much of this material escaped, but enough was left for the planets to condense out of it.

THE EARLY HISTORY OF THE EARTH[37]

Most theories of the origin of the earth say that in its early years the earth was in a molten or semi-molten state. The heat for this situation had been provided by the gravitational forces pulling the material together and by the friction of the earth as it passed through the relatively dense early solar system atmosphere. These heat sources were supplemented by the energy from the decay of radioactive substances contained in the material of the earth.

In its molten condition, the heavier elements sank to the center, the lighter ones came to the surface, and the intermediate ones arranged themselves in between. All sorts of chemical reactions occurred; water vapor and carbon dioxide arose from the melt to combine with other gases which were in the atmosphere. Slowly the planet cooled, and the first layer to solidify was probably the one 20 miles beneath the surface. Then the surface began to form into the first hazy outlines of continents. As the earth cooled, and thus contracted, tremendous convulsions shook it; liquid rock surged up, and great chunks of solid material floated in the fluid. The gases surrounded the earth with thick clouds of vapor.

As the cooling progressed, the land took further shape, and finally the water fell and large portions of it did not boil back into the atmosphere. The oceans took shape; great upheavals continued as the land contracted further; erosive processes produced the soil. At last, even though the inside of the earth was at several thousand degrees temperature, the surface temperature was in the range where life could exist. The atmosphere probably contained water, methane, carbon dioxide, ammonia, and some other substances. The seas were

37. H. C. Urey, *The Planets, Their Origin and Development* (New Haven: Yale University Press, 1952), pp. 105-162.

still relatively warm, and the stage was almost set for the transition from the inorganic (non-living) to the organic (living) realm.

THE TOTAL PICTURE

Let us now summarize the most widely accepted picture of the origin of the universe. About 6 billion years ago, all of the matter and energy of the universe were highly compressed in a compact clump. This ball had a temperature up in the billions of degrees, and it was composed of the basic building blocks of atoms in a state of chaotic agitation. Because of the tremendous pressure, it began to expand explosively. The temperature fell, and as it did so the constituents started to form atoms. As the gaseous matter surged outward, turbulence, gravitational forces, and further cooling produced gigantic clouds of gas separated from each other by tremendous distances.

Within each of these clouds, the particles began to clump up to form billions of smaller clouds. Many of these clouds started to condense into stars. Around the star that is our sun, a platelike cloud of dust formed. Turbulence in this material caused the condensation of the solar system, including the earth. The earth then appeared as a molten mass of matter. Slowly it cooled; the surface rocks solidified; the first continents took shape; water condensed to form the oceans; erosive, thermal, chemical, and mechanical processes worked the surface. And so after a few billion years, the earth was ready for another major event: the coming of life.

SCRIPTURAL VIEW

THE BIBLICAL MATERIAL

It is generally acknowledged that final or ultimate answers in the matter of creation cannot be attained through research (science) or reason (philosophy).[38] If, however, God exists, and if he has chosen to reveal to mankind information concerning the origin of the universe, then there is a possible source for the final answers. Christians have always held that God has spoken to mankind, and that these communications include some pertinent information concerning the origin of the universe.[39]

Before we examine this material, it is of utmost importance that the nature of biblical language be understood. Biblical language is not the precise language of modern-day science; it is popular, phenomenal, and ofttimes poetical.[40] Thus we are not to look for intricate detail, but for basic underlying principles. It is also well to be

38. H. Dingle, *Nature*, CLXXIII (1954), 574. A. H. Strong, *op. cit.*, p. 374.
39. T. C. Hammond, *op. cit.*, pp. 58-60.
40. B. Ramm, *The Christian View of Science and Scripture* (Grand Rapids: Eerdmans, 1954), pp. 65-80.

reminded that the Bible's major aim is to tell us *who* made the universe, and not *how* it was made. These remarks apply particularly to the early chapters of Genesis, for recent researches into ancient literature assure us that these passages are not to be interpreted literally, but poetically or allegorically.

The basic biblical statements concerning the creation come from the books of Genesis and Hebrews. They read as follows: "In the beginning God created the heavens and the earth" (Genesis 1:1). "By faith we understand that the world was created by the word of God, so that what is seen was made out of things which do not appear" (Hebrews 11:3).

Other scriptural excerpts support and amplify these.[41] In order to analyze the biblical view, the passage from Genesis will be broken down into three phrases: (a) In the beginning, (b) God created, (c) the heavens and the earth.

The first phrase *in the beginning* appears to involve the concept of time. Christianity holds that God is eternal, which means that he is timeless. The realm of his existence does not involve a past, present, and future, since God is independent of time. In fact, it is generally asserted that God created time just as he created matter.[42] Unlike God, we operate in and are restricted by time. There then seem to be two realms, that of God's existence known as eternity, and that of our existence known as time. The realm of time can be seen to be included in the realm of eternity, since God created time and set it into operation. Hence the Scriptures would seem to say that God created the universe and simultaneously created the realm of time in which it operates. Just what the exact nature of the beginning was, the Scriptures do not say.

The second phrase *God created* indicates that an act was performed. The time required for this act of creation is not specified; it could have taken a trillion years. or only a second. Consideration of other Scripture passages shows that the act of creation was a creation out of nothingness. Thus neither matter, nor space, nor time is eternal; all were created by God.[43]

Consideration of the third phrase *the heavens and the earth* is

41. Gen. 2:1, 4; Exod. 20:11; I Sam. 2:8; II Kings 19:5; I Chron. 16:26; Neh. 8:6; Job 9:8-9, 26:8-13; Psa. 8:3, 19:1, 24:1, 33:6-9, 74:16, 89:11, 90:2, 96:5, 102:25, 104:2, 121:2, 124:8, 136:5-9, 146:6, 148:3-5; Prov. 3:19, 8:27, 16:4, 26:10; Eccl. 3:11; Isa. 37:16, 42:5, 44:24, 45:12, 18, 48:13, 51:13; Jer. 10:12, 31:35, 32:17, 33:2, 51:15; Amos 5:8, 9:6; Zech. 12:1; Mark 10:6, 13:19; Acts 4:24, 7:50, 14:15, 17:24; Rom. 1:20, 11:36; I Cor. 8:6; II Cor. 5:18; Eph. 3:9; I Tim. 6:13; Heb. 1:1, 3:4, 11:3; Rev. 4:11, 10:6, 14:7.

42. Exod. 3:14; Deut. 32:40; Psa. 90:2, 102:12-14, 27; Isa. 41:4; I Cor. 2:7; Col. 1:7; Eph. 1:4; I Tim. 1:17, 6:16; Heb. 9:14; Jude 25. See also A. H. Strong, *op. cit.*, pp. 275-278.

43. Strong, *op. cit.*, pp. 374-389.

now in order. The phrase probably implies what the Hebrew writer could see when he looked up into the sky at night. Regardless of what he may have thought the size of this to be, he probably felt that it was all that there was in existence. In other words, he thought that he was viewing the whole universe. Thus the phrase would appear to be referring to the whole creation.[44]

In summary, then, the three phrases appear to be saying these things: (a) time and the universe came into being simultaneously, (b) the universe was created by God out of nothing, (c) the universe is defined as being the whole of creation, and (d) no reference to a date is made, and thus any age for the universe is allowed. In the sections to follow, these four ideas and the two theories of the origin of the universe will be compared.

THE SUPERDENSE STATE THEORY

This theory can fit quite well with the picture of creation as given in Scripture.[45] It provides for (a) a unique event which might be identified with the creation, namely the explosion of the great lump of matter and energy. Even if this lump had a previous history, there is nothing in the theory to preclude God's having brought the matter into being at some previous time or even back in the reaches of infinity. The superdense state theory likewise allows (b) the possibility that the lump of matter could have been called into being by God out of nothingness, either just prior to the explosion, or at some time previous to it, or even back into infinity. The theory is one which also provides for (c) a situation in which the whole universe was involved, and (d) a universe which has an age (since the explosion) of about 6 billion years.

Various persons have speculated on events before the explosion,[46] some postulating that the universe alternately expands and contracts throughout infinite time, others feeling that the universe formed the gigantic lump by contracting from infinity. At the present time, however, these two ideas are neither supported nor denied by any direct scientific evidence, even though some people believe that there

44. *International Standard Bible Encyclopedia*, ed. J. Orr (Grand Rapids: Eerdmans, 1952), p. 3106. J. Strong, *Dictionary of the Hebrew Bible* (New York: Methodist Book Concern, 1890), pp. 17, 118. J. L. E. Dreyer, *A History of Astronomy, op. cit.*, pp. 2-3.

45. P. W. Stoner in *Modern Science and Christian Faith* (Wheaton: Van Kampen, 1950), pp. 9-22. A. R. Short, *Modern Discovery and the Bible* (Chicago: Inter-Varsity, 1952), pp. 29-31, 89-92. R. E. D. Clark, *Creation* (London: Tyndale, 1950), pp. 5-13. Ramm, *op. cit.*, pp. 143-156.

46. G. Gamow, *The Creation of the Universe* (New York: Viking, 1952), pp. 29-30. P. Couderc, *op. cit.*, pp. 100, 193. J. T. Davies, *op. cit.*, 121.

are a few indirect indications.[47] Thus, as of now, nothing certain can be said with regard to any pre-explosion stage; in fact, no surety that there was any such stage can be given.

THE STEADY STATE THEORY

As with the previous theory, this one does not necessarily present any difficulties from the standpoint of the Christian writings. Several authors have shown that the steady state idea may be easily put into a Christian context.[48] With regard to (a), the theory does not seem to provide an event which lends itself to being interpreted as the original act of creation as does the superdense theory. Nonetheless, the theory definitely does not exclude a creation event. It is possible that a complete operating system such as proposed by the steady state theory could have come into being out of nothingness at some past time or even back in infinity. With reference to (b), the theory fits, since it regards the creation of matter to be out of nothing, and thus would allow the Christian to postulate God as Creator. In fact, the recognition of creation of this type automatically carries with it the recognition of the possibility of the whole system coming into being out of nothingness, either gradually or almost instantaneously. In considering (c), the steady state idea does not recognize the whole universe as being involved in one unique act of creation. However, as was pointed out above, it distinctly does not rule such an act out. Another possibility is that the third phrase of Genesis 1:1 (the heavens and the earth) may be thought to refer to a local situation only, for example, only what can be seen with the unaided eye. If such is the interpretation, then there is no difficulty, for the steady state theory recognizes that the galaxial clusters and galaxies had origins. Finally, with regard to (d), this theory denies that any discrete date for the origin of the universe as a whole can be given. This does not mean, though, that there could be no such date. It simply implies that although the ages of particular planets, stars, and galaxies may be estimated, no means are available for ascertaining a date at which the steady state system itself could have come into being out of nothingness.

In brief, then, it can be seen that neither the superdense state theory nor the steady state theory necessarily conflicts with the biblical view of creation, as some have claimed. Especially is this true if one regards the major messages of Genesis 1:1 to be that all the world and all that is in it depends on God for its origin and its continued existence.

47. G. Gamow, *op. cit.*, pp. 29-35. *Scientific American*, CLXXXX (1954), 63 and CLXXXXV (1956), 145. A. R. Sandage, *American Scientist*, CLXXXXV (1956), 171.
48. J. H. Thomas, *loc. cit.*

CONCLUSION

Most scientists today express serious doubts about the steady state theory, preferring the superdense state theory to it. However, we must never forget that all our scientific ideas relating to ultimate questions of the universe come under the category of hypothesis.[49] They are subject to constant revision. It is quite widely believed that only relatively few facts about our universe are known.[50] From these few facts, many models (interpretations) can be and have been drawn up. But just because a certain model fits the few bits of observational data that we now have does not mean that it is the true picture. It is known that some theories which are physically false may provide answers which are not incompatible with present experience.[51] History shows us that models which seemed to explain the whole universe have been easily upset by just one newly observed fact.[52] The universe behaves entirely independently of the attempts of men to describe and understand it, and hence any statement based upon a model can never be as valid as an observed fact.

No person can come to the problem of cosmogony without preconceived ideas. Since one of the basic beliefs of Christianity is its concept of God as Creator, the question of cosmogony is particularly controversial in our society. Attempts to avoid the idea of creation are found throughout the scientific literature, indicating the presence of much prejudice. Many writers are not content to leave the idea alone, which would be the strict scientific attitude since science does not deal with ultimate origins, but instead they take particular pains to set forth and promote belief in possibilities for a universe without an origin.

Perhaps the superdense state theory is true; perhaps not. Maybe we have gotten down the wrong trail, and some other theory, not even dreamed of today, will turn out to be more nearly correct. But regardless of the coming and going of models and interpretations of the facts (and we may rest assured there will be more), we can always turn our eyes skyward and know that the heavens are telling us of the glory of God and the wonder of his works.[53]

A noted archaeologist has recently pointed out that the creation account of Genesis is quite unique in ancient literature.[54] He says

49. G. J. Whitrow, *op. cit.*, chap. 10.

50. H. Dingle, *Nature*, CLXXIII (1954), 576.

51. E. H. Betts, *J. Trans. Vict. Inst.*, LXXXIII (1951), 127. H. Dingle, *Science*, LXX (1954), 517.

52. F. W. Cousins, *J. Trans. Vict. Inst.*, LXXIII (1951), 126. D. S. Evans, *Discovery*, IX (1950), 305. G. P. Thomson, *New Republic*, CXXIV (1951), 19.

53. W. M. Smart, *op. cit.*, p. 235.

54. W. F. Albright in H. C. Alleman and E. E. Flack, *Old Testament Commentary* (Philadelphia: Muhlenberg, 1948), p. 135.

that it reflects an advanced monotheistic viewpoint, and that it provides us with a sequence of phrases which modern science cannot improve upon. He goes on to state that recent scientific cosmogonies show such a disconcerting tendency to be short-lived that it may be seriously doubted whether science has yet caught up with the biblical story. Thus we may conclude that with reference to our positions as scientists we must not make a premature judgment on the mechanism of creation, but as children of the One True God we may affirm with the inspired author of the book of Hebrews that by faith we understand that the world was created by the word of God.[55]

55. Heb. 11:3.

Chapter Three

THE ORIGIN OF LIFE

By WALTER R. HEARN AND RICHARD A. HENDRY

THE CONTROVERSY OVER SPONTANEOUS GENERATION

When Charles Darwin was writing *The Origin of Species by Means of Natural Selection,* the possibility of "spontaneous generation" was still a very controversial question. That idea — that living things may arise from inanimate matter under certain conditions — had been firmly held by almost everyone from ancient times, because it *seemed* to be an everyday occurrence. For example, insects could be seen developing from mud and slime, maggots were obviously formed in decaying meat, etc. Aristotle taught that even higher forms of life arose spontaneously from decaying animal and vegetable matter, and such teachings had persisted through the middle ages. At the beginning of the seventeenth century J. B. van Helmont published a recipe for obtaining mice by letting a dirty shirt and some wheat germ ferment for twenty-one days![1]

After the invention of the microscope, people thought they could actually watch swarms of tiny living creatures coming to life before their eyes. Furthermore, living organisms appeared even after boiling had apparently killed any living things which might already have been present. Many observers were convinced not only by what they saw, but also by the fact that God had commanded, "Let the waters bring forth living creatures," a command which they considered had never been rescinded.

Why, then, with this almost universal belief that spontaneous generation was possible, based on the testimony of such learned men as Aristotle, Newton, William Harvey, Descartes, van Helmont, and others, was there still any question about the matter in 1859? Simply because, when experiments were carefully performed to test the hypothesis, they sometimes gave one result and sometimes another. For instance, Francesco Redi in 1668 was able to show that

1. William Bulloch, *The History of Bacteriology* (London: Oxford, 1938); see Chapter IV, "Spontaneous Generation and Heterogenesis," for a detailed account of early writings and the later controversy. For a shorter account see Charles Singer, *The Story of Living Things* (New York: Harper, 1931), Chapter XII, "Biogenesis and its Implications." See also Chapter I of Oparin, reference 10, below.

worms did *not* appear in meat which had been covered with muslin so that flies could not deposit their eggs in the meat. On the other hand, John T. Needham in 1749 sealed up infusions of meat and other organic substances in vessels and heated the vessels to sterilize them, but consistently found them to be swarming with living microorganisms a few days later when he opened the vessels and examined the infusions under a microscope. However, Lazzaro Spallanzani in 1765 criticized Needham's experiments on the grounds that the vessels had not been heated sufficiently to kill microorganisms or their "germs" already present, and he himself did many experiments with more prolonged heating and more careful sealing of the vessels; in all cases in which he was sufficiently careful to exclude air which had not been adequately heated, living organisms did not appear. Needham objected that such prolonged heating would ruin the life-giving properties of the air and the organic matter; Spallanzani tried to meet these objections with more careful experiments. Many other investigators designed experiments of their own, but by the middle of the nineteenth century the question was still undecided.[2]

Although many experiments tended to disprove the old idea of the possibility of spontaneous generation, it was extremely difficult with the scientific methods available at that time to avoid the accidental contamination of a sterile medium by contact with microorganisms or their spores present on dust particles in the air, on pieces of apparatus, or in the breath of the investigator. We must remember that microbiology is really a very recent science, although we now take such things as pasteurization of milk and sterile surgical technique for granted. As a matter of fact, it was the climax of this very controversy over spontaneous generation which led to the modern concept that *all* microorganisms arise only from living microorganisms or their spores. This concept has made the preparation of pure cultures of specific organisms and the science of bacteriology possible. But in 1859, when Darwin wrote that "science as yet throws no light on the far higher problem of the essence or origin of life,"[3] he was accurately describing the situation.

At the very time Darwin was publishing these words in *The Origin of Species,* however, the great French chemist Louis Pasteur was engaged in the famous series of experiments which eventually settled the question in the minds of most people. In a triumph of

2. J. B. Conant, ed., "Pasteur's and Tyndall's Study of Spontaneous Generation," No. 6 in *Harvard Case Histories in Experimental Science* (Cambridge: Harvard University Press, 1953); published in 2 vols. in 1957: II, 489-539.

3. Charles Darwin, *The Origin of Species by Means of Natural Selection,* with additions and corrections from the 6th and last English edition, two vols. in one (New York: Appleton, 1905), II, 294.

the experimental method, Pasteur established that all of the previously observed cases of supposed spontaneous generation could be
explained on the basis that the observers had not been sufficiently
careful to exclude the possibility of contamination of their media.
The French Academy of Sciences awarded a prize to Pasteur for this
convincing demonstration. Of course, not everyone was convinced,
notably Felix A. Pouchet, and many experiments were still done in
an attempt to prove that Pasteur was wrong. One investigator,
Henry C. Bastian, was able to arouse some interest in spontaneous
generation after publication of Pasteur's experiments, but it was
later shown that there was a reasonable explanation for Bastian's
positive results — an explanation not favorable to spontaneous generation. Bastian used infusions of hay for his experiments, heated
them as thoroughly as Pasteur had prescribed, and still found micro-
organisms present when he opened his flasks. The spores of the hay
bacillus happen to be unusually resistant to heat, and when this
fact was realized, the strength of Bastian's arguments disappeared.

Pasteur himself may have felt that spontaneous generation was
theoretically impossible, but he always expressed willingness to
accept the possibility if it could be demonstrated to have occurred.
He realized the logical impossibility of proving a universal negative,
and never claimed to have proven that living things *could not* arise
or *had not* arisen in the past from non-living matter.[4] Darwin, in
1872, after reading Bastian's book, *The Beginnings of Life,* was still
skeptical, and wrote in a letter to his friend A. R. Wallace, "His
general argument in favour of Archebiosis [Bastian's term for
spontaneous generation] is wonderfully strong, though I cannot
think much of some few of his arguments. The result is that I am
bewildered and astonished by his statements, but am not convinced;
though, on the whole, it seems to me probable that Archebiosis is
true." And also, in the same letter, "I should like to live to see
Archebiosis proved true; or if false, I should like to see it disproved,
and the facts otherwise explained; but I shall not live to see all this."[5]

As a result of the conclusive experiments of Pasteur and John
Tyndall, and of the interest soon aroused by Darwin's writings, the
evolution of already living forms began to attract the major attention
of biologists, and the question of origins of the original forms tended
to drop out of men's minds. As the study of biology progressed, two
philosophical points of view among biologists also continued to
develop: "mechanistic" biologists emphasized that living processes
were the ordinary physical and chemical processes of the inanimate

4. R. J. Dubos, *Louis Pasteur, Free Lance of Science* (Boston: Little, Brown,
1950), pp. 395-399. See also Chapter VI.
5. Francis Darwin, ed., *The Life and Letters of Charles Darwin* (New York:
Appleton, 1896), II, 346-348.

world; "vitalists" insisted that some other principle, or "vital force," was operating in living things. With the fairly modern development of biochemistry, many of the most mysterious properties of living things have become explainable by the known laws of physics and chemistry. As a result, most of the old vitalistic concepts have become historical curiosities among practicing biologists today.[6]

CURRENT VIEWS ON THE ORIGIN OF LIFE

Recently, with the mechanistic approach dominant in biology, and with a much better understanding of the chemical reactions which take place in living organisms, attention has again been focused on the problem of the origin of life. A number of scientific conferences have been held to discuss the problem, and an ever-increasing number of technical papers related to it are being published in the scientific literature. In addition, the subject has caught the popular fancy, and many non-technical articles are already appearing, some with startling titles about scientists "creating life." This does *not* mean that Pasteur's experiments have been challenged by the results of more modern ones; indeed, all of the evidence of the science of bacteriology since Pasteur's day has added weight to his conclusion that living things do *not* arise spontaneously in sterile media. However, scientists are now seriously considering the possibility that conditions on the earth's surface must at one time have been very different from what they are today, so that living things *might* have arisen from inanimate matter long ago. Furthermore, they believe that *if* this is true, we ought to be able to learn something about how such a process could have taken place.

Not only were the geochemical conditions of the earth's surface and atmosphere probably different, it is reasoned, but there are also two other factors which would have made the original process uniquely different from any of our attempts to duplicate it or to observe it in nature. In the first place, the total length of time available for the whole original process to take place would have been tremendously longer than anything we would be able to duplicate. Secondly, if some simple form of life *did* develop in nature now, it would have to compete with the highly advanced forms which have been "selected" or favored because of their relatively high efficiency, and the primitive form would probably not survive long enough to be observed. Darwin himself pointed this out very clearly.[7] At any rate, it is certainly possible today for a scientist to discuss possible ways in which life might once have arisen from

---

6. For a review and defense of a modern concept of vitalism, see L. R. Wheeler, *Vitalism, Its History and Validity* (London: H. F. & G. Witherby, 1939).

7. Francis Darwin, *op. cit.,* II, 202-203 and footnote.

inanimate matter, without being accused of ignorance of Pasteur's famous experiments and conclusions.

T. H. Huxley argued in 1868 in his essay, "On the Physical Basis of Life"[8] that the origin of life probably involved only the arrangement of ordinary matter into a suitably complex relationship; the nature of this "sarcode," "protoplasm," or stuff of life was almost completely unknown at that time, and no one could even guess the nature of the forces which might have brought about such an arrangement. In 1953, J. W. S. Pringle began a discussion on "The Origin of Life" by referring to Huxley's essay and then stating that we have only slightly more evidence than Huxley had, and that, furthermore, many of the experiments which might shed light on the question have still not been tried.[9] However, it is safe to say that the development of many different branches of science in recent years has narrowed down the number of *possible* mechanisms and provided some basis for choosing the most reasonable hypotheses. Today, therefore, we have a much better notion of what kinds of experiments we should do to help us choose the *best* hypothesis.

The book by A. I. Oparin, *The Origin of Life*,[10] first published in 1936, represents one of the most significant contributions to the thinking in this field and has influenced most of the recent writers on the subject. Oparin emphasized the possibility, even the necessity, of the formation of very complex molecules in that long period of the earth's existence before there were any living things. It was not necessary to assume that the gap between the non-living and the living had been bridged in one jump; indeed, according to Oparin, it was more reasonable to assume that a very long period of development of complex molecules and their aggregates took place before the appearance of anything we would recognize as being completely "alive." Oparin proposed some possible mechanisms for this "chemical evolution" and showed how a kind of "natural selection" could have operated to bring about molecular complexes sufficiently stable to serve as the immediate "precursors" of the first living organisms.

Only a very brief description of current views on this question can be presented here, but in order for even a brief account to be

8. T. H. Huxley, "On the Physical Basis of Life," 1868, published in various collections of his writings, including *Autobiography and Selected Essays*, ed. A. L. F. Snell (New York: Houghton Mifflin, 1909).

9. J. W. S. Pringle, "The Origin of Life," *Symposia of the Society for Experimental Biology*, VII (1953), 1-21.

10. A. I. Oparin, *The Origin of Life*, translation with annotations by S. Morgulis (New York: Macmillan, 1938). 2nd Edition, paper bound (New York: Dover, 1953). 3rd Edition, *The Origin of Life on the Earth*, trans. by Ann Synge (New York: Academic Press, 1957).

understandable it will be necessary first to discuss some basic principles of physical chemistry and their relationship to biochemistry.[11]

ATOMS, IONS, AND MOLECULES: THE STUFF OF LIFE

Chemical analysis of all types of organisms has shown that they
are composed of atoms of the ordinary elements in the periodic
table, chiefly the lighter non-metals (H, O, C, N, S, P, Cl) and
lighter metals (Na, K, Ca, Mg) with traces of heavier elements
(Fe, Cu, Zn, Co, Mn, I, and others). Some of these are in the form
of electrically charged "ions," such as Na^+, K^+, Cl^-, and HCO_3^-,
the concentrations of which, although rather small, seem to be
extremely important to living things. We know quite a bit about the
role these ions play in physiological functions, and in some cases we
now understand the biochemical reactions in which specific ions
participate.

Most of the atoms in living things, however, are in the form of
"organic compounds." Such compounds got their name because the
vitalists used to think that compounds produced by living organisms
would have special properties not shared by "inorganic" compounds.
It has turned out that the properties of organic compounds can be
traced to the properties of the elements of which they are composed
and the types of chemical bonds which hold the atoms of these
elements together. These are called "co-valent" bonds to indicate
that they are formed by the *sharing* of valence electrons between
atoms and *not* by the complete gain or loss of electrons which results
in the formation of ions such as those mentioned above. When ions
form compounds, such as NaCl (ordinary table salt), the ions are
held together by simple electrostatic attraction between their charges.
The covalent bond, although it predominates in molecules produced
by living things, is an ordinary chemical bond, and is found also in
many compounds never associated with living organisms. The study
of biochemistry is made difficult by the fact that many compounds
of importance in living things are tremendously large and complex,
being made up of thousands of individual atoms held together by
thousands of covalent bonds. The "proteins" and "nucleic acids,"
whose molecular weights range up into the hundreds of thousands,
are perhaps the most important examples. In fact, they are the most
complicated molecules known.

Proteins have been shown to be "polymers" consisting of about
twenty different kinds of small molecules, called amino acids, which
are hooked together by covalent bonds to form long "peptide" chains

11. For details and references to the original literature for the following
sections, see a modern biochemistry textbook such as J. S. Fruton and S. Simmonds,
General Biochemistry (2nd ed.; New York: Wiley, 1958).

much like a string of beads. If the chains are long enough, they may be coiled up like a spring or helix, or folded back and forth. These folded configurations (called "secondary" structures to distinguish them from the "primary" or covalent peptide structure) are known to be held together by ionic bonds and by a type of bond which is in a sense intermediate between covalent and ionic, the so-called "hydrogen bond." Of course, with twenty different amino acids to be strung together in different ways, there are many different possible arrangements of the peptide chains, and each of these may have different ways of coiling or folding. By slightly altering the primary structures (e.g., by removing the last amino acid in the chain) or the secondary structures (e.g., by slightly unfolding the chains), biochemists have learned that the biological functions of protein molecules are very specifically related to their chemical structure. For example, the hormone insulin, a protein small enough to have had its complete amino acid sequence worked out recently, loses its power to lower the blood sugar concentration of diabetic animals if its structure is disturbed in even very minor ways. And even the simplest organisms we know of seem to be composed largely of these huge but delicate protein molecules! (See Fig. 1.)

Recent investigations of the structure of nucleic acid molecules are very exciting, because one type of nucleic acid containing the sugar ribose (and called RNA, for ribose nucleic acid) seems to be important in the bio-synthesis of the proteins mentioned above, and the other type containing desoxyribose (and therefore called DNA) actually seems to be the molecule which carries the hereditary characteristics from one generation to another. In other words, DNA seems to be *the* chemical substance that does the work of the genes in the chromosomes, discussed in later chapters. Many lines of evidence have indicated that this is so, and recent discoveries about the structure of DNA fit in beautifully with this concept.[12] The DNA molecules are apparently always of tremendous size, which has made investigation of their structure very difficult. Actually, they are made of fewer different types of "monomers" than the proteins, and seem to be arranged in more rigidly defined secondary structures. There are only about four types of building blocks, this time of the class of purine and pyrimidine "bases" rather than amino acids, each connected to the same type of sugar molecule (ribose in RNA and desoxyribose in DNA), with these sugars linked together as esters of phosphoric acid (the phosphoric acid accounting for the acidic properties of the nucleic acids). The repeating units strung together in the chains are thus: base-sugar-phosphate, with the four types of

12. R. L. Sinsheimer, "First Steps Toward a Genetic Chemistry," *Science*, CXXV (1957), 1123-1128.

bases alternating in a definite but still unknown pattern. The secondary structure of DNA has been shown to consist of two of these "polynucleotide" chains spirally wound around each other in a "double helix" resembling a two-strand rope. The bases from one chain face the bases from the other chain on the inside of the helix, and only certain pairs can fit together and be held by hydrogen bonds. In other words, calling the bases A, B, C, D for simplicity, A-B and C-D are the two pairs that fit; when A occurs in one chain, B must occur opposite it and not C, D, or another A. This means that one chain is not a duplicate of the other one, but rather a "complement" of it; if the helix were to be unwound and a new chain of DNA synthesized to fit each of the chains, we would then have two sets of helices exactly like the first set we started with. This structural feature accounts in a truly remarkable way for what must be happening when genes duplicate! It is now generally believed that the order of the four bases along the DNA chain itself serves as the "code" or pattern of heredity. And of course, all living organisms contain these extremely complex nucleic acid molecules. (See Fig. 2.)

ENERGY AND ENTROPY: THE SECOND LAW

Now the interesting thing about such giant molecules is that we would at first glance expect them to be less stable than small molecules. Energy has to be put in to form a covalent bond, so that a compound with many bonds has more energy than a smaller compound with fewer bonds. To say that one molecule has more energy than another is equivalent to saying it is less stable; if it has more energy it can react in more ways — it can "do" more things — and some of these will involve breaking its bonds. Here is another way to look at it: Since breaking a bond usually involves a collision with an atom of another molecule, it is easy to see that the larger a molecule is, the better a target it is for a bond-breaking collision. So, as a general rule, we expect complex molecules to be less stable than simple molecules.

The tendency for energy differences to be leveled off is one that we are all familiar with in one way or another. Gravity tends to pull high objects down to the same level of potential energy as that of lower objects, hot objects give up their higher heat energies to their cooler surroundings, etc. In a similar way, there is a tendency for molecules with large amounts of chemical energy to react and give up some of their energy. The precise statement of this tendency toward "energetic" or "thermodynamic" equilibrium is called the Second Law of Thermodynamics. One way of stating the Second Law is to say that in a closed system, one in which energy does not come in or go out, the energy of the system tends to spread randomly throughout all parts of the system. The measure of this random-ness is called "entropy." That is, as the energy becomes distributed more evenly throughout the system, we say that the entropy of the system is increasing.

One of the most characteristic properties of living things is their ability to reverse this trend toward random distribution of energy and actually to concentrate energy in complex chemical compounds. It is *not* true that in so doing they violate the Second Law (as some have claimed), because no living organism is a closed system; energy is constantly flowing through it as long as it is alive. But it *is* true that living things seem to be the only systems capable of *continuously* utilizing a portion of the energy passing through them to *decrease* entropy within the system.

How does an organism accomplish this? Biochemistry is steadily unraveling the chemical reactions involved in the breaking down of foodstuffs (catabolism) and the building up of the complex mol-ecules of the organism (anabolism). The sum of these two processes is called *metabolism*. We already know many details of processes which yield energy (called "exergonic" processes), and of many synthetic reactions which require energy (called "endergonic" proc-esses). In some cases we even know how two such metabolic processes are linked together in the organism, one furnishing the chemical energy necessary for the other. A striking observation is the high degree of similarity in certain metabolic processes throughout the animal and plant kingdoms, in spite of exceedingly great differences in outward forms. There are differences in metabolism, of course — some of them very outstanding. The ability of green plants but not animals to carry out photosynthetic reactions is the most obvious example, but there are many others. Often different species, or even different individuals in the same species, may synthesize distinctly different compounds for the same purpose. Thus, horse hemoglobin is not structurally the same protein as human hemoglobin, although both perform the same function of absorbing oxygen for transport by red corpuscles in the blood; it has recently been established that not even all human beings synthesize the same type of hemoglobin molecules. But in spite of such variations, most living things do seem to carry out essentially the same basic types of biochemical reactions.

STRUCTURE AND FUNCTION: THE CYCLE OF LIFE

From an ordinary chemist's point of view, it is truly remarkable that living things are able to carry out the reactions of metabolism at all. The organic chemist knows how difficult it is to form covalent bonds! The reacting atoms must collide with enough energy to over-come the repelling force of their electron clouds — that is, with enough "energy of activation." Therefore, a reaction mixture must be heated continuously, sometimes for hours, to speed up the molecules sufficiently (increasing their kinetic energy) to get them to react. But metabolic reactions in living cells go on easily at temperatures far below those that would be necessary to drive the same reactions to completion in the laboratory. This mystery (which was once quite commonly attributed to a "vital force") was cleared up largely by the discovery of *enzymes,* molecules which have the ability to catalyze (speed up) specific chemical reactions. Enzymes themselves have turned out to be complex protein molecules, but merely molecules. Many have been isolated from the cells which produced them, and even crystallized like ordinary compounds. These crystal-line enzymes seem to have the same degree of catalytic power they had before they were removed from the cell. Their high specificity means that for the hundreds of chemical reactions carried out in a single cell, there must be hundreds of these different types of enzyme molecules; this means that protoplasm must be far more complicated than the early biologists ever dreamed — and new complications are being discovered every day. Each of these enzymes must itself be synthesized within the cell! This leads us to the very fundamental "life cycle" of structure and function: the enzymes catalyze metabolic reactions by virtue of their particular chemical structures, and these structures are synthesized by the very same kinds of chemical re-actions. (Which came first, the catalyst which makes the reactions go, or the reactions which make the catalyst?)

WHAT ARE THE MINIMUM REQUIREMENTS FOR LIFE?

It is just this kind of question which has always made the origin of life such an insoluble problem. How could such a complicated cyclic system ever get started? If we could find simpler patterns of metabolism or less complex catalytic molecules, we might get some hints. However, even the simplest forms of life we know today seem to make use of the same types of huge protein molecules as catalysts, and therefore must be able to synthesize them. There may be a few living freaks in the museum of nature, but so far they have not yielded much useful information. Some organisms which use variant schemes of metabolism may yet give us information about more "primitive" systems than the ones common today. For example, organic compounds are the usual source of energy for all organisms except green plants (which absorb radiant energy from the sun), but certain chemosynthetic microorganisms can get the energy they need by oxidizing iron or elemental sulfur instead.[13]

The catalytically active sites of some enzymes are actually part

13. J. R. Porter, *Bacterial Chemistry and Physiology* (New York: Wiley, 1946), pp. 635-661.

of smaller molecules attached to the large protein part. In some cases, these smaller "co-enzyme" molecules have been shown to have some catalytic power by themselves. This may give us a hint of a way the cycle of life might have begun without having to start with an already overwhelmingly complicated system. That is, the original bio-catalysts may have been much simpler than the enzymes we isolate today.[14]

At the borderline between the living and the non-living it becomes very difficult to decide where we would draw the line as to whether a given system was "alive" or not. Such a question was brought up by the discovery of viruses. Viruses are smaller than any other living things known (if indeed they are living organisms), and they cannot metabolize by themselves; but they can "infect" or invade a host cell and use the metabolic reactions of the cell to reproduce themselves. Viruses seem to have the "pattern" part of the reproductive apparatus (they are made up chiefly of nucleic acid) but lack the metabolic machinery for taking the energy out of foodstuffs to use for synthetic reactions. Are viruses alive? Probably not by our ordinary criteria, but they are certainly more complicated for their size than any clearly non-living things we know. And now biochemists have even taken certain viruses apart to yield stable smaller particles which could be put back together to yield the original virus with the same infective properties.[15] This work is certainly a long way from "creating life," as some newspaper stories called it, but it is impressive. It demonstrates that highly complex arrangements of atoms can be relatively stable apart from metabolizing systems, and therefore *might* have preceded metabolism originally. (See Figs. 3, 4, and 5.)

Cytochemical studies also show that whole units of a cell's metabolic machinery may be associated with definite sub-cellular structures in the protoplasm, and that these may be isolated in a condition that is still functional. For example, from bacteria a subcellular membranous material has been separated which still has the ability to synthesize enzymes, even though it is now much less complicated than the cell of which it was a part.[16] It is not unreasonable to imagine that the first organisms with complete metabolic systems

14. Melvin Calvin, "Chemical Evolution and the Origin of Life," *American Scientist*, XXXXIV (1956), 248-263.

15. H. Fraenkel-Conrat and R. C. Williams, "Reconstitution of Active Tobacco Mosaic Virus from its Inactive Protein and Nucleic Acid Components, *"Proceedings of the National Academy of Sciences of the United States of America*, XXXXI (1955), 690-698. For a popular account, see H. Fraenkel-Conrat, "Rebuilding a Virus," *Scientific American*, CLXXXXIV (1956), 42-47.

16. O. E. Landman and S. Spiegelman, "Enzyme Formation in Protoplasts of *Bacillus megaterium*," *Proceedings of the National Academy of Sciences of the United States of America*, XXXXI (1955), 698-704.

could have been formed by the union of several less complex systems, each of which had the power to catalyze certain types of reactions. This would be a prototype of the "symbiosis" biologists are familiar with among living organisms.

GEOCHEMICAL CONSIDERATIONS:
THE ORIGIN OF ORGANIC COMPOUNDS

The lines of evidence mentioned above give us suggestions about what *might* have happened. To get more definite information about what *did* occur, we would have to find out, if possible, the nature of the earth's crust and atmosphere while life was originating, and then try to duplicate these conditions as closely as possible in the laboratory.

There is still considerable disagreement about the stages the earth went through before life actually appeared. One distinguished scientist, H. C. Urey, has emphasized that an entirely different type of atmosphere from our present one was probably characteristic of the earliest stages of the earth's history.[17] The main feature of this pre-biological atmosphere, according to Urey, was the presence of hydrogen and absence of oxygen, giving it *reducing* rather than *oxidizing* properties. Oxygen was originally in the form of water and metallic oxides, carbon in the form of carbides and methane, nitrogen possibly as ammonia. Urey believes that such conditions, while unfavorable to life as we know it today, would have promoted the formation of organic compounds which might later have been used in the original organisms. Urey's ideas have been challenged by other scientists,[18] but they have led to some interesting experiments.

A student of Urey's, Stanley L. Miller, tested Urey's hypothesis in 1953 by making up a "sample" of his proposed primitive atmosphere, circulating methane, water, ammonia, and hydrogen in a closed system through an electric arc. When he analyzed the aqueous solution at the end of several days, he found it to contain many different organic compounds, including several of the amino acids, the building blocks of proteins![19] Since then, many investigators have performed similar experiments using various sources of energy other

17. H. C. Urey, "On the Early Chemical History of the Earth and the Origin of Life," *Proceedings of the National Academy of Sciences of the United States of America*, XXXVIII (1952), 351-363.

18. W. W. Rubey, "Development of the Hydrosphere and Atmosphere, with Special Reference to the Probable Composition of the Early Atmosphere," *Geological Society of America, Special Paper No. 62*, (1955), pp. 631-650.

19. S. L. Miller, "Production of Some Organic Compounds Under Possible Primitive Earth Conditions," *Journal of the American Chemical Society*, LXXVII (1955), 2351-2361.

than an electric discharge, and have shown that many types of compounds can be produced.[20]

If the evidence for such drastically different atmospheric conditions during the early stages of earth's history is really good, there seems no reason to doubt that the formation of organic compounds *did* occur before life originated. In fact, we would have to conclude that at least the simpler compounds *must* have been formed, since their formation under similar conditions has now been demonstrated in the laboratory.

THE BIG PROBLEM: FORMATION OF COLLOIDAL SYSTEMS

The next step, the combination of these simpler organic molecules into the giant "colloidal" complexes of protein and nucleic acid, is the step about which we have the least information at present. We do know of certain types of molecular aggregation to form colloidal systems, but the formation of the biologically important polymers has not been observed under any conditions except the influence of an already living cell or a metabolizing sub-unit of a living cell. Some enzymes have been isolated which catalyze certain steps in the synthesis of proteins and nucleic acids, but the details of the over-all processes are not yet known. Providing an adequate explanation for the original aggregation into complex but stable colloidal systems is probably now the most serious problem for any proposed mechanism for the origin of life.

In recent years, as we have learned more about the structure of the biological polymers, we have begun to appreciate some of the forces (such as hydrogen-bonding) which may actually confer stability to such large molecules. It may be that when we know more about such forces, the spontaneous formation of large molecules under certain conditions may seem much more reasonable than it does today. It is also possible that these polymeric molecules of importance to living things now may not be directly related to the original aggregates. It is impossible to imagine life getting started without *some* kind of structure, but there are other types of structural molecules which might have been utilized in the beginnings of life. J. D. Bernal has suggested the concentration of organic molecules by absorption on clay, a substance whose catalytic power still makes it of use in certain industrial applications; "right-handed" and "left-handed" quartz crystals in such clay might even have helped give rise to the molecular asymmetry now characteristic of

20. For references to some original papers, see S. W. Fox, "Origin of Protein," in Letters, *Chemical and Engineering News*, XXXV (1957), x.

biological molecules.[21] A number of other suggestions have been made, some probably more logical than others, but there is no basic reason to doubt that considerable structural organization could have occurred by natural processes before the first "living" organisms came into being.[22]

It may be helpful to consider a "model" of such an aggregating process. Take a number of short pieces of wire with a hook bent in one end and a ring in the other. Each small "molecule" is obviously more stable individually than a chain of them linked together; but if they are allowed to "react" by shaking them together in a hat, they will spontaneously form "polymers," and it will be easier to reach in with a hook and "isolate" one of these "unstable" chains than one of the "stable" small molecules! In other words, certain small, reactive molecules may be regarded as having a tendency to aggregate "built into" their structures.

HOW DID LIFE ORIGINATE? SCIENTIFIC EVIDENCE

It now seems reasonable to believe that the earth's early atmosphere and the constitution of its crust favored the formation of organic compounds, at least locally, and that over the long periods of pre-biological time very large amounts of chemical energy were accumulated in this way.

It seems highly possible, although still not clearly demonstrated, that natural forces existed which would have favored the formation of highly complex molecules and aggregates of such molecules, and that the chemical structures of such complexes could have had some ability to catalyze certain types of chemical reactions. If any of the reactions catalyzed were more favorable to the synthesis of the catalyst than others, a mechanism such as "natural selection" could begin operating, even at this pre-biological level.[23] Gradually, this process could conceivably lead to increased catalytic efficiency, given the randomness characteristic of molecular interactions and sufficient time.

21. J. D. Bernal, "The Origin of Life," New Biology, No. 16 (London: Penguin, 1954), pp. 28-40.

22. See discussions by J. B. S. Haldane, N. W. Pirie, and J. W. S. Pringle in New Biology, No. 16 (London: Penguin, 1954). See also G. Wald, "The Origin of Life," Scientific American, CLXXXXI, No. 2 (1954), 44-53; A. Gulick, "Phosphorus as a Factor in the Origin of Life," American Scientist, XXXXIII (1955), 479-489; H. F. Blum, "Perspectives in Evolution," American Scientist, XXXXIII (1955), 595-610; S. W. Fox, "Evolution of Protein Molecules and Thermal Synthesis of Biochemical Substances," American Scientist, XXXXIV (1956), 347-359. See also references 10, 14, 23, and 24 of the present essay.

23. G. Allen, "Reflexive Catalysis, a Possible Mechanism of Molecular Duplication in Prebiological Evolution," American Naturalist, XCI (1957), 65-77. See also reference 14, above.

It also seems likely that many of the metabolic reactions of modern living things could have arisen separately in these pre-living complexes, and that a complete metabolic machine may have appeared only after long periods of "chemical evolution" of such systems.

There are many interesting suggestions and some evidence concerning the possible sequence of metabolic pathways developed by the first living things.[24] Energy requirements may have first been met by utilizing the energy of pyrophosphate or other inorganic molecules, later by rearrangement of the atoms in certain organic compounds (anaerobic fermentation), then by photosynthesis, and finally by oxidative metabolism; it is possible that these developments may have taken place over the long periods of time required for a change from a reducing atmosphere to an oxidizing atmosphere. Indeed, the development of such processes may have been an essential part of this change, for example, in the liberation of free oxygen into the atmosphere by photosynthesis and the production of atmospheric carbon dioxide.

While there is still much uncertainty about these things, there is no reason to believe that logically necessary "gaps" will remain as our understanding develops. The possibility of doing experiments to settle some of these questions is now fairly good, and many scientists are interested in doing them.[25] This does not mean that scientists will necessarily ever be able to "create life," although this certainly seems within the range of scientific possibility; it does mean, however, that reputable scientists *do* have faith that life arose from inanimate matter through a series of physico-chemical processes no different from those we can observe today. If Christians cannot accept this, at least as a legitimate hypothesis, there will inevitably be conflict at this point.

HOW DID LIFE ORIGINATE? BIBLICAL PASSAGES

The emphasis of the entire Bible is on an omnipotent God who is the Author of the whole universe and all that it contains. The explicit passages in Genesis describe his creative activity in the form of a brief but beautifully poetic narrative, emphasizing his divine purpose and the orderliness of his plan as it unfolds. It seems to the authors of this chapter, who are biochemists and perhaps prejudiced by their scientific training, that the Bible gives little specific information about the *ways* in which God has worked in nature, possibly

24. S. Kirkwood, "The Origin of Life," *Chemistry in Canada*, VIII (1956), 25-30.
25. W. P. Woodring, "Conference on Biochemistry, Paleoecology, and Evolution," *Proceedings of the National Academy of Sciences of The United States of America*, XXXX (1954), 219-224.

because such details are irrelevant to the major theme of his revelation of himself. The type of physico-chemical mechanisms he may have used in the creation of life seems to be left as an open question. The Bible does unequivocally state that God *is* the Creator and that therefore we are indebted to him and responsible to him; this statement is intended to have the same impact on all men whether or not they understand the mechanism of enzyme synthesis or the thermodynamics of open systems. Men may believe in him as Creator or reject him, but they cannot legitimately claim to do so on the grounds of their understanding or lack of understanding of nature. It does seem clear that the biblical description of God's creative activity may include an instantaneous, explosive, *ex nihilo* type as well as a sustaining or developing type; admittedly our word symbols become inadequate as we try to grasp the significance of either of these concepts. Some writers use the term "special creation" for the first type, and many "creationists" seem to place their major emphasis on special creation.

A CHRISTIAN VIEW OF THE ORIGIN OF LIFE

Many devout Christians have found little difficulty in accepting the evidence for the age of the earth presented in an earlier chapter and the gradual development of living forms to be discussed in subsequent chapters, regarding this as an illustration of God's use of natural forces in a process of continuous creative activity. Where large gaps in the record of geological or biological development exist, some Christians have felt these to be evidence for God's special intervention in a sudden creative act, while others have not felt the necessity for such a belief. The gap between non-living matter and life has always seemed so large, however, that most Christians have probably felt a need to assume at this point an extraordinary and sudden act of special creation.

A number of scientists themselves, particularly in the past, have been so impressed by the complexity of living things that they have emphasized that only a highly improbable event could bring matter into such an intricate arrangement. Many Christians have eagerly accepted such conclusions as that of Lecomte du Noüy[26] as indicative that life must have arisen by a sudden (i.e., highly improbable) creative act of God. But most scientists regard Lecomte du Noüy's probability calculations as meaningless because they are convinced that the gap from the non-living to life was bridged gradually over long periods of geologic time and not in a single "jump." Moreover,

---

26. P. Lecomte du Nouy, *Human Destiny* (New York: Longmans, Green, 1947). Paperbound (New York: New American Library, 1949), pp. 30-39.

there is considerable danger in assuming a sudden supernatural intervention as the only possible interpretation of an observed event which, on the basis of our present knowledge, we regard as highly improbable. A Christian must be as ready to acknowledge God as the ultimate cause of phenomena he can understand as he is ready to say "God must have done this" when he does not understand the mechanisms behind some phenomenon; if not, he will find his concept of God shrinking instead of growing with his understanding of God's creation. To any person who regards the Bible as God's revelation there remains, of course, the legitimate question of limitations imposed by the actual words of Scripture. The authors of this chapter consider the expressions in Scripture regarding the creation of life to be sufficiently figurative to imply little or no limitation on possible mechanisms. Others may disagree with this conclusion.

Scientific investigations must always be mechanistic in their outlook, because it is only in this narrowed frame of reference that the scientific method can operate.[27] It is probably true that many nonbelievers have welcomed mechanistic interpretations of phenomena, and especially of the origin of life, feeling that such interpretations would make belief in God unnecessary. Such an attitude is indicative of a basic misunderstanding of the Christian idea of God and the way by which we come to know him. Belief in God is never forced upon us, no matter what our level of understanding of natural processes. God cannot be found by scientific knowledge any more than he can by scientific ignorance. The mechanistic view and the teleological, philosophical, or theological view of nature are complementary to each other and not antithetical.

The problem of the origin of life illustrates this situation. How did life originate? The Christian may answer unhesitatingly, "God created it," but he should realize that this is not a complete answer. The scientist may say, "We are not yet certain, but probably it happened something like this —," and outline the sort of reasoning presented in this chapter and the evidence behind it. But even if he could describe precisely the mechanisms by which life came into being, his answer could still never be a complete one by itself.

How did life originate? The concerted attempt to find an answer to this fascinating question by the experimental method is just beginning. There are now many attractive theories to be tested and modified by new information from many areas of investigation. No one can accurately predict the extent of new discoveries or the effects

27. See John Baillie's address to the British Association meeting in Edinburgh, 1951, entitled, "Natural Science and the Spiritual Life," published in full by Oxford, and in shortened form as "Christianity in an Age of Science," in *Science and Faith Today* (London: Lutterworth, 1953).

they may have on our concepts of nature and of life itself. Christians need not regard this great adventure of discovery with suspicion or fear, but may take part in it enthusiastically and even joyfully, confident that they are in a sense thinking the Creator's thoughts after him as they learn to understand his ways. After all, we believe that God has created life — why should we not be interested in how he created it?

Chapter Four

GENETICS

By Donald S. Robertson and John Sinclair

INTRODUCTION

The average person is of the opinion that the idea of evolution began with Darwin, whereas natural explanations of plant and animal origins had been proposed for some time prior to the publication of *The Origin of Species by Means of Natural Selection.* One might well ask, then, what was so unique about Darwin's theory that won for it such wide acceptance, while earlier ones had failed? One of the most important reasons for its success was his suggested *mechanism* known as "natural selection." This mechanism is based on the theory of Malthus who held that living things tend to multiply faster than their food supply. Darwin suggested that as a result of the ensuing overpopulation there would be a struggle for the existing food, and those organisms with traits that would bestow the greatest advantage in this struggle would succeed in producing the most offspring, while those with less advantageous or detrimental traits would not be so successful.[1] In this way nature is continually selecting new traits from the reservoir of variation found in a population, which in time will be incorporated into the species as a whole.

Natural selection is as important to the theory of evolution today as it was when Darwin first suggested it. In this chapter we shall be concerned with one aspect of natural selection, namely, the factors responsible for variation within a population — the variation within which nature does its selecting.

The fact that there is considerable variety in living forms was as obvious to Darwin as it is to us. He made much of the variations exhibited by the breeds of pigeons, horses, and other domesticated animals. Such variations are found in most populations of living things, including man. In fact, interracial differences exhibited by the human population serve as an excellent example of variation

1. For the sake of simplicity, only the struggle that results from a limited food supply has been considered. Darwin, however, recognized that other limiting factors in an organism's environment would enter into this struggle for existence.

within a species. Variability is one of the outstanding characteristics of most species; this is true not only for animals but also for plants and is found even in the bacteria and viruses.

Although Darwin was impressed by variation in populations of living things, and made use of this fact in his theory, he never could explain adequately what was responsible for producing it. This was because the mechanism of inheritance was not understood by the biologist of his day. Many accepted the erroneous belief that environmentally induced changes in organisms were passed on to their offspring, a theory known as the inheritance of acquired characteristics. Darwin's theory of inheritance was an attempt to explain how the environment could induce changes in the hereditary material. To do this he proposed the mechanism of pangenesis in 1868.[2] He thought that little particles called "gemmules" were continually passing from all parts of the body to the reproductive organs. When the environment modified a part, this would induce a corresponding change in the gemmules which through incorporation into the hereditary stream would be transmitted to their offspring.

A theory of evolution demands a hereditary mechanism which will explain the origin of variation in a population and for the inheritance of variations once they are produced. However, the biological world knew of none until 1900, when three scientists, de Vries, Correns, and von Tschermak, learned that the discovery of such a mechanism had been reported in 1865 by an Austrian monk named Gregor Mendel. Mendel, working with peas in a monastery garden, in what is now Czechoslovakia, discovered the basic principles of heredity which laid the foundation for all modern work in this field. The results of his experiments were reported to the Natural History Society of Brunn in 1865 and published in the annual proceedings of this society in 1866.[3]

Thus in 1900 the modern study of heredity began, based on the fundamental laws first discovered by Mendel and substantiated thereafter by many other workers. From these studies the field of science called genetics developed. It is this field which provides the modern evolutionist with the explanation for the origin of variation and its transmission that is necessary for his theory.

To understand inherited variation we must know the basis of the *differences* among individuals. Have you ever wondered why one person has brown eyes, another gray, or another blue, or why some

2. Charles R. Darwin, *The Variation of Animals and Plants Under Domestication* (New York and London: Appleton, 1920), II, 338-387.
3. For an English translation of this paper see Edmund W. Sinnott, L. C. Dunn and Th. Dobzhansky, *Principles of Genetics* (4th ed.; New York: McGraw-Hill, 1950), pp. 463-493.

have red hair while others have brown or blond? The geneticist has been able to show that these traits and many others are determined by factors called "genes" that are passed from one generation to another through the sex cells of the parents.

THE GENE

What are these units of heredity, called genes, that are so important to genetics? Although they are too small for the scientist to see, he has nonetheless been able to accumulate considerable information about them. For example, he knows that genes are carried on chromosomes, thread-like structures found in the nucleus of the cell, which have been known and studied for some time. By the beginning of this century it had been determined that there was a very precise mechanism called "mitosis" for distributing the chromosomes to each daughter cell in cell division (Fig. 6), and a complicated set of divisions called "meiosis" for distributing them to the sex cells (Fig. 7). These observations led workers to speculate that the chromosomes might be the carriers of the genes. It was finally possible, by making use of aberrant changes in these structures, to show that this was actually the case and even to locate which particular region of a chromosome controls a given trait. For example, a duplication on the X chromosome of the fruit fly *Drosophila* results in an eye resembling a bar, suggesting that this segment of the chromosome is responsible for the normal development of the eye.

Thus, in spite of not being able to see the genes, the geneticist has been able to demonstrate that they are carried on the chromosomes of the nucleus, and even has been able to locate specific genes in specific regions of the chromosomal complement. However, the scientist has had considerable difficulty in determining just what it is at a particular gene locus that is responsible for producing a given effect. Recent research has enabled him to make several operational assumptions about the nature of the gene.

Work on the chemistry of genes would seem to indicate that very probably they are made up of desoxyribose nucleic acid (DNA), a complicated organic compound. A model of the DNA molecule, recently proposed by Watson and Crick,[4] has stimulated a great amount of interest and speculation. This work on the structure of DNA, coupled with recent studies of its synthesis during cell division,

---

4. J. D. Watson and F. H. C. Crick, "Molecular Structure of Nucleic Acids," *Nature*, CLXXI (1953), 737-738. Cf. also ch. 3 of this book. J. D. Watson and F. H. C. Crick, "The Structure of DNA," *Cold Spring Harbor Symposia of Quantitative Biology*, XVIII (1953), 123-131.

has led to the suggestion of several possible models of how chromosomes and genes are duplicated.[5] (See Fig. 2.)

Genes are also usually considered to be indivisible by crossing-over (see pp. 76f.), and often are considered to be associated with a single primary physiological effect, like the change in a single enzyme.[6] Another characteristic typical of genes is their ability to change or mutate. Such changed genes are faithfully reproduced through many generations until they are in turn changed. Individuals showing the characteristics of the mutation are called mutants and will, of course, differ from their ancestors in the trait controlled by that gene. Since, for the most part, genes are very stable, they only very rarely undergo mutation. In man, for example, it has been estimated that the mutation which produces hemophilia (the bleeder's disease) occurs only thirty-two times out of every million sex cells produced. Other genes of man show similar stability with mutation rates of one in 10 to 80 million sex cells.[7] In spite of the fact that individual genes are stable, the process of mutation itself is not a rare event in living things because living things have thousands of genes which are potentially capable of mutating. For example, Morton, Crow, and Muller[8] have estimated that in man about .06-.15 lethal and detrimental mutations occur per sex cell per generation. The geneticist has found ways to speed up the mutation rate by treating living things with X-rays, mustard gas, ultraviolet light and other physical and chemical agents. For the most part, these merely speed up the over-all mutation rate, producing the same kinds of mutations which take place spontaneously. A gene can also be described as the unit which is modified in a mutant.

There has been much speculation as to what happens to a gene when it undergoes mutation, and how changes in the genes affect the appearance of the organism. In a bread mold, *Neurospora,* at least three different genetic strains are known that cannot complete the conversion of anthranilic acid to indole because they possess defective (mutated) genes controlling this step. Research has shown that these defective genes lie at the same place on a specific chromosome and thus are considered to be "alleles" (see p. 76). These alleles

5. Herbert Taylor, "Time and Mode of Duplication of Chromosomes," *The American Naturalist,* LXXXXI (1957), 209-221. J. Herbert Taylor, "The Duplication of Chromosomes," *Scientific American,* CLXXXXVIII (1958), 36-42.

6. Enzymes are organic catalysts which control most chemical reactions in living things.

7. James V. Neel and Harold F. Falls, "The Rate of Mutation of the Gene Responsible for Retinoblastoma in Man," *Science,* CXIV (1951), 419-422.

8. Newton E. Morton, James F. Crow and H. J. Muller, "An Estimate of Mutational Damage in Man from Data on Consanguineous Marriages," *Proceedings of the National Academy of Sciences, U. S.,* XXXXII (1956), 855-863.

could be the result of various changes in the chemical structure of this section of the chromosome which would affect the surface configuration of this region. It has been suggested that such a modified surface would be reflected in the gene product (probably an enzyme) that controls this step in the production of indole. Since the shape of the enzyme is believed responsible for the way it initiates changes in the materials on which it works, one can readily visualize how changing its shape would affect its ability to work, just as a slight change in the shape of a key would affect its ability to open a lock. As a result of this lost or altered function of an enzyme, the chemistry of the organism will be altered, which in many instances will result in a changed appearance of the organism with the mutated gene.

How much of the area of the chromosome is responsible for the surface configuration (specificity) of a single enzyme? Are the chromosome areas overlapping, so that part of the area that determines one enzyme would also be a part of the template for another enzyme or another part of the same enzyme? These are questions which need to be answered before the gene can be adequately defined.

We see, then, that genes are not easy to define. If a mutant change is the loss of a single atom cluster, and if this cluster's place of attachment can be separated from other adjacent places of attachment by crossing over, this site could be considered a gene. If the mutant effect is due to a modified spatial integration of a chromosome segment, this segment could be considered a gene. The definition of the gene, then, is determined by the hierarchical level at which the modification occurs.

To summarize: the gene is considered to be the unit of heredity. At the present time the chemical structure of genes is felt to be closely related to DNA. Genes are known by the changed appearance of an organism when genic material is altered by a mutation. Mutations are thought to be caused by chemical changes in the gene. The mutation of a gene is thought to result in an altered enzyme which results in an altered chemistry. The place of mutation along the chromosome can be located. Genes may exert their effect by acting as a template. The size, spatial orientation, and integration of the genes are still almost unknown.

BASIC PRINCIPLES OF GENETICS

Although the scientist still has much to learn about what a gene is and how it operates in the living organism, nonetheless he has been able to discover a good deal about how genes behave when they are passed on from one generation to another. Mendel set forth the two basic principles of genetics in 1865: they are the principles of "segregation" and "independent assortment."

SEGREGATION

The carriers of the genes, the chromosomes, are present in the nuclei of the cells of an individual in two duplicate sets which are identical as to structure and the gene loci which they carry.[9] One of these sets is contributed by the mother through the egg and the other by the father through the sperm. Because of the paired condition of the chromosomes the gene loci are also paired. However, this does not mean that a gene found at a particular gene locus in a particular chromosome is always identical to its partner carried on the other chromosome of the pair. For example, there are three genes (A, B and O) that can occur at the gene locus responsible for determining the blood group to which a person belongs. The alternative forms of a gene which can occur at a particular gene locus are called "alleles." A person can have any two of these alternatives or alleles. Some people have two similar alleles (e.g., AA, blood type A; BB, blood type B; and OO, blood type O), while some have two different alternatives[10] (e.g., AB, blood type AB; AO, blood type A; and BO, blood type B).[11]

In the production of sex cells the chromosome number is reduced in half by meiosis (see Fig. 7). This is done in such a manner as to insure that each sex cell receives one member of each of the pairs of chromosomes. Since the sex cells carry only one representative of a pair of chromosomes, it follows that they will also carry only one representative of each pair of genes. If a person has two different alleles such as in the case of a person of AB blood type, these alleles will be segregated into different sex cells during meiosis, resulting in the production of two types in equal frequency: A-bearing and B-bearing.

INDEPENDENT ASSORTMENT

The principle of independent assortment states that at the time sex cells are formed different pairs of genes segregate independently.

---

9. There is one exception to this generalization, which forms the basis for the chromosomal method of determining sex. The generalization as outlined holds for females, but in males there is one pair of chromosomes where the members are not identical. In males this pair consists of one long chromosome (called X) and one short one (called Y). Females have two X chromosomes.

10. If the two alleles are alike the person is said to be "homozygous" for the gene (e.g., AA, OO, etc.), and if they are different he is "heterozygous" for the genes (e.g., AB, AO, etc.).

11. Notice that a person carrying the genes AO is A type. The O gene does not express itself in the presence of A (or B). A gene such as O, which is masked by the presence of its allele, is said to be "recessive," while the allele doing the masking is said to be "dominant." Since both A and B express themselves when they are present in a single individual they are said to be incompletely dominant with respect to each other.

Thus in man, who has been estimated to have about twelve thousand pairs of genes, this principle would imply that at the time sex cells are formed the alternatives of each of these pairs of genes are segregating independently of each other. However, it was soon found that the principle of independent assortment was an oversimplification, for genes that are carried on the same chromosome tend to be inherited together because of the physical linkage the chromosome provides. In spite of the fact that genes are carried on the same chromosome, they can still assort themselves with respect to each other by a process called "crossing-over" which allows for the exchange of chromosomal segments between pairs.

The behavior of genes at the time sex cells are formed has been compared to a game of chance which is played by the parents.[12] Each parent has a pair of counters (genes) corresponding to the twelve thousand or so hereditary traits. In playing the game each parent selects at random one counter from each pair and places it in a pile on the table. Each of these selections corresponds to a gene carried in a sex cell while the pile of counters represents the genetic endowment received by the child, and contains the same number that each of the parents possesses. Each time a sex cell is produced a new random selection of counters is made. As a result, no two sex cells a person produces carry quite the same combination of genes (counters). Since this is so, no two people, with the exception of identical twins, receive exactly the same hereditary material.

THE BASIC PRINCIPLES OF GENETICS AS APPLIED TO EVOLUTION

In the early part of this chapter it was pointed out that variability is essential for the evolutionary theory and that the lack of an explanation for variability was one of the shortcomings of Darwin's theory. Biologists today believe that the discoveries in the field of genetics which have been outlined above, have largely overcome this deficiency.

Genetic research has established that a population of organisms has many different alleles present, which are being shuffled continually through sexual reproduction and the accompanying segregation, independent assortment, and crossing-over. As a result of this shuffling, there are produced new combinations of hereditary traits. It is believed that the gene combinations are what the environment selects. As new gene combinations are realized, generation after generation, they interact with the environment; and those that produce favorable traits tend to survive whereas those resulting in unfavorable characteristics are lost. In this way the environment acts to alter the gene frequencies in the population. Thus, to the present-

12. N. H. Horowitz, "The Gene," *Scientific American*, CLXXXXV (1956), 78-90.

day biologist, evolution is basically the result of a "... change in the genetic composition of populations."[13]

POPULATION DYNAMICS

The study of the genetic constitution of whole populations is the concern of the population geneticist. He is interested in determining gene frequencies and how they change. Such men as Haldane, Fisher, Wright, and others have formulated the mathematical models necessary to explain these changes under various conditions and have evaluated the role of selection, mutation rates, and population size on gene frequencies. How some of these and other factors influence gene frequencies will now be considered.

POPULATION GROWTH

An understanding of the reproductive potential that is found in all populations is essential in the study of population genetics and natural selection. Populations tend to increase geometrically. If a small number of bacteria are placed in a test tube of nutrient, they will increase in numbers slowly at first, then more rapidly. Each parent divides into two bacteria, then each of them divides into two, so that at each cell division the number of bacteria is doubled. It is readily seen how rapidly the population soon begins to grow (Fig. 8).

A good example of the rapid growth of a population is demonstrated in a series of events that took place in Kearn County, California, in 1927. In the winters of 1924 and 1925 a campaign against the coyotes was conducted to protect the sheep. The poison that was put out killed weasels, kite, foxes, skunks, coyotes, and all the other mammalian predators of mice. There was abundant food and shelter in the grain and corn fields. The winters were mild, and the nesting habits of the mice protected them from the weather. Two years later sheep were grazed in this area, destroying the food and shelter. This led to a vast migration of hordes of mice. Entire haystacks were reduced to chaff. Two tons of mice were sifted out of a large granary in one day. Highways were slippery with dead mice. Mice were in people's clothes, on their beds at night, and chewing holes in the walls and flooring of their houses. Usually the number of mice is fairly constant. In this example, we have seen how an extermination of normal predators led to an increase, whereas the loss of their food and shelter by sheep grazing led to migration, loss of fertility, and wholesale slaughter.

Another example of a rapid population increase was found in the planting of fish in the Salton Sea. The first few broods had an

---

13. Theodosius Dobzhansky, *Genetics and the Origin of Species* (New York: Columbia University Press, 1951), p. 16.

abundance of food and practically no predation, so they increased rapidly in numbers. The number of deformed fish in these early broods was high; but in subsequent years they disappeared as competition became more intense. However, the defective genes responsible for them are still present, so that deformed fish will continue to be born, though they will be eliminated so rapidly by natural selection that they will be seen only rarely.

These examples of rapid population growth illustrate the latent abilities of a population to expand rapidly if allowed to do so. However, most populations are not able to multiply as rapidly as their potential will allow because of predation, limited food supply, etc. It is, in part, this continual tendency of a species to produce more offspring than can be accommodated within the species habitat that leads to the selective survival of the more beneficial gene combinations.

THE HARDY-WEINBERG FORMULA

The basic formula of population genetics is the Hardy-Weinberg formula for the frequency of genotypes in a random breeding population:

$$(pA + qa)^2 = p^2AA + 2\ pqAa + q^2aa, \text{ where } p + q = 1.$$

A and a represent allelic genes, p is the frequency of the A allele, and q is the frequency of the a allele. This formula can be used to determine gene frequencies and the frequencies of various genetic traits expected in a population once the gene frequencies have been determined (e.g., if: $p = 20\%$ and $q = 80\%$, then:

$$4\%\ AA + 32\%\ Aa + 64\%\ aa = 100\% \text{ of all kinds.)}$$

Variations of this formula can be used to predict gene frequencies under conditions of negative or positive selection. Strictly speaking, these formulas apply only in the ideal case where there is a large random breeding population in which every member of one sex is a potential mate of any individual of the opposite sex. These conditions are rarely, if ever, found, and therefore the answers given are only approximate.

POPULATION SIZE

The size of the population is thought to be very important in the evolution of a species. Gene frequencies change very slowly in large populations, but in small ones the change can sometimes be very rapid. In a small population a chance fluctuation in gene frequency can exert a tremendous effect upon the gene frequency in succeeding generations, while a similar fluctuation in a large population may hardly be noticed. A very simple example might be useful to illustrate this point. Assume a population where the alleles *A* and *a* are segregating. In this population there will be individuals that have the genes *AA,* those with *Aa* and those with *aa.* Now, assume that two members of this population with the genes *Aa* mate and produce four offspring. Each parent will produce *A* and *a* bearing sex cells in equal frequency (see p. 76). On the basis of chance, it is possible that only the *a* bearing sex cells from both parents will function in the formation of each offspring. If this happens the *A* gene is completely lost as far as the offspring of this union is concerned, resulting in only *aa* progeny. The laws of probability tell us that such an event is expected once out of every 256 matings where both parents are *Aa* and four offspring are produced. Now, if these parents were members of a large population the elimination of the *A* allele from their descendants would not affect the gene frequency appreciably, since there would be many other offspring produced from other matings and chance fluctuations in the opposite direction could be expected in these offspring, which would result in no net change in the gene frequencies. However, if the total population was a small one, consisting of no more than the two original parents, then this chance fluctuation could result in the complete elimination of one allele from the population. The frequency of *a* would change from 50 percent to 100 percent in one generation and of *A* from 50 percent to 0 percent. The change of gene frequency due to chance fluctuations like this is called "genetic drift." While this is a rather crude example of drift, it does serve to illustrate how population size can have a marked effect on the gene frequencies in a population and hence affect its evolution.

Today it is generally held that evolution proceeds most rapidly in a large population that has been subdivided into more or less isolated subgroups. Within the subgroups changes in gene frequencies can result due to mutation, drift, and selection more rapidly than if there was only one random breeding population.

Factors that could subdivide a population could be such things as physical barriers (e.g., mountain ranges), sexual incompatibility (either physiological or psychological in origin) or other barriers occurring in a portion of the range of the population.

SELECTION

Certain recent events are probably the result of the incorporation of rare genes by most individuals of a population. In certain areas where DDT was used as a fly spray, the farmers began to notice that an increasing number of the flies were no longer being killed by the fly spray. These flies were the survivors of the original few which possessed genetic resistance to DDT. This same sort of resistance to poisons has been found among bacteria. In one case where it has been possible to determine the biochemical basis for resistance it was found that an essential enzyme had a reduced affinity for its metabolite, but its affinity for the drug was reduced *way down,* so that even though the normal metabolite was processed less efficiently, the enzyme now was scarcely hindered by the drug. These examples and the sickle-cell anemia example (see pp. 82f.) illustrate how mutations can give a selective advantage and so increase in their relative frequency.

To summarize: it needs to be emphasized that many of the conclusions of population genetics are only tentative. In many instances, they have been arrived at by purely mathematical means which frequently include some simplifying assumptions. Their validity can be determined only through their application to populations as we find them in nature. This has not always been done. With this in mind, we have seen that populations have a tendency to increase geometrically, but that usually there is a relatively constant number of individuals. It is known that populations possess variability and are characterized by the frequency patterns of this variety. It is also known that on the average the better adapted individuals in any situation usually survive and pass on their genes, resulting in changes in gene frequencies. Formulas that enable the geneticist to estimate gene frequencies and their rate of change under different conditions have been derived.

How are the results of modern genetics related to Darwin's theory of evolution? Darwin understood geometrical increase and environmental checks leading to the survival of those organisms better adapted. He did not know the nature of, nor the origin of, variability. He thought that its source was unlimited and that it could occur in any direction. He did not understand the way in which a population responds to natural selection. He thought that variations selected against were lost. He did not know that the genes for the eliminated traits and their mutation potential remained. He believed that varieties selected were preserved, not knowing that any particular gene combination in sexually reproducing organisms is lost with the individual possessing it, and will never be repeated. He did not know that evolution can occur only by a change in gene frequencies or by new genes.

AREAS OF DIFFICULTY

Most of what has been considered so far has been only introductory, to familiarize the reader with basic genetic principles and how they are thought to apply to evolution. However, in applying these principles there are certain areas of difficulty that should be considered in some detail.

MUTATIONS

Thus far, it has been shown that heritable variability results from variability in the genes of the population. However, to explain evolution it will be necessary to know what is responsible for producing new variations in the genes. As evolution proceeds, it does so at the expense of existing variation and therefore there must be a continual source of new ones. This source is the process of mutation which was described above (see p. 74).

One of the outstanding characteristics of the vast majority of mutations, which has not been mentioned as yet, is the harmful effects they produce in the organism possessing them. This creates somewhat of a problem for the modern theory of evolution. "The mutation process constantly and unremittingly generates new hereditary variants — gene mutations and chromosomal changes. These variants accumulate in populations of sexually reproducing and cross-fertilizing organisms, and form a great store of potential variability.... And yet, a majority of mutations, both those arising in laboratories and those stored in natural populations, produce deteriorations of viability, hereditary diseases, and monstrosities. Such changes, it would seem, can hardly serve as evolutionary building blocks."[14] However, within recent years, with the study of the genetics of microorganisms, beneficial mutations have been demonstrated. These are mutations that impart resistance to drugs and antibiotics. However, the significance of such mutations in the total evolution of a form is somewhat difficult to evaluate.

Several hypotheses are suggested to explain why most mutations observed today are detrimental:

(1) It is postulated that mutations rarely, if ever, affect just one characteristic of the organism, for beside the most obvious changes produced, there are other less obvious ones. It may be that in some instances the most obvious change might be detrimental while some of the less obvious associated changes may have real adaptive advantages that balance or outweigh the harmful effect. The mutation responsible for sickle-cell anemia in man may be an example of such a case. People suffering from this disease have red blood cells which form a sickle shape. The sickle-cells are destroyed and a severe anemia results. It has been shown that people suffering from this disease have an abnormal type of hemoglobin which is responsible for the distortion of the red blood cells.[15] Some people have a mixture of both the normal and the sickled type and are said to have the sickle-cell trait. Such individuals do not seem to be incapacitated,

14. *Ibid.*, p. 73.
15. Linus Pauling, Harvey A. Itano, S. J. Singer and Ibert C. Wells, "Sickle Cell Anemia, a Molecular Disease," *Science*, CX (1949), 543-548.

while those with 65 percent or more sickle-cell hemoglobin suffer with anemia. Neel[16] has presented evidence that those suffering from the disease have two doses of the sickle-cell gene, while those with the trait have one sickle-cell gene and one gene for normal hemoglobin.

Allison[17] has shown that persons with the sickle-cell trait are less susceptible to malaria than those without it. Of fifteen adults having the trait who were inoculated with malaria, only one caught it, while fourteen out of the fifteen individuals without the trait who were inoculated with malaria came down with it. This resistance to malaria could explain why up to 40 percent of some tropical populations have this trait, in spite of the fact that individuals who receive two doses of the gene will almost inevitably die from anemia. This harmful mutation has been retained and its frequency built up by selection, because those who receive only one dose of it survive malaria better than those who have normal hemoglobin. In populations where malaria is not found this mutation is extremely rare, because of the high mortality of those possessing a double dose.

(2) Some have suggested another reason why most mutations observed today are harmful.[18] Since the process of mutation has been going on in a given population for some time, all the mutations which are advantageous to the population under a given set of environmental conditions have already been incorporated as part of the characteristics of the species. Any additional alteration by mutation is apt to upset this delicate balance. It is only as the species enters a new environment with new adaptive demands that many mutations will have a chance of being advantageous.

(3) Another explanation as to why observed mutations do not appear to have survival value is that the mutations which are normally observed are those that produce marked changes in the organism. These are more likely to be harmful than those that cause only slight alterations. However, the latter types of changes are so subtle that they are often overlooked. It is thought that evolution really proceeds by the accumulation of many of these "micro-mutations," each of which produces such a small difference that its effect cannot be observed readily. Thus only the more obvious

16. James V. Neel, "The Inheritance of Sickle Cell Anemia," *Science*, CX (1949), 64-66.

17. A. C. Allison, "Protection Afforded by Sickle Cell Trait against Subtertian Malaria Infection," *British Medical Journal*, I (1954), 290-294. Allison, "Aspects of Polymorphism in Man," *Cold Spring Harbor Symposia on Quantitative Biology*, XX (1955), 239-255. Allison, "Sickle Cells and Evolution," *Scientific American*, CLXXXXV (1956), 87-94.

18. Edward O. Dodson, *Genetics* (Philadelphia: Saunders, 1956), pp. 227-228. Adrian M. Srb and Ray D. Owen, *General Genetics* (San Francisco: W. H. Freeman, 1952), p. 253.

detrimental mutations are seen while the small mutations which include the beneficial ones go unnoticed.

NEW GENES

A successful theory of evolution not only requires an adequate explanation of variation, but it must also include a mechanism for producing new genes. It is reasonable to assume that most, if not all, of the genes in the ancestors of a form control activities essential to the life of the organism. Therefore, as new functions are added, new genes will be required to control these. What is the source of these new genes? One theory is that they come from the duplication of old ones.[19] This process of duplication has been observed in living things. It is known that short segments of a chromosome can be duplicated, as well as whole chromosomes and complete chromosomal complements. Such duplications result in extra genic material which, it is reasoned, are now free to change by the process of mutation to take on new functions. E. B. Lewis summarizes this process as follows: "We hold to the viewpoint that new genes arise from pre-existing genes, and we picture the origin of a new gene as being generally accomplished by a two-step process: namely, (1) the establishment of a duplication of that gene (or a higher repetition) and (2) the occurrence in one of the two (or more) genes thus formed of a 'mutation to a new function,' the result of which will be termed the 'new gene.' "[20] The work with pseudo-alleles has been suggested as evidence to support the contention that genes can take on new functions.

In the section on basic principles of genetics, it was mentioned that frequently more than one form of a gene can occur at a particular location on a chromosome, and that the different possible forms are called alleles. For most of the mutations that geneticists work with there are at least two alleles, the normal one found in most individuals of the population and the mutant form. However, some loci can have many alleles. For example, in the fruit fly *Drosophila* there are at least twelve different alleles known to occur at the white eye locus on the sex chromosome. One characteristic of alleles is that they usually affect the same structure of the organism and usually produce similar changes. Thus, all the alleles at the white-eye locus affect eye color and, generally speaking, reduce the amount of pigmentation from that produced by the normal allele. Frequently genes at different loci in the chro-

19. G. W. Beadle, "Genes and Biological Enigmas," *Science in Progress*, ed. G. A. Baitsell. (Sixth series; New Haven: Yale University Press, 1949), pp. 244-245.
20. E. B. Lewis, "Pseudo Allelism and Gene Evolution," *Cold Spring Harbor Symposia of Quantitative Biology*, XVI (1951), 159.

mosomal complement can produce similar effects. Although the effects produced are similar, such genes are not allelic since they occur at different positions on the chromosome. Thus, appearance alone is not a sufficient criterion for judging if two genes are allelic. It must also be demonstrated that they occupy the same gene locus. Let us take an example to make this point clear. Suppose that there are two flies that have white eyes. How are we going to find out if the gene responsible for white eyes in fly A is an allele to that in fly B? The standard test is to breed them with one another. If the genes are non-allelic, the trait will not show up in their immediate offspring.

Another characteristic of allelic genes is that they cannot be separated by crossing-over (see pp. 76f.) because they occupy the same place on homologous chromosomes. According to the classical theory of genetics, crossing-over can take place only between non-allelic genes. However, this simple picture was disturbed when several workers succeeded in getting crossovers between two genes that otherwise behaved as alleles (i.e., had similar effects and showed the mutant trait when combined in one individual). In these instances we have genes that behave as alleles as far as the expression of their traits are concerned, but not as far as crossing over is concerned. Such genes are called pseudo-alleles.[21]

How does this work with pseudo-alleles support the biologist's theory as to the origin of new genes? It will be recalled that geneticists have suggested that a new gene results from the duplication of an old one and the subsequent mutation of one of the duplicated genes so that it can perform a new function. It has already been pointed out that the geneticist has had evidence for the duplication of genes for some time, usually involving whole blocks of them. However, evidence for the second step was lacking until the discovery of pseudo-alleles. Some geneticists feel that pseudo-alleles demonstrate a mechanism which accomplishes both of the required steps. For here are genes that for a long time were thought to be alleles but now are shown to be closely adjacent genes that have very similar, though in most cases slightly different, effects. The most widely accepted explanation for this has been that pseudo-alleles represent duplicated genes, as evidenced by their similar effect on the organism, which are beginning to diverge in function, as evidenced by slight functional differences that are usually observed. Now the geneticist is making two assumptions here: (1) that the gene is particulate in nature, and (2) that crossing-over takes place only between genes. However,

21. For a good review of work in this field see: M. M. Green, E. B. Lewis, J. R. Laughnan, Clyde Stormont, and S. G. Stephens, "Symposium on Pseudo-allelism and the Theory of the Gene," *American Naturalist*, LXXXIX (1955), 65-122.

if some slight changes are made in the usual assumptions, most of the work with pseudo-alleles no longer appears to be convincing as evidence for the origin of new genes (one can only be speculative here, since the gene cannot be seen).

If it is assumed that some genes, while being particulate in nature, can at the same time be rather large particles consisting of two or three subparts which can be separated by crossing-over — a separable complex, in other words — and that this complex does not function correctly unless it has all the normal parts present, then pseudo-alleles cannot be thought of as genes on the way to taking on a new function. The different pseudo-alleles would then represent alleles in which a different part of the gene-complex had been changed. The crossing-over which is observed between pseudo-alleles would be responsible for recombining different parts of the complex. One may think that the difference in these two pictures is just a matter of terminology. However, the basic difference between these two views is that the traditional one visualizes the pseudo-allele as being a series of closely linked genes, each of which has a different function, whereas the complex-gene view visualizes them as being all one large gene responsible for only one function but with the ability to be altered in different regions which can be separated by crossing over. Much of the evidence from pseudo-alleles can be interpreted on this basis.

CHROMOSOMAL EVOLUTION

The chromosomal complement is an important anatomical feature which can be used in the classification of living organisms. Studies have revealed that there is considerable variation in the chromosomal pattern of different species. One very useful variation is in the number. Each species is characterized by a given number of chromosomes (see Chapter 5). For example, man has 46, the fruit fly 8, the corn plant 20. Besides number, other criteria can be used in distinguishing the chromosomes of different species, such as the relative lengths of the different chromosomes, and certain internal structural patterns. When species which are similar anatomically are studied they are often found to have similar chromosomal patterns, which had led to the conclusion that change in the anatomical pattern of a species is frequently accompanied by change in the chromosomal pattern. Rather extensive analyses of these chromosomal differences have been made between some species of both plants and animals. It has been found that in many instances the differences can be explained by changing the sequence of genes within the chromosomes and by exchange of blocks of genes between chromosomes of two different pairs. The changes in the chromosomes in which the order of genes is inverted are called "inversions." Those changes which involve the transfer of blocks of genes from one chromosome to a chromosome of a different pair are called "translocations." It has been demonstrated that such changes take place spontaneously, and can also be induced by treatment with X-ray and other radiations. Analysis of chromosome pairing in inter-species hybrids of *Drosophila* reveals differences in species which can be explained by the accumulation of inversions and translocations.[22] In *Drosophila,* inversions seem to have occurred much more frequently than translocations while in other organisms such as the plant *Crepis,* and the fly *Sciara,* differences between closely related species seem more often to involve translocations.

These chromosomal rearrangements are thought to play an important role in evolution in at least two ways. First, they help to form a sterility barrier between incipient species, and secondly, they produce associated anatomical changes.

These chromosomal rearrangements are sometimes heterozygous (i.e., one set of normal chromosomes and one set with an inversion or translocation). When they are they lower fertility. An individual heterozygous for a translocation produces less offspring than one homozygous (i.e., both sets of chromosomes carrying the same arrangement) for the normal arrangement. Inversions also lower fertility when heterozygous. However, in many instances, when a species becomes homozygous for an inversion or translocation, normal fertility is restored. This is particularly true for plants. In *Drosophila,* most translocations are lethal when homozygous, but some are known which lower the viability little if at all. If sufficient homozygous translocations and inversions are accumulated in one individual, the hybrid between it and the parental stock would be completely sterile. This is suggested as having happened in some *Drosophila* species which have been analyzed.[23] However, there are a couple of difficulties with this hypothesis. One is that the heterozygotes in many instances produce less offspring than those not carrying the rearrangement and would thus be at a competitive disadvantage. However, Dobzhansky and Pavlovsky[24] have described a case in *Drosophila tropicalis* where flies heterozygous for an inversion seem to have an adaptive advantage over normal flies, which suggests that it might be possible to overcome the harmful effects of sterility if advantageous genes are

22. Theodosius Dobzhansky and C. C. Tan, "Studies on Hybrid Sterility, III: A Comparison of the Gene Arrangement in Two Species, *Drosophila pseudoobscura and Drosophila miranda,*" *Zeitschrift für Induktive Abstammungs-und Vererbungslehre,* LXXII (1936), 88-144.

23. *Ibid.*

24. Theodosius Dobzhansky and Olga Pavlovsky, "An Extreme Case of Heterosis in a Central American Population of *Drosophila tropicalis,*" *Proceedings of the National Academy of Sciences, U. S.,* XXXXI (1955), 289-295.

associated with a rearrangement. Another difficulty in the way of accumulating many chromosomal rearrangements is, as has been mentioned above, that most of them are lethal when homozygous in *Drosophila*. However, viable homozygous translocations are known, so it may just be a matter of accumulating the proper ones. It should also be mentioned that in plants most homozygous rearrangements such as inversions and translocations do not seem to affect viability in the least.

Chromosomal rearrangements are thought to be important in the evolution of some forms not only because they produce a sterility barrier, but also because they produce anatomical changes as well. This is thought to be true in forms like *Drosophila*, and, to a lesser extent, in plants. In *Drosophila* there are frequently found changes in the gene action associated with a change in position such as takes place when chromosomal rearrangements are induced. Such changes are called position effects.[25] Thus rearrangements can also change the appearance of an organism by altering the genes in its immediate neighborhood.

To summarize: in this section we have considered some of the difficulties with the mechanism of evolution as proposed by the geneticist. These difficulties lie in three areas: (1) mutations as the origin of new variation, (2) the origin of new genes, and (3) chromosomal evolution. Although we have seen that there are difficulties in each of these areas, we have also seen that there have been proposed plausible explanations which have suggested how evolution might proceed in spite of them. In most instances these explanations are based on rather meager evidence, yet they are consistent with present-day knowledge and therefore serve as useful working hypotheses for future work in these areas. Only time and further experimentation will tell if they are valid.

This means that at the present time two positions are possible with respect to the difficulties. One can assume that they represent a basic deficiency in the modern theory of evolution. Hence, they stand as a testimony to its non-validity. Or one can assume that the theory of evolution is true and that these difficulties will be explained in the light of future research, research which may be stimulated by some of the possible hypotheses that have been suggested. Or, possibly, as so often happens in science, some entirely new line of research may be developed which will throw light on these areas. What one makes of these difficulties will depend on what basic assumptions one brings to them.

---

25. For a good review of this subject see: E. B. Lewis, "The Phenomenon of Position Effect," *Advances in Genetics* (New York: Academic Press, 1950), III, 73-115.

DISCUSSION

In evaluating the contribution of genetics to evolution and its significance to the Christian, we must remember that the scientist has assumed a mechanistic universe which he feels can be understood if properly observed and analyzed. His working hypothesis while engaged in scientific endeavor has no room for a God that can fortuitously interrupt this smoothly working machine. Since this is the working hypothesis of science, it was only a matter of time before theistic explanations of origins were abandoned in favor of mechanistic ones. Thus the theory of evolution came along as an inevitable consequence of the scientific procedure.

Before the theory of evolution was formulated, the field of biological origins was outside of the realm of science. For, as long as one held that God had created living things as we find them, instantaneously and out of nothing, there was no room for experimentation. But when Darwin presented his theory of evolution, the scientist was free to experiment in this area as well. However, real experimentation in evolution was not possible until the rediscovery of the Mendelian principles at the turn of the century. The work before this time was primarily of a descriptive nature obtained from a comparison of living forms and those that had lived in the past. These studies provided only circumstantial evidence that evolution had taken place.

Although Darwin had suggested the mechanism of natural selection to go along with his theory, it, by itself, was insufficient because it depended on variation in the population, for which he had no adequate explanation. With the rise of genetics, the scientist was able to hurdle the last barrier that hindered the taking of a purely mechanistic approach to the origin of living things. The fruits of such an approach we have considered in this chapter.

How can the scriptural descriptions of origin be reconciled with what we have been considering from genetics? Two positions are possible. One is to emphasize the difficulties which the scientist encounters in his theories. As we have proceeded in this chapter, we have seen that the evolutionary theory is not without its problems. There have been pointed out problems associated with mutations as a source of variation. It has also been suggested that no adequate source of new genes has been demonstrated, and certain difficulties encountered in chromosomal evolution have been mentioned. Some evangelical Christians have felt that these problems are of such a magnitude as to create serious doubts about the validity of the mechanism of evolution as proposed by the geneticist, and that only the supernatural intervention of God will adequately explain the facts.

The view that the present-day mechanism of evolution is inadequate is not championed solely by evangelical Christians, however. Such an eminent geneticist as the late Dr. Richard B. Goldschmidt for years suggested that these principles, which are held in such high esteem by most geneticists, work only on the level of the species, and are inadequate to explain the origin of higher categories.[26] The only difference between Goldschmidt and the creationist at this point is that the creationist calls God into the picture to bridge the gaps while Goldschmidt suggests another mechanistic explanation. Although most evolutionists feel that Goldschmidt's explanations are inadequate, they prefer them to the creationist's because Goldschmidt suggests a process which can be tested through further experimentation while the creationist's position presents them with a process outside the field of science. However, it is only fair to point out that it is solely the natural bias of some scientists toward naturalistic explanations that forces them to take this view, and that the present-day evidence will permit one to take a creationist position.

There is another way in which this evidence from genetics can be incorporated into a theistic explanation of origin. In order to understand the significance of this interpretation, one must consider that what the Christian is concerned with is the relationship of God to his creation. The Scriptures seem to teach that the universe as we observe it continues to exist because of the activity of God. The Christian's God, while above and beyond the physical universe, is nonetheless intimately related to it. This relationship is so intimate that the universe would cease to exist if it were not for the activity of God. Now, since the scientist is dedicated to discovering the principles by which the universe does exist, the laws and theories which he formulates become, to the Christian, very precise definitions of God's activity in the natural realm. The scientist thus shows the Christian that his God is one of law and order. Now, why should it be assumed that God acts any differently in creation than he is acting in sustaining the universe? If his *modus operandi* has remained unchanged, then it should follow that it may be possible for the scientist to describe God's activity in creation as well as his activity in sustaining nature. Viewed in this light, the discoveries in genetics may be nothing more than such a scientific description.[27]

26. Richard B. Goldschmidt, *The Material Basis of Evolution* (New Haven: Yale University Press, 1940). Goldschmidt, "A Geneticist Views Evolution," *American Scientist*, XXXX (1952), 84-98. Goldschmidt, *Theoretical Genetics* (Berkeley: University of California Press, 1955).

27. This is just one of several ways to reconcile scientific discoveries with the biblical account of origins. (Another way has been discussed on page 89.) As is the case with all such attempts of reconciliation, one does not find 100 per cent acceptance of this or any other theory, for all have their characteristic difficulties. Some object that this theory makes it impossible to distinguish the creation of

In conclusion, it is interesting to note that it is impossible to demonstrate God's creative activity from within the realm of scientific discovery, just as it is also impossible to demonstrate his sustaining activity. However, these relationships of God to his creation are not anti-scientific just because they cannot be demonstrated by science. They are concepts that are outside of the realm in which science operates and thus science has little if anything to say about their validity. These are questions that must be answered by faith.

---

life and man from any other natural phenomena. Also it is hard for some to conceive of mutation, predation, starvation, etc., as the *creative* mechanisms of God. As a final criticism of this theory, it should be noted that evolution as it is commonly understood among scientists is an explanation in terms of natural process alone. The scientist will object to making God a part of this process for he will feel that if evolution is an adequate explanation there is no need to bring God into it. It is only the Christian, who is trying to develop a philosophy of life that will take into account his religious experience *and* scientific discovery, who will see any need for making such a synthesis.

Chapter Five

THE ROLE OF HYBRIDIZATION IN EVOLUTION

By Irving W. Knobloch

Most readers, by the time they have reached college, will be familiar with the term "hybrid." Examples such as hybrid corn or the mule immediately come to mind. There are thousands more, however, generally unknown to the layman, and it will be part of our task to bring these to the reader's attention.

We may begin this discussion by asking ourselves what is meant by a hybrid. Some biologists call the result of every cross between two individuals of a line or race a hybrid. This can be done because each individual is genetically different from every other individual, except in the case of identical twins. In modern practice, however, the term hybrid is restricted to the product of a cross between individuals of different varieties or species. A well-known example of a species cross is that between the dog and the wolf.

A related question may now be asked: are wider crosses possible than just between species? Before this question is answered, it is well to review the scheme of classification one finds in textbooks. The animal kingdom is divided into a number of larger groups or phyla (singular: phylum). Some of these are the molluscs, the jelly-fishes and the chordates. Each of the phyla are further subdivided into sub-phyla and these into classes. For example, the phylum chordata includes the sub-phylum vertebrata, and this sub-phylum is divided into the fish, amphibian, reptile, bird and mammal classes. The classes have orders, the orders contain families, the families contain genera, and these are made up of one or more species. This classification is complete enough for our purpose.

One would expect that crosses between individuals of the *same* species would be easier to make than between individuals of *different* species. Matings between two human beings (the same species) are more productive than matings between a dog and a wolf (different species). One must not forget, however, that human matings are not always fertile, there being some sterility known in both human males and females. To go a step further now, it should be more difficult to make a successful cross between species of *different* genera than it is to make a cross between species of the *same* genus, and in general this is the case. A few successful crosses between species or different genera are as follows: cattle and bison, aegilops and wheat, sugar cane and sorghum, and wheat and rye. For those unfamiliar with genus and species names, an example may be given. *Bos taurus* (cattle) can be crossed successfully with *Bison americanus* (bison). *Bos* and *Bison* represent different genera and *taurus* and *americanus* represent species in their respective genera. Families are higher categories than genera, and crosses between individuals in different families are rare indeed. One such inter-family cross is known among the birds, and one or two others have been reported. Among some fishes, crosses are possible between individuals belonging to different orders.[1]

It will become apparent later, if not now, that the more similar the hereditary units or genes are in two mating individuals, the more successful is likely to be the cross, other factors being equal. The classification scheme outlined above is based upon external similarities which, in turn, are founded to a large degree upon genetic kinship. Therefore, the higher up in the scheme we go in attempting crosses, the more differences in genes we encounter and the more unsuccessful is likely to be the cross. In the Appendix there appears a list giving a few of the many hybrids known today.

One must not, however, rely too closely upon outward appearances of mating individuals before one decides whether the cross will be productive. There are two species belonging to the fruit fly genus which look very much alike, but their offspring are sterile.[2] On the other hand, there are two moths which appear quite different from each other, and yet they produce perfectly fertile offspring.[3]

Having defined our topic somewhat, we might go back a bit and inquire as to whether the subject of hybridization is a new or an old topic.

It may be surprising to learn that crossing is the oldest known method for producing new varieties and species. The Greek physician Galen (130-200 A.D.) knew of hybrids, and he further noted that these hybrids were intermediate in appearance between their parents. This intermediacy is not universal, however, because one or the other parent may pass on "dominant" genes which may make the hybrid resemble the parent contributing (in the egg or sperm) the dominant genes.

The great botanist Linnaeus made plant crosses, as did Kolreuter, Focke, Naudin, Winge, Knight, Gaertner and many others. Charles Darwin, the father of the natural selection idea which revolutionized

1. G. C. Robson, *The Species Problem* (London: Oliver and Boyd, 1928).
2. *Drosophila melanogaster* x *D. simulans.*
3. *Paecilopsis pomonaria* x *P. isabellae.*

human thought in the last half of the nineteenth century, recognized hybrids. He knew that some crosses produced sterile offspring whereas others originated fertile ones; and that varietal crosses were more successful than species crosses. In 1890 Darwin published the second edition of his book *The Variation of Animals and Plants Under Domestication.* He repeated what he had said earlier, but further noted that some species which cross with difficulty may produce fertile offspring. In those plants which have both pollen and pistils on the same plant, it is possible to take pollen from plant A and pollinate the pistil of plant B, and take the pollen of plant B to pollinate the pistil of plant A. This would be a reciprocal cross. Darwin noted in 1890 that a cross might work only one way in some cases. Something prevented a cross in the opposite direction. Darwin evidently did not think of hybridization as a very important method of forming species, being content to concentrate his attention on the phenomenon of natural selection which, in the last analysis, does not form or initiate species but simply allows favorable variations to continue their existence.

THE FIXITY OF SPECIES

We must pause now to consider an objection frequently raised by some people. They make the statement that species do not cross or, if they do, the offspring are sterile. This belief is based, partly at least, on statements in the Bible that each created organism reproduced after his kind. This is taken to imply that the word "kind" and the word "species" mean the same thing. If such were the case, we could not have any changes and species would be "fixed." We feel it out of order, however, to make such a daring assumption. We shall assume, therefore, that the two words mean something different, and that we can have species changes by, for example, hybridization. Incidentally, we may also have species arising by gene mutation or change, by rearrangements in the parts of chromosomes, and by a doubling, tripling, and so forth, of the chromosome number.

WHAT IS A SPECIES?

There have been almost as many definitions of a species as there are biologists. This is due to the great variations which some species exhibit. A species may be considered as a large or small population of individuals having so many genes in common that their variation pattern is slight when compared to the variation pattern of the population of a related species. Some populations are large, being composed of thousands, millions, or even billions of individuals. The human species, for example, is composed of over two billion individuals. Other species populations are small and confined to a particular area. Examples of such small populations are the Chatham Island robin (twenty to forty pairs), the lizard *Lacerta simoni* (sixty to eighty individuals) on a 100 square yard rock in the Canary Islands, and the evening primrose[4] (about five hundred plants in certain New Mexico valleys).

As indicated above, some of the confusion about species definitions is due to the great variability exhibited by some species. The human species is a very variable one, being composed of at least three races (according to some) and many sub-races. A certain spider[5] may have white stripes or red abdominal colors. A fish[6] has eight color phases. A butterfly[7] has sixty to seventy color phases, and smooth brome grass[8] has four races. If we contrast these facts with the slight variability exhibited by such species as the gingko tree, we may gain some appreciation of the species problem.

We must recognize, however, that species are populations of individuals which can or cannot interbreed with other species, which may or may not produce offspring after crossing and which can consist of very similar or quite different morphological entities. This will become clearer as we proceed.

THE DETECTION OF HYBRIDS

When two species are crossed artificially, there can be no doubt as to the hybrid nature of the offspring. The cattalo is a hybrid of cattle and bison. Plant and animal breeders have made countless crosses in an effort to produce worthwhile new species or varieties. It is not quite so easy to detect a hybrid in the *wild*. The hybrid nature of Brewster's Warbler and of Lawrence's Warbler was not determined without much study. Heiser[9] says that the detection of a hybrid demands a combination of methods dealing with structure, measurement, and physiology. A commonly used combination of some of these methods is called the "hybrid index method," the details of which need not concern us here.

In some cases one may make a guess as to the parents of a suspected hybrid, and by crossing these supposed parents, one may actually produce a facsimile of the suspected hybrid. This happened in the case of a plant called galeopsis.[10] One must be careful not to

4. *Oenothera organensis.*
5. *Theridion ovatum.*
6. *Epinephelus striatus.*
7. *Heliconius melpomene.*
8. Irving W. Knobloch, "Tetraploid Bromegrass," *Bulletin of the Torrey Botanical Club*, LXXX (1953), 131-135.
9. Charles Heiser, "Natural Hybridization with Particular Reference to Introgression," *Botanical Review*, XV (1949), 645-687.
10. *Galeopsis tetrahit.*

suppose that one or two breeding attempts to synthesize a hybrid are enough. It may be that "nature" made many, many attempts before "she" succeeded in producing a certain hybrid. The hybridizer is generally not as patient as is nature.

As Charles Darwin recognized, a cross may go in one direction but not in another. If one desires to see if two species or varieties will cross, one must put the pollen from one onto the stigma of the pistil of the other and vice versa.

Some workers believe that a low percentage of good, full pollen grains (fifty per cent or less) is a good indication of hybrid ancestry. They realize that this, however, is not a very reliable guide since low temperatures and other causes may likewise be responsible for poor pollen.

Closely allied with pollen failure is the failure of chromosomes to pair in reduction division. The reader may recall from his biology work that it is assumed that there are hereditary units called genes. There are two genes of the same or similar kind in each cell, one coming from the father and the other from the mother. When an organism forms sex cells such as eggs or sperms, the number of chromosomes and genes is reduced by one-half because the similar genes line up opposite each other or pair, and then only one of each pair goes into the sex cells. When two sex cells of opposite kind unite with each other, the double number is again restored. In some hybrids there are not always two genes of the same or similar kind, and pairing prior to reduction is either not possible or is not too successful. Here again we must not assume that all hybrids have irregular cell divisions. Huskins[11] cautions us against falling into this trap. He believes that irregularities may be brought about by conditions other than hybridity. On the other side of the picture we have known hybrids which exhibit normal or almost normal meiotic (reduction) pictures. Hybrids showing such regularity are, according to Stebbins,[12] found within the genera of the dogbanes, lettuce, tomato, poppy, bean, poplar, nightshade, dandelion, and other plants. It should be plain by this time that to tell whether or not an organism is a hybrid is not a task for the amateur.

INTROGRESSIVE HYBRIDIZATION

Hybrids have been studied rather intensively in the last twenty to thirty years, and a surprising phenomenon has been noted, namely,

11. C. Leonard Huskins, "Criteria of Hybridity," *Science (New Series)*, LXIX (1929), 399-400.
12. G. Ledyard Stebbins, Jr., "The Cytological Analysis of Species Hybrids II," *Botanical Review*, XI (1945), 463-486.

the integrating of a hybrid with its parents. The original first generation hybrid may backcross repeatedly with one or both of its parents. There is a certain sunflower[13] growing out on the West Coast which crosses repeatedly with an eastern sunflower[14] which has been naturalized there. Natural hybrids can be found in disturbed habitats. Where many are found together, the first and second generation hybrids are mingled with the results of backcrosses to the parents. The entire population is very variable. The hybrids show low fertility, but with repeated backcrossing, according to Heiser,[15] the fertility increases.

There are two species of tradescantia or wandering jew which have been the subject of a rather intensive investigation by Dr. Edgar Anderson. One[16] grows in full sun on the tops of cliffs in the Ozark Mountains, whereas another[17] prefers the woodland shade at the base of the cliffs. These two species cross, the hybrids cross among themselves, and also backcross with their parents. Introgression is also believed to occur in certain animals such as the fishes and toads, among others.[18]

THE MAINTENANCE OF HYBRIDS IN NATURE

From what has been written above, some readers may choose to believe that hybrids become submerged by backcrossing, and hence the entire process is a blind alley as far as evolution is concerned.

There are two plants[19] in Tennessee which occupy different areas near the upper regions of the Harpeth River. A number of different populations of hybrids were found by Rollins,[20] some containing thousands of individuals. The hybrids were scaled on a "hybrid index" and found to display relatively intermediate characteristics between their reputed parents. It also seems that the hybrids *do not* backcross to the parents.

Huxley noted that two species of alfalfa[21] cross and produce vigorous offspring. This crossing has gone on since the seventeenth century, and in one area of France the hybrid has *displaced* the

13. *Helianthus bolanderi.*
14. *Helianthus annuus.*
15. Heiser, *loc. cit.*
16. *Tradescantia canaliculata.*
17. *Tradescantia subaspera.*
18. T. Dobzhansky, *Genetics and the Origin of Species* (3rd ed.; New York: Columbia University Press, 1951), p. 299.
19. *Lesquerella densipila* and *L. lescurii.*
20. Reed C. Rollins, "Interspecific Hybridization and Its Role in Plant Evolution," Report of the Eighth International Congress Botany, 1954, pp. 172-180.
21. *Medicago sativa* and *M. falcata.*

parents.[22] A similar situation exists in Great Britain in respect to two species of the genus *Centaurea*. The case of the two warblers has been mentioned previously. Mayr[23] found that both the Brewster's and the Lawrence's warblers arise from the same parents.[24] The hybrid warblers are evidently fertile since they are able to backcross to the parents. Thus, in these cases, we have an example where crossing does lead to something new and quite different. Many others could be cited,[25] but we shall restrict ourselves to mentioning the loganberry, which originated in 1881 from a cross of two species.[26] Here again we have a valuable result from the recombination of genes.

THE PREVENTION OF HYBRIDIZATION

Two species, otherwise able to cross, might not combine genes in a hybrid if they are geographically isolated. Mountain ranges, desert areas, grassy plains, and bodies of water may keep crossable species apart. There are numerous examples in the biological literature of two species which cross easily when brought within range of each other. Two species of grouse,[27] normally separated, will cross in captivity. The same is true of some thrushes[28] and some snails.[29] A cross between two species of sycamore[30] and a cross between two species of catalpa[31] have been intensively studied, and it was found that in both of these cases reduction division goes on regularly in the hybrids and fertile seeds are formed.

Another type of isolation is sexual isolation, in one form or another. Two kinds of lettuce[32] bloom at different times of the year, and so do not cross in nature. Fertile hybrids can be obtained, however, when the two are crossed by the plant breeder. In other related plants, the pollen tubes of one species may be too short to travel down the pistil of another species.

In animals there may be an aversion to crossing between species.

22. Julian Huxley, *Evolution, the Modern Synthesis* (New York: Harper, 1943), p. 342.

23. Ernest Mayr, *Systematics and the Origin of Species* (New York: Columbia University Press, 1942), p. 262.

24. *Vermivora pinus* x *V. chrysoptera*.

25. E.g. *Primula Kewensis (P. verticillata* x *P. floribunda); Aesculus carnea (A. hippocastanum* x *A. pavia).*

26. *Rubus idaeus (R. i. strigosus* x *R. ursinus (R. vitifolius)).*

27. *Lagopus scoticus* and *L. lagopus.*

28. *Luscinia megarhyncha* and *L. luscinia.*

29. *Clausilia dubia* and *C. bidentata.*

30. *Platanus occidentalis* and *P. orientalis.*

31. *Catalpa ovata* x *C. bignonioides.*

32. *Lactuca graminifolia* and *L. canadensis.*

The ultimate of this seems to be reached in man himself, where there frequently is aversion displayed within the *same* race.

Differences in copulatory organs may prevent some crossing in animals. The sperm may fail to reach the egg, or if it does, it may fail to penetrate the "foreign" egg. Should it gain an entrance to the egg, the maternal protoplasm of the egg cell may be of such a nature as to cause its death. Another event which may happen is that the male's chromosomes may be ejected from the dividing fertilized egg or zygote.

In most of the isolating mechanisms, chance plays a great part. Wind and insect pollination in plants are largely chance events. In the external fertilization, existing among fish and amphibia, chance may bring together the gametes of certain species which might not otherwise cross. By chance, a geographic barrier may be removed, thus permitting hybridization.

STERILITY AND FERTILITY

It is commonly held among certain groups that species are set apart from each other by insurmountable barriers of sterility. Sailer[33] has this to say about this viewpoint: "The evidence has now piled up to a point where only the most obstinate of the uninformed continue to hold the view that hybrid sterility is a necessary species criterion." This is to say that *not all hybrids are sterile.* There are many which do fall into this category, however. What events promote sterility in a species cross?

Robson and Richards[34] present a sequence of events which is worth considering. The sperm may fail to reach the egg; the egg is fertilized but development ceases at an early stage; feeble or malformed F_1 (first generation) individuals may be formed; vigorous F_1's may be produced but which are sexually abnormal; the F_1 hybrids are fertile in one or the other sex, but not in both; the F_1 is completely fertile but the F_2 (second generation) individuals are weak or sterile; and last, complete fertility, generation after generation. An example of a fertile F_1 and partially sterile F_2's occurs in the case of a cotton cross, *Gossypium hirsutum* var. *punctatum* x *G. tomentosum*. The same phenomena have been seen in *Zauschneria cana* x *Z. septentrionalis.* A case of false sterility involves the hybrids from the cross *Linum perenne* and *L. austricum*. In these, the seeds are only ap-

33. R. I. Sailer, "Interspecific Hybridization among Insects with a Report on Crossbreeding Experiments with Stink Bugs," *Journal Economic Entomology,* XLVII (1954), 377-383.

34. G. C. Robson and O. W. Richards, *The Variation of Animals in Nature* (London: Longmans, Green, 1936), pp. 156ff.

parently inviable since they germinate readily when the seed coat is removed.[35]

Dr. M. J. D. White sums up a great deal of our information about hybrid sterility in the following words:

> The whole subject of the causes of sterility is a very complex one. Each of the parents in any species cross probably contains within its chromosomes a large number of genes controlling the development of the sex organs, the course of sperm and egg formation, the motility of the sperms and their ability to survive in the female genital tract, and a number of other physiological processes essential to fertile reproduction. If all these genes are sufficiently alike in the two parent forms, they may build up a compatible system in the hybrid so that the latter is wholly or partially fertile. On the other hand, if there is an incompatibility between the genes of the parent species, we have a general disturbance of sex cell formation, a failure of pairing or of chromosome twining at reduction division, or the suppression or modification of some essential stage or process in reduction division or the latter stages of sex cell formation.[36]

When White speaks, in the last sentence, of the modification of some essential stage of reduction division, he refers, in part, to the fact that the chromosomes of the parents do not always pair properly in the hybrid. Stebbins believes that dissimilarity between maternal and paternal chromosomes is the main cause of sterility in plants whereas in animals the most prevalent cause is abortion of the sex organs.[37]

We need to emphasize that good species do cross in nature and that not all of them are sterile. We have placed in the Appendix a partial list of hybrids known to be fertile. (See also Figs. 9 and 10.)

No one knows how many hybrids there are in nature, and no one knows how many fertile hybrids there are. We have been searching the literature to ascertain the answers to these questions. Our preliminary search has turned up over twenty thousand hybrids thus far. In the larger number of papers on hybrids, the authors make little or no effort to ascertain fertility, being content to determine the parenthood or the meiotic picture during gametogenesis or sporogenesis. The list given in the Appendix represents, therefore, only a small proportion of the fertile hybrids which may exist.

In plants, at least, one other fact needs to be taken into consideration before the fertility or sterility of a cross can be evaluated. We have reference to the environmental conditions obtaining at the time of the cross or immediately following a cross. In elm crosses, L. P. V.

35. T. Dobzhansky, *loc. cit.*

36. M. J. D. White, *Animal Cytology and Evolution* (London: Cambridge University Press, 1954), p. 263.

37. G. Ledyard Stebbins, *Advances in Genetics,* IX (1958), 147-215.

Johnson[38] found that in some years viable seed was produced while in other years inviable seed formed. If one had made only a cursory examination of such hybrids and in an unfavorable year, one would have concluded that the hybrid was sterile in that no progeny could be produced. A study of the literature on crossing experiments leads one to suspect that many studies have not been tried on a large enough basis to judge the fertility of the offspring.

FERTILITY AND POLYPLOIDY

Each species of plant or animal has a characteristic number of chromosomes although some species have a series of numbers, e.g. *Bromus inermis,* which has 28, 42, 56 or 70 chromosomes.[39] In other words, the regular number may be doubled, tripled, and multiplied in an even higher series.

Let us represent the chromosomes of a cell of a plant by the letters AABBCC, there being two chromosomes of each kind (one coming from each of the two parents). If, as in the callus tissue of a tomato, this number becomes doubled, we would have an auto-tetraploid with four of each kind of chromosomes, AAAABBBBCCCC. This type of doubling has been known to occur. We are more concerned in this chapter with those cases where doubling has occurred after crossing. Let us cross two species with the chromosome complements AABBCC x DDEEFF. Reduction division in the first species produces gametes ABC and reduction in the second species produces gametes DEF. The hybrid has chromosomes ABCDEF. In such a case there are no two chromosomes alike, there is no homology, there is no pairing, and the hybrid would probably be sterile.

If the chromosomes should be doubled, then the organism has the chromosomes AABBCCDDEEFF, and pairing can take place. Such organisms are called allotetraploids and are frequently fertile. Huxley[40] mentions that allopolyploidy has undoubtedly played an important part in the evolution of plant genera. Fothergill[41] believes that the allopolyploids are of common occurrence in nature. Dobzhansky says, "Along side this slow method of species formation (mutation) there exists a mechanism of rapid emergence of new species by the multiplication of chromosome sets, and since the ancestral species may continue to exist side by side with the polyploid, the organic diversity is augmented by the chromosome doubling."[42]

---

38. L. P. V. Johnson, "Fertilization in *Ulmus* with Special Reference to Hybridization Procedure," *Canadian Journal of Research,* XXIV (1946), 1-3.

39. Knobloch, *loc. cit.*

40. Huxley, *op. cit.,* pp. 340ff.

41. Philip G. Fothergill, *Historical Aspects of Organic Evolution* (London: Hollis & Carter, 1952), p. 224.

42. T. Dobzhansky, *loc. cit.*

It has been estimated that about thirty-five per cent of the flowering plants are polyploids of one sort or another. In crop plants polyploids have been important, as in tobacco, cotton, wheat, oats, plums, sugar cane, apples, pears, loganberries, and strawberries. The origin of allopolyploids is not entirely theoretical, since they have been synthesized in forty or more instances and have regular chromosome pairing.[43] The same author believes that doubling has produced some large, complex, widespread genera but, since no new characters are forthcoming, the method operates in more or less of a closed system. (See Fig. 11.)

VARIATION POSSIBLE IN HYBRIDS

One of the facets of the hybrid problem not given sufficient attention is that concerned with the possibility of crosses between species giving rise to not one but *many* hybrids. Not all eggs or sperms are alike in most individuals and many combinations are possible. Two parents differing in only twenty characters can form about one million combinations.[44] The possibility of there being an exact double of the present reader in this world is, for this reason, very remote. We have already mentioned the fact previously that we can get two recognizably different warblers from crosses between the same parental species.

THE DISTRIBUTION OF HYBRIDS AMONG THE PHYLA

Some biologists believe that there are very few hybrids in nature and others deny their very existence. Such ideas are untenable in view of our present knowledge. Since we can estimate the number of *species* in nature with only fair accuracy, it is not surprising, therefore, that we have a lesser knowledge of the number of *hybrids*. To remedy this latter situation, we have made a search of the literature for reputed hybrids and their parents. Below will be found the results of that survey. Two things, above all, should be borne in mind by the reader. One is that the list is not complete, one reason for this being the inaccessibility of some of the literature. Second, some reputed hybrids of an earlier day may have been erroneously reported as such. This is possible because earlier workers did not have the wealth of information on this subject which we possess today. Allowing for errors and incompleteness, and bearing in mind that many hybrids existing today remain to be discovered and that others are being formed at present, the list is impressively long.

43. G. Ledyard Stebbins, Jr., *Variation and Evolution in Plants* (New York: Columbia University Press, 1950), pp. 326ff.
44. Heribert Nilsson, "The Problem of the Origin of Species Since Darwin," *Heredity*, XX (1925), 227-237.

Reputed Hybrids in the Plant and Animal Kingdoms

Plants

Thallophytes	64	
Bryophytes	7	
Pteridophytes	158	
Spermatophytes	12,500	(exclusive of the orchids) [45]

Animals

Mollusca	5
Echinodermata	31
Arthropoda	240
Pisces	167
Amphibia	101
Reptilia	37
Aves	1599
Mammalia	300

THE IMPORTANCE OF HYBRIDIZATION

Many authorities believe that interspecific hybridization has played an important role in evolution. The list of hybrids in the Appendix, incomplete as it is, confirms their opinion.[46]

If hybridization plays only a minor role in evolution, as some maintain, it is very strange indeed that there are so many vigorous, fertile hybrids in existence today, and more are being found each year by those who earnestly search for them.

That changes in species are taking place today by hybridization and other methods, no one can doubt. This poses a serious question for those who have been taught that the Bible rules out changes. It is my opinion that the Bible is not at all specific on this point. "Kinds" still reproduce after their kind, but children never look exactly like their parents. Granted that man *was* created, mutations and crossings have produced the three races and the multitude of groups within those races. Conservative Christians can believe in the divine creation of the major groups of organisms and still be modern enough to believe in the natural laws of change.

45. There are many thousands of orchid hybrids reported in the literature.
46. Charles C. Sibley, "Hybridization in the Red-eyes Towhees of Mexico," *Evolution*, VIII (1954), 252-290. Rollins, *loc. cit.* G. Ledyard Stebbins, Jr., *Variation and Evolution in Plants*, p. 251. C. Evelyan Hutchinson, "Marginalia," *American Scientist*, XLI (1953), 628-634. Irene Manton, *Problems of Cytology & Evolution in the Pteridophyta* (London: Cambridge University Press, 1950), p. 251. H. G. Baker, "Hybridization and Natural Gene Flow Between Higher Plants," *Biological Review*, XXVI (1951), 302-337. Robert W. Long, "Hybridization Between the Perennial Sunflowers, *Helianthus salicifolius* and *H. grosseserratus*," *American Midland Naturalist*, LIV (1955), 61-64.

APPENDIX

List of Fully or Partially Fertile Hybrids Reported in the Plant and Animal Kingdoms*

ANIMAL KINGDOM

MAMMALS

Macaca mulatta x *M. irus*
*Panthera leo*x *P. tigris*
Canis aureus x *C. familiaris*
Canis familiaris x *C. f. dingo*
Canis familiaris x *C. lupus*
Canis familiaris dingo x *C. lupus*
Mustela putorius furo x *M. p. p.*
Thalarctos maritimus x *Ursus arctos a.*
Thalarctos maritimus x *Ursus arctos middendorfii*
Mus musculus x *M. musculus bactrianus*
Mus musculus x *M. musculus molossinus*
Mus musculus x *M. musculus spicilegus*
Mus musculus x *M. musculus wagneri*
Peromyscus gossypinus x *P. leucopus*
Peromyscus leucocephalus x *P. polionotus albifrons*
Peromyscus maniculatus x *P. polionotus*
Peromyscus maniculatus x *P. leucocephalus*
Peromyscus maniculatus gambelii x *P. m. sonoriensis*
Chinchilla brevicaudata x *C. laniger*
Cavia aperca x *C. porcellus*
Cavia cutleri x *C. porcellus*
Equus asinus x *E. a. africanus*
Equus caballus x *E. przewalskii*
Bison bison x *B. bonasus*
Bos banteng x *B. indicus*
Bos gaurus x *B. indicus*
Bos gaurus x *B. taurus*
Bos taurus x *B. indicus*
Capra caucasica x *C. hircus*
Capra falconeri x *C. hircus*
Capra hircus x *C. ibex ibex*
Capra hircus x *C. ibex sibirica*
Ovis ammon x *O. aries*
Ovis aries x *O. canadensis nelsoni*
Ovis aries x *O. musimon*
Ovis aries x *O. orientalis cycloceros*
Ovis musimon x *O. canadensis*
Ovis musimon x *O. orientalis vignei*

Ovis aries x *O. orientalis vignei*
Axis axis x *Cervus elaphus xanthopygus*
Cervus canadensis x *C. elaphus*
Elaphurus davidianus x *Cervus elaphus*
Muntiacus reevesi reevesi x *M. muntjak vaginalis*
Odocoileus peruvianus x *O. virginianus truei*
Lama glama x *L. pacos*
Lama glama x *Lama vicugna*
Lama huanacus x *L. glama*
Lama pacos x *L. huanacus*
Lama pacos x *L. vicugna*
Sus barbatus x *S. scrofa*

FISH

Mollienesia latipinna x *M. sphenops*
Xiphophorus helleri x *Platypoecilus maculatus*

AMPHIBIA

Bufo americanus x *B. fowleri*
Bufo americanus x *B. terrestris*
Bufo americanus x *B. woodhousei*
Bufo fowleri x *B. woodhousei*
Bufo terrestris x *B. fowleri*
Bufo terrestris x *B. woodhousei*
Colias alexandra x *C. eurythene*

BIRDS

Columba turbata x *C. livia*
Stigmatopelia senegalensis x *Streptopelia alba*
Streptopelia alba x *S. risoria*
Streptopelia alba x *S. humilis*
Streptopelia douraca x *S. risoria*
Streptopelia humilis x *S. risoria*
Streptopelia risoria x *S. semitorquata*
Streptopelia risoria x *S. decaocto*
Streptopelia risoria x *S. roseogrisea*

*This is only a partial list. It is included to contradict the common and erroneous impression that hybrids are seldom if ever fertile.

Turtur turtur x T. orientalis
Zenaida vinaceo-rufa x Zenaidura
 carolinenesis
Anas platyrhynchos x A. acuta
Gennaeus melanotis x G. nycthemerus
Serinus canarius x Carduelis carduelis

INSECTS

Bombyx mori x B. mandarina
Celerio euphorbiae x C. vespertilio
Celerio euphorbiae x C. hippophaes
Celerio euphorbiae x C. lineata
Celerio euphorbiae x C. gallii

Epicnaptera tremulifolia x E. ilicifolia
Euschistus variolarius x E. servus
Pediculus capitis x P. corporis
Pergesea elpenor x P. porcellus
Poecilopsis pomonaria x P. isabellae
Pygaera anachoreta x P. curtula
Pygaera pigra x P. curtula
Achaeta campestris x A. bimaculata
Aedes polynesiensis x A.
 pseudoscutellaris
Culex pipiens x C. quinquefasciatus
Eupithecia innotata x E. unedonata
Trimerotropis maritima x T. citrina
Tephrosia bistortata x T. crepuscularia

PLANTS

Apocynum androsaemifolium x A.
 cannabinum
Betula pubescens x B. verrucosa
Silene vulgaris x S. maritima
Senecio lyallii x S. scorzoneroides
Quamoclit coccinea x Q. pennata
Dudleya anthonyi x D. farinosa
Castanea pumila x C. sativa
Nothofagus cliffortioides x N. fusca
Nothofagus solandri x N. truncata
Quercus cerris x Q. suber
Quercus emoryi x Q. gravesii
Quercus robur x Q. sessiliflora
Aegilops ovata x Triticum dicoccoides
Aegilops ovata x Triticum durum
Agrostis tenuis x A. alba
Bromus mollis x B. racemosus
Bromus mollis x B. hordeaceus
Euchlaena mexicana x Zea mays
Hordeum vulgare x H. agriocerithon
Paspalum urvillei x (P. malacophyllum
 x P. dilatatum)
Poa ampla x P. compressa
Poa ampla x P. scabrella
Poa ampla x P. pratensis
Poa ampla x P. arida
Poa arachnifera x P. pratensis
Poa arida x P. scabella
Poa canbyi x P. pratensis
Poa compressa x P. pratensis
Poa gracillima x P. scabrella
Poa scabrella x P. pratensis
Poa scabrella x P. compressa
Saccharum officinarum x Erianthus sara
Saccharum officinarum x Sorghum
 halapense
Saccharum spontaneum x S. officinarum

Sorghum vulgare x S. halapense
Triticum compactum x Aegilops
 triuncialis
Triticum dicoccoides x Aegilops ovata
Triticum dicoccum x Aegilops ovata
Triticum dicoccum x Aegilops
 triuncialis
Triticum durum x Aegilops ovata
Triticum durum x Agropyron
 intermedium
Triticum durum x Agropyron
 elongatum
Triticum monococcum x Aegilops
 uniaristata
Triticum polonicum x Secale cereale
Triticum spelta x T. polonicum
Triticum spelta x Aegilops triuncialis
Triticum timophaevi x T. monococcum
Triticum turgidum x T. monococcum
Triticum turgidum x T. dicoccum
Triticum turgidum x Aegilops
 ventricosa
Triticum turgidum x Haynaldia villosa
Triticum vulgare x Aegilops triuncialis
Triticum vulgare x Aegilops triaristata
Triticum vulgare x Agropyron
 intermedium
Triticum vulgare x Agropyron
 elongatum
Triticum vulgare x T. durum
Triticum vulgare x T. turgidum
Linum usitatissimum x L.
 angustifolium
Myrtus bullata x M. obcordata
Pinus contorta x P. banksiana
Pinus mugo x P. sylvestris
Platanus orientalis x P. occidentalis

Armeria maritima x *A. plantaginea*
Populus alba x *P. tremula*
Populus balsamifera x *P. nigra*
Populus laurifolia x *P. nigra italica*
Aesculus pavia x *A. hippocastanum*
Nicotiana alata x *N. langsdorffii*
Nicotiana digluta x *N. tabacum*
Nicotiana glauca x *N. langsdorffii*

Nicotiana rustica x *N. paniculata*
Nicotiana suaveolens x *N. alata*
Nicotiana tabacum x *N. otophera*
Nicotiana sylvestris x *N. tomentosiformis*
Solanum henryi x *S. verrucosum*
Solanum nigrum x *S. luteum*
Tilia cordata x *T. platyphyllos*

Chapter Six

SYSTEMATICS AND SPECIATION

By Wilbur L. Bullock

THE PROBLEM OF THE SPECIES

As indicated by the title of Charles Darwin's major work on the subject of evolution, one of the most basic tasks of the biologist is that of studying the "origin of species." This problem includes two phases of study: an investigation of the true nature of a species, and the investigation of the processes which determine that nature and separate one species from another. Both of these phases of study are outgrowths of that most basic of all biological studies, the classification of living organisms into some filing system which makes sense when applied to all living things. Inasmuch as Darwin's *The Origin of Species* was partly the result of his justifiable dissatisfaction with the prevailing species concept of his day, it is important that creationists carefully re-examine what Darwin and his followers had to say with particular attention to current thinking on the subject. In doing this as it concerns the "species," as in other phases of a critical evaluation of evolution, it is important that we understand the terms that are being used and that have been used in regard to this important problem, as well as that we look into the history of man's understanding of the classification of living things.

Principles of Classification

That branch of science which is concerned with the classification of plants and animals is called *taxonomy,* and, as in any other field of human endeavor, its work must be done according to the rules. But before we get involved in these rules we should take a brief look at the types of pigeonholes that the taxonomists use. Although to the uninitiated these categories frequently have rather awe-inspiring names, these names are really used only for convenience and in the interest of standard practice.

In some respects we are already acquainted with taxonomic procedure. For example, should we make a study of the types of man-made shelters in a residential community, we could distinguish various categories. We might first set up two large groups, one of which included dwellings proper, while the other included those shelters used for human possessions. We might break down the dwelling places into those which are single units and those which furnish shelter for more than one family, such as duplexes, apartments, and perhaps hotels. On the other hand, we could decide that this criterion for classifying dwelling places was not convenient and conclude that the materials of which the houses were made was of greater significance. So we would erect categories to take care of wood, brick, cement block, etc. The reader can undoubtedly think of many other possible arrangements.

Over the years, as people have looked at the plant and animal kingdoms, they have recognized that these kingdoms can be divided into a relatively small number of large groups which are now known as *phyla* (singular *phylum*). In the animal kingdom about ten of these phyla include the majority of the animals that exist or have existed on the earth. In addition, there are a number of small groups of animals that cannot be assigned to these larger groups and many of these are being recognized as separate phyla. However, even the most intensive splitting of this kind would not result in more than twenty-five or thirty phyla to include the hundreds of thousands of species of animals.

When these phyla are examined more carefully it can be seen that there are fairly definite groups within them which are known as *classes*. Thus, all of the animals that have shells at some stage of their development, have a type of larval stage known as a "veliger," and certain other anatomical features are grouped in the phylum Mollusca. In turn, several classes of mollusks can be recognized. So, for example, there are the Gastropoda, which have a large foot and usually a spiral shell; these are the snails. There are the Pelecypoda, in which the shell is composed of two valves and which are generally sedentary in their life habits; these are the clams and their allies. Continuing this process of dividing larger groups into smaller groups we find that each class may have several *orders*; each order may have several *families*; each family may have several *genera* (singular *genus*); each genus may have several *species*. Finally, as we shall see later, each species, after it has been studied carefully, may be found to have several subspecies which may be further divided into races, populations, etc. After going through this long chain we arrive at the ultimate biological entity, the individual. With this convenient type of grouping in mind let us look at the classification of the common hard-shelled clam or quahog, *Venus mercenaria*. The place of this species in the animal kingdom can be outlined as follows:

Phylum — Mollusca
  Class — Pelecypoda
    Order — Eulamellibranchiata
      Family — Veneridae
        Genus — Venus
          Species — *Venus mercenaria*

It should be noticed that by combining the name of the genus with the species name we come up with the "scientific name" of this clam. This system dates back to the time of the Swedish biologist, Carolus Linnaeus, who introduced this standard procedure in his various works on plants and animals. This system of "binomial nomenclature" appeared in a few publications prior to the time of Linnaeus, but the system is generally attributed to him because of the comprehensive nature of his work and the degree of consistency with which he applied it. For the animal kingdom the apex of Linnaean consistency was reached in the tenth edition of his *Systema Naturae,* which was published in 1758.

This method of using the name of the genus and the species name has contributed considerably to our understanding of the animal and plant kingdoms. Thus, the clam referred to above is variously known among laymen as the round clam, the hardshell clam, the little neck clam, or the quahog. However, by the use of the binomial nomenclature it can be referred to the world over as *Venus mercenaria* Linnaeus, 1758. The use of the name of Linnaeus and the date is a further aid in that we acknowledge that this species was first described by our Swedish friend in his 1758 publication.

WHAT IS A SPECIES?

During the evolution-creation debates that were so popular in the first quarter of the twentieth century, one of the most important conflicts centered around the problem of "fixity of species." At that time it was generally assumed that "kind" in Genesis 1 and "species" in biology were synonymous. Therefore, since Genesis implied that these kinds or species were stable units, many Christians became ardent defenders of the fixity of species. Indeed, precedence for a stand on the immutability of species had already been set by such biological greats as Agassiz and Cuvier, while the main exposition of the concept could be traced back to Linnaeus himself. In the past fifty years considerable thought and study have gone into the species concept and some important changes have been made which bear heavily on this old problem of species fixity. A challenging problem thus presents itself to the Christian biologist. What is the relationship between "kind" and these newer concepts of species, and is there a

Christian concept of species? Mixter[1] made a contribution to this problem by pointing out that the word "kind" is a rather general term which may have several meanings. He further pointed out the difficulties involved in assuming synonymy between "kind" and "species." Without any further consideration of the former term at this time, let us consider the problem of species as it manifests itself in that area of modern biology known as taxonomy or systematics.

At first sight the naming and describing of animal forms seems to be a relatively simple task. Certainly Adam had no great difficulty, as we are told in Genesis 2:19,20: "And out of the ground the Lord God formed every beast of the field, and every fowl of the air; and brought them unto Adam to see what he would call them: and whatsoever Adam called every living creature that was the name thereof. And Adam gave names to all cattle, and to the fowl of the air, and to every beast of the field." However, our difficulties soon become apparent when we actually try to catalogue the forms we see in the world around us. This dilemma is perhaps best illustrated by the remark of the entomologist: "Where am I to put a beast of a bug when the next one that's exactly like it is entirely different the next time you look at it?" Not only does this exclamation of exasperation indicate difficulty in assigning an animal form to its taxonomic niche (or species), but it intimates that the niche itself is none too reliable.

The task of defining the species is one of formidable proportions. Such is the difficulty of the task that many have been led to deny the reality of the species. Historically, we can follow through from the fixed species of Linnaeus to the relative "passing parade" concept of Haeckel and Darwin, to the modern polytypic species of Mayr, et al. As these attitudes varied in time, so do they vary with the particular animal or plant group involved and with the approach of the taxonomist. In this manner there is little correlation between the species of bacteria, protozoa, helminths, insects, or vertebrates. For example, witness the awkwardness of applying a bacterial species concept to helminths (parasitic worms) as done by Wilhelmi: " 'Species' of helminths may be defined tentatively as a group of organisms the lipid-free antigen of which, when diluted to 1:4000 or more, yields a positive precipitin test within one hour with a rabbit antiserum produced by injecting 40 mg. of dry-weight, lipid-free antigenic material and withdrawn ten to twelve days after the last of four intravenous injections administered every third day."[2]

Among the earliest concepts of species is that which considers the species to be a group of animals of similar morphology (structure)

1. R. L. Mixter, *Creation and Evolution*, ASA Monograph, No. 2 (West Lafayette, Ind.: American Scientific Affiliation, 1953).

2. R. W. Wilhemi, "Serological Reactions and Species Specificity of Some Helminths," *Biological Bulletin*, LXXIX (1940), pp. 64-90.

and not overlapping in this respect with any other group. This is basically the concept of Linnaeus and, although it is now a much-maligned concept, it is still used by many modern taxonomists. In actuality, this is the species concept implied by "type" specimens in museum collections. Students of many of the invertebrate phyla use it in cataloguing new forms. Indeed, it would be impossible to begin a taxonomic study of an unworked group without a morphological introduction. However, this concept has its shortcomings. The selection of characters that are "significant" tends to become quite subjective. Besides, the significance of these characters varies from one group to another. Rensch[3] illustrates this by noting that folds in the shell mouth of certain snails are reliable for species identification whereas in other snails individual variation makes them useless. Still other examples of the inconsistency of "significant characters" are indicated by Mayr.[4]

Another approach to a species concept, and one that has achieved considerable popular acclaim, is made on the basis of interbreeding. One of the better known manifestations of this concept is illustrated by the statement that "all forms belong to one species which can produce fertile hybrids." This is a very appealing definition but it has many limitations. (1) It cannot apply to the Protozoa or to the hermaphroditic groups. (2) There are too many obvious exceptions. Moore[5] showed that crosses between geographically widely separated races of the frog *Rana pipiens* produced defective "hybrids," whereas crosses between two species *R. pipiens* and *R. palustris* from the same area produced normal hybrids capable of reproduction. Still another example of the unreliability of this definition is illustrated by the shad genus *Pomolobus*. These marine fishes go up the bays and rivers to spawn in brackish water during the spring of the year. At least in the region of Durham, New Hampshire, *P. aestivalis* and *P. pseudoharengus* overlap in their spawning seasons. Apparently, in the past, there were separate spawning seasons and hence clearly recognizable separate species. Now much interbreeding is taking place, so that it is quite difficult to distinguish the two species. Thus the presence or absence of fertile hybrids is not a reliable species character.

A somewhat improved version of the interbreeding species concept

3. B. Rensch, *Kurze Onwersung für zoologisch-systematische Studien* (Leipzig: Akademische Verlagsgesellschaft, 1934), p. 94.

4. E. Mayr, *Systematics and the Origin of Species* (New York: Columbia University Press, 1942), pp. 22-32.

5. J. A. Moore, "Incipient Intraspecific Isolating Mechanisms in *Rana pipiens*," *Genetics*, XXXI (1946), 304-326. "Hybridization between *Rana palustris* and Different Geographical Forms of *Rana pipiens*," *Proceedings National Academy of Science*, XXXII (1946), 209-212.

is that of Mayr: "Species are groups of actually or potentially inter-breeding natural populations, which are reproductively isolated from other such groups."[6] Since this definition emphasizes reproductive isolation and natural populations it avoids the indefiniteness of the hybrid sterility concept but still retains some of its limitations. It cannot be applied to many invertebrate groups, nor does it explain the hybrids between sympatric species. (Species of a genus are considered sympatric if they are found together in part or all of their range.) However, this definition of Mayr is the most workable species concept at the present time and is, therefore, the most widely accepted generalization of the problem today.

Still other species concepts have utilized genetics, physiology, or immunology as their basis. However, general application of these criteria have yielded little but confusion in the taxonomy of the greater part of the animal kingdom. It is not surprising, then, to find many adherents to what Mayr characterizes the "practical species concept," namely, that a species is a systematic unit which is considered a species by an authority on the group.[7] This concept reduces the species to the depths of subjectivity. It creates an ephemeral, highly limited species which serves only a given group of authorities on a given group of animals or plants.

Thus it can be seen that at the present time there is no real concept of species that is applicable to the entire animal kingdom. Indeed, it is easy to become pessimistic about the very existence of the species as a valid biological unit. However, most authorities in the fields of taxonomy and evolution still maintain that the species is a real and useful entity (e.g. Mayr,[8] Goldschmidt,[9] and Huxley[10]). This is particularly true for animal groups which are well "worked" taxonomically. In these groups the various factors in variation (geography, temperature, altitude, etc.) are more clearly understood and it is in these groups (e.g. birds) that the "polytypic" species dominates the scene.

The polytypic species is a concept which had its beginnings with Kleinschmidt[11] in his *"Formenkreis* theory." This *Formenkreis* was a sort of super species which took into account the factors involved in the variations of populations under differing environmental conditions. Kleinschmidt further recognized the strong possibility of

6. Mayr, *op. cit.,* p. 120.

7. *Ibid.,* p. 115.

8. *Ibid.*

9. R. Goldschmidt, *The Material Basis of Evolution* (New Haven: Yale University Press, 1940).

10. J. S. Huxley, *The New Systematics* (Oxford: Clarendon Press, 1940).

11. O. Kleinschmidt, "Arten oder Formenkreise?," *Journal of Ornithology,* XLVIII (1900), 134-139.

supernatural intervention in bridging the gaps between related *Formenkreise*. Such a concept — minus the supernatural intervention — is the basis of Goldschmidt's modern mutationist theory. Unfortunately, what Kleinschmidt lacked in genetics, Goldschmidt lacks in making any contribution to the species problem. In general, the polytypic species has led to the lumping of many varieties, previously described as distinct species, into a few species. Such a concept applied to man leads to the inclusion of all living and fossil men into one, or at most two, species. The reverse procedure as applied to man leads to a great diversity of terms and serves only to support favored phylogenetic fancies.[12] Some species, as pointed out by Huxley,[13] appear to vary little and hence are considered monotypic. Such species present few difficulties in their recognition and limitation.

One more problem should be considered: the "subspecies." To Goldschmidt (as well as Kleinschmidt) the subspecies merely indicates the multiplicity of variations *within* the species. To the majority of present-day evolutionists (e.g., Mayr and Dobzhansky), however, the subspecies represents an incipient new species. Should this latter concept prove correct, then Christians must certainly look for the units of creation (kinds?) elsewhere than at the species level. Should mutationism triumph then this new species concept might solve the problem. Much long and laborious taxonomy must be performed before anything definite can be said about the limitations of the species unit.[14]

In summary, the species concept in modern biology is far from settled. The prevailing opinion is that the species is a real entity, but whether this can be defined to satisfy all plant and animal groups is problematic. Consequently, the species at present is basically a human concept. It provides an interesting biological problem, but probably does not bear any real relationship to the "kinds" of Genesis. It is possible that further developments in this field will shed light on this complex problem. Meanwhile, one is ill advised to champion the cause of fixity of species under the banner of Christianity.

VARIATIONS IN ANIMALS

As one reads through *The Origin of Species* it becomes increasingly apparent that the differences between individuals of the same or similar species played as much of a role in Darwin's thinking as did

12. R. R. Gates, *Human Ancestry* (Cambridge: Harvard University Press, 1946), pp. 366-369.
13. *Op. cit.,* p. 10.
14. This subject has been reviewed recently by J. G. Edwards and W. L. Brown in *Turtox News* for October and November, 1956, and March, 1957.

the similarities between major groups. Indeed, Darwin later (1868) published a two-volume work on *The Variation of Plants and Animals Under Domestication*. Several of Darwin's predecessors had also been impressed with the variability of living forms, but it remained for Darwin to arrange the data in some semblance of order and, by means of his principle of natural selection, to produce an explanation that made some sense. Less than half a century later, when the basic nature of heredity and variations became known through the rediscovery of the publications of Gregor Mendel, many of Darwin's observations on the subject of variation were justified, although a large part of his explanation of the mechanism of variation had to be discarded. But what should be the explanation of these variations within the framework of existing knowledge and of the Bible? In order to be able to suggest some possible answer to this question it is important to understand something about the nature of variations in living organisms. In the interest of simplicity we will confine our consideration to the animal kingdom.[15]

Variations can be roughly divided into two major groups: those that originate primarily as a result of the genetic or hereditary makeup of the animal, and those that are induced primarily by external factors. However, closely related to these are other more or less obvious factors. For example, most people are aware of the differences manifest in many animals by sex. These sexual differences may be associated only with the organs of reproduction or they may affect other body systems. Birds frequently show sexual differences in color patterns. Fish may show not only these color differences but may show differences in the structure of their scales, the shape of their fins, or in general body outline. There are many instances where these differences have led to the description of males and females as different species until their true relationships were discovered. Many of the "lower animals" show even more drastic and amazing differences. In some forms the male may be reduced to a small parasite on the female, may be present only at certain times of the year, or may even be completely unnecessary and nonexistent! In this last instance sexual reproduction is performed by females alone in the process of parthenogenesis.

Of greater concern to us in this chapter, however, are those variations which are primarily determined by non-genetic factors. Among the more obvious of these are variations associated with age. Many new species of animals were described as valid species before it was realized that they represented a different age group of a previously known form. Certainly anyone who has attempted to

15. See also Chapter 5 for a discussion of similar problems in the plant kingdom.

identify immature shore birds is only too well aware of the fact that the young are often very different from the parents. In sea gulls, for example, even the rank amateur has no trouble separating the herring gull from the slightly larger and more northern black-backed gull. But first-year birds are a different matter, and only a person with considerable birdwatching experience can readily separate the two species. For many years *Fundulus pallidus* was regarded as a distinct species of killifish from the coast of the Gulf of Mexico. Recently, Gunter has shown this "species" to be the young of the common Gulf killifish, *Fundulus grandis*.[16] Similar difficulty is experienced in identifying the young of many other animals including snails, starfish, and parasitic worms.

Even more extreme differences associated with age are to be found in those animals which undergo marked change (metamorphosis) in their life history. Two of the commonest examples of this phenomenon are the frogs and the butterflies. Frog eggs hatch into the small fish-like creatures known to most boys as tadpoles or pollywogs. After a period of growth in which these animals must stay in the water and behave like fish, they undergo a transformation. The tail is lost by absorption into the body, the digestive tube diminishes to one-fourth of its size, and the animal develops four legs. It is now ready to leave the water, at least temporarily, and behave like a grownup frog. The story of the butterfly is even more spectacular as the eggs hatch into the small wormlike creatures known as caterpillars. After these hungry little animals consume enormous quantities of food — usually plant material — they enter into a "resting stage" in which about the only thing they rest from is eating! In this stage (the pupa) a drastic reorganization of the whole body takes place, so that what went to "sleep" as a caterpillar "wakes up" as a beautiful butterfly. Obviously, the recognition of a particular caterpillar as one and the same species comes only after carefully controlled observational work.

Another phenomenon which occurs in many of the lower animals is a source of even greater difficulties until careful studies are made of the entire life histories. This is the problem of "alternation of generations." In some of the coelenterates (jellyfish and their allies), as well as in some of the worms and other groups, the offspring of the male and female parents are not only very different in appearance from their parents but are sexless as well. These asexual individuals then produce the next generation which is composed of males and females. The classic example of this type of alternation is found in jellyfish such as those belonging to the genus *Obelia*. The small free-swimming jellyfish produce eggs and sperm which produce the asexual generation. This generation is very unlike the parent in that instead of being free-swimming they are attached and arranged in colonies which look more like plants than animals. Eventually, some of these members of the colony give rise to offspring that are typical jellyfish and are free-swimming males and females. In such a situation the offspring do not look at all like their parents but rather like their grandparents. Certainly, the difficulties in setting the limits of the species in such a group are considerable. The final solution of the problems of these groups can come only after long, careful study of the life history has been made. Even more spectacular changes take place in the development of the trematodes or flukes, a large group of parasitic flatworms.

Of greater importance to the problem of the nature of the species and its origin are those variations which are obviously associated with the environment of the organism. These features are generally termed "adaptive" and are considered in their application to comparative anatomy in Chapter 9 of this book. However, on the level of the lower taxonomic categories, such as species and genus, these reactions of an animal to its environment may and frequently do give rise to considerable difficulty in defining the limits of the species. One aspect of the environment is the influence of the seasons. Many of our birds have such pronounced changes of color in the fall and again in the spring that it is almost like learning the features of two different birds to recognize that they are one and the same species. Indeed, just as immature birds have been considered as distinct species from the adult until their true relationship has been proven, so the different seasonal plumages have given rise to "different" species of birds. That many of these seasonal features are environmental has been shown by demonstrating that the development of sex organs in many birds and mammals is largely dependent on the hours of daylight that occur at different times of the year. It has been possible to stimulate the development of the sex organs of these animals by artificially increasing the light hours in the middle of the winter. Likewise, the retrogression of these organs can be effected by diminishing the hours of light.

Even more drastic are the seasonal variations of many of the smaller lower animals. In some of these forms the problem is relatively simple, as in the case of the fairy shrimp *(Eubranchipus)* which lives as an adult in the numerous temporary pools associated with the spring thaw. During the remainder of the year this animal exists in the form of eggs that are highly resistant to desiccation. In others, such as some of the water fleas *(Cladocera)*, there are marked differences in the same species among the several seasonal forms.

All of these differences have given rise to confusion that has been cleared up only after long and detailed study of these animals in the laboratory and in the field. And many are still not cleared up!

Of far greater significance to the problem of the origin of species is the variation that can be observed in animals throughout their geographic range. Most groups of animals which have a wide distribution show differences between populations living in different parts of the range; and those populations are most different if selected from the opposite extremes of their range. Basically, these variations appear to be the result of the action of the environment through temperature, moisture, altitude, light, and the other living organisms (plants and animals) that live in this environment. Inasmuch as these variations are the cause of more difficult and subtle problems in the recognition and limitation of the species it is important that their nature and ramifications be clearly understood.

First, let us consider the variation that can take place within a generally accepted single species of wide distribution. Moore[17] found that the frog *Rana pipiens* is found from Canada to Panama and is made up of a number of geographic races which differ in many characters. For example, the more southerly frogs have smaller eggs which are laid in looser masses than those of their more northerly relatives. Furthermore, these eggs are favored in their development by warm temperatures, whereas they are more markedly slowed down by cooler temperatures. That this is a temperature factor is shown by the fact that the frogs from Costa Rica, a southerly but high altitude situation, were more similar to the frogs from Vermont than to the frogs of southern Florida, although Costa Rica and southern Florida are nearly in the same latitude. Similarly, in the breeding experiments mentioned earlier, the frogs from Vermont could not produce offspring with the frogs from Florida but they could with the frogs from Costa Rica. This latter race could not breed with the frogs from Florida.

At this point the question might well be asked, why do we consider these frogs which do not breed to belong to the same species? The major reason, on the basis of Mayr's definition of the species as given earlier, is that we have from Canada to Panama a continuous series of interbreeding populations. There is no place where we can separate one race from another unless we select widely separated populations. But so long as the populations are all connected by intermediate forms that can breed with either group they must all be considered part of the same species. How is it then, as mentioned

17. Moore, "Incipient Intraspecific Isolating Mechanisms in *Rana pipiens*," *loc. cit.* "Hybridization between *Rana palustris* and Different Geographical Forms of *Rana pipiens*," *loc. cit.*

earlier, that other "species" can breed with *Rana pipiens* and still remain distinct species? It is important to recognize at this point that these fertile hybrids were produced in the laboratory and do not occur in nature; in other words, the two species cannot be considered as part of the same system of "actually or potentially interbreeding populations." In their natural environment they are prevented from becoming such by various factors such as difference in breeding season and preference for different breeding locations. Should the environmental situation change so as to break down these barriers and thus enhance the interbreeding — as in the case of the shad genus *Pomolobus* referred to above — then there would be hybrids produced that would soon eliminate the distinctive species characteristics of both species. Further aspects of this problem will be considered in the next section of this chapter.

In summary, there are many factors involved in the many ways in which animals within a species may vary. Before any limits can be set as to where one species ends and another begins all of these variations must be considered. The most important variations that occur within the species are those associated with geographic and climatic differences to the point where members of an admittedly valid species can no longer interbreed.

ISOLATION AND SPECIATION

Intimately associated with the phenomena of geographic and climatic variation is the role which these processes play in the formation of species. It should be apparent at this point that the definition we give to the word "species" is going to determine our conclusions to a great extent. It has been shown earlier that for the conservative Christian scholar the synonymy of the biological "species" with the biblical "kind" is not only unwise but completely untenable. This proposition must be re-emphasized at this point in order that the Christian may get the proper perspective in evaluating much of the literature on the subject of evolution. Perhaps the simplest accurate description of the process of evolution as understood by present-day biologists is that given in the words of the following paragraph.

"Species have a natural tendency to vary. In any given population the nature of the environment will determine which of these variations is beneficial to the members of that population. Those variations which are disadvantageous will operate to the detriment of the animals in which they occur so that these animals will eventually die out. On the other hand, those variations which are beneficial will enhance the survival of the animals in which they occur. Therefore, these animals will increase in numbers. If our population is at the fringe of the geographic distribution of the species involved or becomes isolated from other populations of the species, it soon becomes sufficiently distinct to be recognized as a separate subspecies. At this point we have a difference of opinion as indicated earlier in this chapter. The majority of biologists (neo-Darwinians) consider that this process continues and results in the formation of new species; i.e., the subspecies is an incipient species. However, another group of biologists (neo-mutationists) consider that more drastic changes are necessary in order to develop new species. A major portion of the differences of opinion lies in the understanding of the limits of variation, the definition of the species, and the nature of the hereditary mechanisms which are responsible."

As will readily be recognized by all who have read Darwin or an accurate summary of his position, the early portion of the above statement is merely a rewording of Darwin's concepts of natural selection and survival of the fittest. In regard to the latter, it is important to notice that this much-abused and overrated aspect of evolution is meaningless as an expression of the popular "ever upward and onward" notion, since the only plausible definition of the term "fittest" in this regard is that these are the individuals which survive under a given set of circumstances. But such a proposition is just the naturalistic way of expressing the theological concept of the providence of God. With the concept that natural selection can and does make changes in populations which result in the formation of subspecies and perhaps even species, there can be little disagreement. But that this is the *only* factor is a considerable understatement of the case. The simple interaction of variation and natural selection would lend itself to a single pattern of change in a given species. In order that several species may be derived from a common ancestor it is necessary that the parent stock give rise to populations which are prevented from interbreeding with one another. This phenomenon is called "isolation."

Isolation can be of several varieties. *Seasonal* isolation occurs when, as a result of the interaction of variation and selection, two or more populations result that reproduce at different times of the year. Under these conditions it would be impossible for these populations to interbreed. Thus two closely related species of European sea gulls breed in the same area about two weeks apart. Reference has been made to a similar mechanism in the frog species *Rana pipiens* and *R. palustris*. Such species are kept isolated by such slight but important differences in the time in which they breed.

The most easily understood type of isolation is *geographic* isolation. In this situation, the separation of different populations takes place as the result of geographic barriers such as the development of deserts, islands, or mountain ranges, or the widening of rivers. Thus, for example, the animal life on either side of large rivers, such as the Amazon River, may be basically similar but still result in the production and recognition of distinct species or subspecies on either side. Even smaller rivers may furnish barriers to animals which can neither fly over them nor swim across them. Thus Dice[18] has found significant differences in the mouse populations on either side of the Snake River in Idaho. Likewise, the Grand Canyon in Arizona has produced significant differences in the populations for many species of the north and south rims by effectively isolating these two areas from one another. Perhaps the most spectacular of these differences occurs in the tufted-eared squirrels, with the Abert's squirrel of the south rim and the Kaibab squirrel of the north rim. Similar differences have been observed in many situations where an unfriendly environment isolates populations of birds, small mammals, insects, etc. Spectacular differentiation has been observed in many groups of land snails in which individual populations have become isolated on small areas of high ground, thus eliminating the possibility of natural inbreeding of these populations. Such situations are difficult to resolve and, until they are carefully studied over a long period of time and a reasonably wide area and compared with similar situations in other areas, these populations may be considered — and have been — as mere populations, subspecies, distinct species, or even different genera.

This consideration of isolation leads us to one of the classic arguments in popular anti-evolutionary literature. It is frequently stated that any organism differing from its parents in more or less obvious ways — whether produced naturally or artificially — will, when it breeds with others of its kind, eventually revert to the natural, wild type. Certainly, were interbreeding with others of its kind completely unrestricted and the environment stable, this would be the case. Indeed, this is the case most of the time. However, the development of distinctive characters in an isolated population or at the extremes of the geographic range of a given species will lead to the development of distinctive populations that eventually become recognized as either subspecies or species. Furthermore, changes in the environment do occur, not only in terms of geological time but even in the time range of one or two human generations. One of the most carefully studied examples of this type is the nun moth (*Lymantria monacha*) studied by Goldschmidt.[19] This moth has been observed in Europe for hundreds of years and during most of that time it was recognized that the light phase predominated over the dark phase so that the latter was a rarity. Within the last hundred years these moths, which

18. L. R. Dice, "Variations in the Deer-mouse (*Peromyscus maniculatus*) in the Columbia Basin of Southeastern Washington and Adjacent Idaho and Oregon," *Contributions from the Laboratory of Vertebrate Genetics, University of Michigan,* XII (1939), 1-22.

19. R. Goldschmidt, "Lymantria," *Bibliographica Genetica,* XI (1934), 1-180.

are prevalent in industrial areas, have "changed" so that the dark phase predominates and the light phase is seldom found. Whether the dark forms have a physiology which enables them to survive the toxic elements of industrial pollution or whether they are better able to escape their predators in these smoky areas has not been settled. But the moth population has changed. A similar situation appears to be involved in the development of DDT-resistant flies, antibiotic-resistant micro-organisms, and tryparsamide-resistant trypansomes where the organisms have been subjected to these originally lethal compounds. While it might be objected that individual smoke and toxic substances are "artificial," these factors do represent valid changes in the environment and the organisms revert to the "wild" type only when the environment is returned to its original condition in a reasonably short period of time.

SPECIATION AND CREATION

From a study of the evolutionary literature it is obvious that speciation is one of the basic aspects of evolution, or as stated earlier in this chapter, evolution is concerned with the origin of species. Inasmuch as conservative Christian thinking has been largely anti-evolutionary, it is most important that this problem of speciation be considered in its relationship to the doctrine of creation. We have seen in the previous sections that the process of speciation makes up a substantial part of the theory of evolution. We have seen further that much of what is included in speciation is not only observable in the fossil record but can actually be observed in living populations at the present time; in short, speciation as a demonstrable process is still going on. In contrast to this, is the process of creation as outlined in the first chapter of Genesis which, as a unique act of God in the past, came to an end and is no longer taking place in its strictest sense. From this it should be obvious that when an evolutionist talks of speciation as evolution he need not be speaking in opposition to creation, although in most cases he is ignoring the possibility of any special act of an almighty God.

On the other hand, it is unfortunate that the average evolutionist uses evolution and speciation as almost synonymous terms. Since speciation can be demonstrated quite conclusively, and since speciation is "obviously" evolution in action, anyone who questions evolution in its larger scope is, therefore, considered an unscientific ignoramus. That this is unfair can be partially established on the basis of admissions by evolutionists themselves. The position of Goldschmidt and his followers that speciation processes alone cannot explain the whole course of evolution is further evidence that the ameba-to-man scope of evolution is not proven from, and, therefore, not synonymous with, speciation. The difficulties in sharply separating "micro-evolution" from "macro-evolution," as Goldschmidt used these terms, have led most biologists to ignore the problems involved in the supposed evolution of the higher taxonomic categories by the same mechanisms involved in speciation.

The authors of the Westminster Confession of Faith spoke of God as executing his decrees in the works of creation and providence. On this basis they went on to consider the process of creation as having taken place in six days (duration not specified) and implied that this was the extent of a unique activity on the part of God the Creator. They then went on to consider God's work of providence as his preserving and governing all his creatures and all their actions. Such a broad and all-inclusive concept of God's activities is certainly in accordance with the Bible and is obviously the place where any consideration of speciation belongs. Therefore, speciation is not a substitute for creation but rather one phase of God's activities as the ruler of the universe. As such, then, speciation sheds little light on the mechanics of creation, although it is possible that God the Creator may have used it, in part, during the "six days" in much the same manner as the car repairman uses some of the same tools as the original manufacturers.

In a similar fashion, speciation is a part of the theory of evolution. It may be that, as a process, speciation can be elaborated to include such a "naturalistic" interpretation of the origin of all life, but the evidence for such a generalization is far from conclusive. Speciation certainly cannot be claimed to prove or even imply the naturalistic origin of all things without God. The whole process is complex enough that those who want to see no design and no Creator can easily do so, while those who look for design in nature can just as easily find it. Speciation demonstrates some orderly change or "evolution." It does not, however, disprove the prime role of God either in a unique creative process "in the beginning" or in his providential control since that time. It most certainly does not do any violence to the simple but eloquent account of Moses in the first chapter of Genesis.

Chapter Seven

THE DISTRIBUTION OF ANIMALS

By V. Elving Anderson

Plants and animals are widely distributed on earth. In fact, no place is so forbidding as to be entirely without living things. At the same time we all realize that the different types of plants and animals are not equally distributed. One of the joys of vacationing is to become acquainted with new kinds of birds, trees, and flowers. A good hunter soon learns the type of terrain which is most likely to have the kind of game which he desires.

The inquiring person, however, is not satisfied with a description of distribution — where to find different creatures. His interest shifts to the more difficult problem of explanation — why this animal is found here but not there. A general rule soon emerges, that the animals living in a particular place are suited for their environment in a variety of ways. This is almost too obvious, since those forms not suited (or not adapted) for the environment would have moved away or died long ago.

In this task of description and explanation it is important that one write from the background of personal experience with an appreciable part of animal life. In the opinion of a recent author, for example, "any young naturalist who thinks he can understand the world and living things and evolution without experiencing the tropics is ... deceiving himself, to his own great injury."[1] We must not assume that the task is a simple one, either, for existing situations are almost endlessly complex, and "they are evidently the products of exceedingly complex movements and counter-movements, spreadings, recedings, disappearances, and replacements of a diversity of animals over the whole of the very complex surface of the world."[2] Those of us who have not traveled and studied widely are thus dependent upon the observations of a large number of persons who have contributed to the study of animal distribution (a field known as zoogeography) and to the related areas of ecology and geology.

Now the reason for including this topic in a book about Darwin

1. Philip J. Darlington, Jr., *Zoogeography: The Geographical Distribution of Animals* (New York: Wiley, 1957), p. 10.
2. *Ibid.*, p. 619.

is that his observations along this line in South America were among the first suggestions to him of evolution. His book *The Origin of Species* contains two chapters which are still considered one of the best discussions of the evolutionary principles of the subject. It will be of interest, therefore, to follow his line of reasoning as well as more recent contributions.

GENERAL CONSIDERATIONS

Darwin opened his discussion of geographical distribution with the observation that "neither the similarity nor the dissimilarity of the inhabitants of various regions can be wholly accounted for by climatal and other physical conditions."[3] One can find very similar types of environment in such widely separated areas as Australia, Africa, and South America. If the physical factors were the sole determiners of distribution we might expect to find similar plants and animals in these three areas, but the fauna and flora are vastly different. It is apparent that a particular environment does not contain all the types of organisms which are adapted to it.

Another approach to the same problem is to study areas within one continent (as South America) which have considerably different conditions. The types of life in these different South American areas resemble each other more closely than they resemble the life in those African or Australian regions which have the same climate.

Of course it is still true that the chances for an animal to survive and produce offspring are closely related to environmental factors: (1) Climate (temperature, moisture, and light), (2) other animals (of the same kind and of other kinds) and organisms causing disease, (3) food (both quality and quantity), and (4) a place in which to live.[4] Any such grouping is somewhat arbitrary, however, since the factors are interdependent. For example, the distribution of plants used for food is influenced by climate. Any attempt to study and describe the nature and effects of natural selection should clearly account for these environmental components. But Darwin's point was that something more than these factors is required for a full explanation.

The second of Darwin's observations was that barriers, or obstacles to free migration, affect plant and animal distribution. You may already know that bird guides for the area east of the Rocky Mountains are different from those for the western region. Those

3. Charles Darwin, *The Origin of Species by Means of Natural Selection,* with additions and corrections from the 6th and last English edition, two vols. in one (New York: Appleton, 1905), II, 129.

4. H. G. Andrewartha and L. C. Birch, *The Distribution and Abundance of Animals* (Chicago: University of Chicago Press, 1954), p. 26.

mountain ranges which run parallel to the equator (such as the Himalaya Mountains) appear to be even more effective barriers than those which run north and south. In a similar manner the types of animal and plant life are often quite different on the opposite sides of oceans, deserts, and large rivers.

This effect of barriers introduces us to a time dimension in the study of distribution. Apparently extensive changes in the distribution of plant and animal forms have occurred, but such changes have been limited (although not prevented) by barriers. Unfortunately some writers have stated that the concept of creation necessarily means that all forms of life are now in the location where they were originally created. No such restriction can be read into the Bible account. The story of the flood (whether one believes it to be local or universal) suggests a redispersal of animals from a *refugium* (as the ark could be designated). Furthermore, in the course of time volcanic and coral islands have emerged from the oceans and have become populated.

Temporal changes in distribution have posed some interesting riddles for the zoogeographers. In earlier years some writers took the easy way out by the extensive use of hypothetical "land bridges." More recently scientists have been more cautious in using bridges for explanation except where strong evidence has accumulated. Human intervention has further complicated the story. The animals on Newfoundland were particularly puzzling for they resembled the types found in Europe even though Newfoundland is part of North America. Lindroth[5] recently learned that as early as the seventeenth century vessels filled with earthen ballast sailed from England to Newfoundland. There the ballast (and the animals unintentionally included) was dumped ashore and fish and lumber were taken on for the return trip to Europe. Thus, with or without man's help, very extensive changes in distribution have taken place.

At this point we might distinguish between *distribution,* the places which happen to be occupied at any particular moment, and *dispersal,* the movement away from a populated place.[6] All animals apparently show, to a greater or smaller degree, a tendency toward dispersal, although this tendency may be accentuated by hunger, warmth, or wind.[7] Some movements may result from competition for the environmental factors listed earlier. On the other hand, the dominant (most successful) forms of animals apparently spread to gain advantages, rather than to escape disadvantages.[8]

---

5. Carl H. Lindroth, *The Faunal Connections Between Europe and North America* (New York: Wiley, 1957), pp. 157ff.
6. Andrewartha and Birch, *op. cit.*, p. 86.
7. *Ibid.*, p. 91.
8. Darlington, *op. cit.*, p. 620.

Another important distinction is between the *distribution* and *abundance* of animals as different aspects of the same problem. Within the geographic limits of the distribution of a species may be found zones with high abundance and also a marginal zone with low abundance.[9] Great changes in abundance have occurred in the past, not too rarely ending in the extinction of a species. Species are thus subject to opposing tendencies — toward dominance on the one hand, and extinction on the other.

The continuity of a species throughout time is clearly the result of the reproductive cycle — birth, growth, and production of the next generation. The next generation will inherit its genes only from those creatures which were able to survive, find a mate, and produce living young. From this point of view we lose sight of individuals and think in terms of groups of individuals, or populations. In a specific geographical area there may exist a population of animals which are free to interbreed. This group of animals is called a "deme" (a local population) and constitutes a sort of "gene pool" since there are no restrictions to interbreeding. In other geographic areas there are other demes which would freely interbreed with this first one were it not for barriers. A "species" may now be described as "a group of organisms so similar in structure and heredity that their demes intergrade, may fuse, and may take the place of each other without essential change in the nature and role of the group as a whole."[10] Within a species, however, certain groups of demes may be distinguished from others, and such subdivisions are called "subspecies" or "races." Breeds of domestic animals and varieties of cross-fertilized cultivated plants are considered races.[11] With these concepts as a background we are ready to go back to Darwin's observations.

DARWIN AND THE GALAPAGOS ISLANDS

In the year 1835 Charles Darwin visited the Galapagos Islands as a naturalist with the English ship *Beagle*. His observations there started his thinking in the direction which later resulted in *The Origin of Species*. These islands lie near the equator some 600 miles west of the coast of South America and were originally formed by the action of volcanoes. The largest island is eighty miles long and has peaks 4,000 feet high. The name Galapagos refers to the giant

9. Andrewartha and Birch, *op. cit.*, pp. 5ff.

10. George Gaylord Simpson, Colin S. Pittendrigh, and Lewis H. Tiffany, *Life: An Introduction to Biology* (New York: Harcourt, Brace, 1957), p. 397.

11. Th. Dobzhansky, *Evolution, Genetics and Man* (New York: Wiley, 1955), p. 138.

land tortoises found there, which have been used both for food and oil.

These islands belong to the class of "oceanic" islands, those which are far from the mainland and which were not connected with any continent in geologically recent times. The Hawaiian Islands are another example. Such islands have no native amphibians or land mammals, although when these forms have been introduced they have spread rapidly. On the other hand, many oceanic islands have aerial mammals (bats), apparently because they could migrate more readily. The second major class of islands is termed "continental," and includes those which are usually separated from the mainland only by shallow straits (such as Newfoundland). The plants and animals of continental islands are usually similar to those on the adjacent mainland, whereas the forms on oceanic islands are often different from those on other islands or on the closest continents.

Darwin was especially intrigued by his study of the Galapagos land birds. Of the twenty-six species of land birds, twenty-one (and perhaps two more) were "endemic" (found nowhere else in the world). In contrast, of the eleven marine species only two were endemic while nine were found elsewhere. He explained this difference between the land and marine birds by pointing out that marine birds could travel from the continent to the islands more easily. However, most of the land birds on the islands (even though of different species) showed a close affinity with those on the continent "in every character, in their habits, gestures, and tones of voice."[12] It was a case of "so much alike, and yet so different."

The story became more complex when he observed that "each separate island of the Galapagos Archipelago is tenanted, and the fact is a marvellous one, by many distinct species; but these species are related to each other in a very much closer manner than to the inhabitants of the American continent, or of any other quarter of the world."[13] To explain these findings he suggested "colonization from the nearest or readiest source, together with the subsequent adaptation of the colonists to their new homes."

In 1938 David Lack visited the islands to study "Darwin's finches" (the most common type of land bird). These finches are dull to look at — all gray brown, short-tailed, with fluffy rump feathers. They build roofed nests, display territoriality, are monogamous, and have extremely few natural enemies. The size varies from that of a small warbler to that of a very large sparrow. "Only the variety of the beaks and the number of their species excite attention — small finch-like beaks, huge finch-like beaks, parrot-like beaks, straight wood-

12. Darwin, *op. cit.*, II, 179, 188.
13. *Ibid.*, p. 190.

boring beaks, decurved flower-probing beaks, slender warbler-like beaks; species which look very different and species which look closely similar."[14] (See Fig. 12.)

Lack found that the specimens of finches from any one island did not form a continuously graded series for any single characteristic — large body to small, thick-billed to thin-billed, or dark to pale plumage. Instead they fell into distinct groups, each group having a characteristic appearance. The individuals of any one group did not normally interbreed with the members of any other. In Lack's opinion interbreeding was primarily prevented by psychological factors associated with breeding behavior.

Let us now restate Darwin's hypothesis as amplified by later workers. A long while ago a few finches somehow made the trip from South America to the Galapagos Islands. They found an ample food supply and none of their old enemies, so they multiplied rapidly. In the course of time mutations occurred even as they had earlier and the genes already present were sorted out into new combinations. But the new environment was different enough from their old South American home that some mutant traits which were formerly at a disadvantage now made them more successful in coping with the environment and producing young. Such traits accumulated as the result of this *natural selection*. Occasionally a few birds travelled to one of the other islands where another set of environmental factors acted to select for somewhat different characteristics.

At a later time some of the birds from the second island could migrate back to the first island with either of two results. If the two groups of birds could interbreed freely and exchange their accumulated gene differences, they would be considered as two subspecies. On the other hand, if they kept distinct with no interbreeding they would be considered two separate species. In other words, one original species would have divided into two species, and we would have an example of the "origin of species." Since this is a crucial point it may be well to include part of Lack's description:

> The commonest method of species-formation in birds is through the meeting in the same region of two geographical forms which have become so different they keep separate. The fundamental problem in the origin of species is not the origin of differences in appearance, since these arise at the level of the geographical race, but the origin of genetic segregation. The test of species-formation is whether, when two forms meet they interbreed and merge, or whether they keep distinct.
> ... When forms differentiated in geographical isolation meet later in the same region, two conditions are necessary if the forms are to persist as separate species. First, they must be sufficiently different genetically not to interbreed

14. David Lack, *Darwin's Finches* (Cambridge: Cambridge University Press, 1947), p. 11.

freely, and secondly, they must be sufficiently different in their ecology to avoid serious competition with each other.[15]

Of course, we must recognize the possibility that some of the "species" of finches are merely striking variants which should be considered subspecies.[16] However, there is apparently no good reason to doubt the accuracy of the classification, and if this is correct, these birds provide strong evidence for the "mutability of species."

The precise mechanism of such a change in species is less well documented. Andrewartha and Birch feel that there is no need to invoke "competition" to explain the observations. They prefer to restrict the term to those cases where food or space is limited (in relation to the number of organisms) or where one species harms the other. They point out that where Lack found species together, their food was superabundant or else they lived on different foods. When they were separated, there was no evidence that they invaded one another's territories. In fact, natural populations rarely consume a large proportion of the food available to them. Andrewartha and Birch suggest rather that if related species have differentiated in geographic isolation, "the chances are that they would also have developed different habits and preferences, so that when they were later brought into the same territory, they would select different sorts of places in which to live."[17]

Does this concept of species change conflict with the Bible account? Unfortunately many writers (including the "father of taxonomy," Linnaeus, in his earlier writings) have insisted that belief in creation necessarily includes belief in the "fixity of species." Such an insistence is not a fair interpretation of the Bible record and has caused much confusion from both the scientific and religious point of view.[18] The approach of Short seems to be more adequate: "Let us make it plain at the outset that we are not disposed to argue that species, or genera, were created at the beginning of time exactly as they are now, and that no changes or variations have taken place. It seems that large variations have as a matter of fact occurred."[19] Otherwise the strong evidence for species change (at the level described above) will be interpreted as evidence against the existence and activity of a Creator.

15. *Ibid.,* pp. 129, 145-146.
16. Dobzhansky, *op. cit.,* pp. 184-187.
17. Andrewartha and Birch, *op. cit.,* p. 463.
18. Frank Lewis Marsh, *Evolution, Creation and Science* (Washington, D. C.: Review and Herald Publishing Association, 1947), pp. 332ff. Russell L. Mixter, *Creation and Evolution,* ASA Monograph, No. 2 (West Lafayette, Ind.: American Scientific Affiliation, 1953), p. 3.
19. A. Rendle Short, *Modern Discovery and the Bible* (London: Inter-Varsity, 1943), p. 35.

THE MARSUPIAL STORY

The story of Darwin's finches was a case history in speciation, at a level sometimes called "microevolution." A different set of problems is presented by the distribution of animals in higher (and thus more inclusive) categories of classification. Here the range of variability is much greater and the total distribution is often world-wide. As an illustration we may turn our attention to some information about mammals (those animals which possess hair and mammary glands).

Mammals have been divided into three groups: the egg-laying "monotremes" (such as the platypus), the "marsupials" (such as the kangaroo and opossum) which carry their young for a long time in a brood pouch, and the "placentals," in which the developing embryos receive nourishment until the time of birth through a placenta. Fossils of marsupials and placentals have been found scattered widely over the earth. However, with the exception of the opossum in North America, living marsupials are almost entirely restricted to Australia. There the marsupials are the dominant (most successful) mammals. In fact, the only native placentals are bats, the dingo dog (possibly introduced in the Pleistocene), and a few rodents.

The dominance of marsupials in Australia may be explained by the relative absence of placentals, for placentals tend to replace the marsupials whenever they occupy the same area. When rabbits were introduced into Australia by man, they spread and multiplied explosively. The absence of marsupial bats is thought to be the result of the presence of placental bats. In North America the opossum has survived, possibly because its activities are restricted to nocturnal periods, thus avoiding competition with placentals. The placental type is apparently more efficient in terms of brain capacity, greater accuracy of temperature regulation, and various details of animal structure.[20]

It is particularly interesting to observe that the Australian marsupials resemble, both in appearance and in ways of life, the placental mammals on other continents. There are, for example, the Tasmanian wolf, the banded anteater, and the marsupial mole. The flying phalanger resembles flying squirrels and the wombat resembles the woodchuck. These observations are usually interpreted as examples of "adaptive radiation" or of opportunism in evolution. This would be like the story of Darwin's finches extended to a much broader scale. However, marsupials do not fill all the available niches. The absence of marsupial bats has already been noted. In

20. Julian Huxley, *Evolution in Action* (New York: Harper, 1953).

addition, there are no aquatic marsupials in Australia and no small dominant gnawing marsupials anywhere.[21]

If we turn now to the fossil evidence, a common interpretation is that Australia became separated from the Indomalayan continental mass before the rise of placental mammals, so that only monotremes and marsupials were present in the original Australian mammalian fauna.[22] The breaking of the land bridge prevented later invasions by placentals. Dobzhansky describes a similar hypothesis for the South American marsupials.[23] During the Tertiary period North and South America were separated, with no land bridge such as the Isthmus of Panama. The study of Miocene and Pliocene fossils shows that the North American mammals were quite different from the South American ones, with only a few families (and no genera) common to both continents. The South American marsupials included forms resembling wolves and saber-toothed tigers. In late Pliocene or in Pleistocene a land corridor arose linking the two continents. Many of the South American marsupials have since become extinct, apparently as a result of the invasion of North American placentals.

The hypothetical sequence of the mammalian groups has been re-evaluated recently by Darlington:

> It used to be thought that the earliest mammals were monotremes, that marsupials were derived from monotremes, and that placentals were derived from marsupials, but it is now known that mammalian phylogeny was not so simple. Mammals split into two or three sub-classes very early in their history. Whether the monotremes were one of the earliest groups is doubtful. ... Marsupials and placentals belong to one ancient sub-class, but, instead of being successive groups, they were parallel ones which existed together well before the end of the Cretaceous. There apparently never was a time when only marsupials, and not placentals, were widely distributed over the world.[24]

A note of caution seems necessary here. Changes in interpretation (like that in the preceding paragraph) might be taken by Christians as evidence that scientists really do not know what they are doing. This is not at all a fair conclusion. Such changes are made possible, and are often necessitated, by the accumulation of more accurate information. This point may illustrate the role of assumptions in the formulation of scientific hypotheses. It would be useless to insist that we attempt no conclusions until "all the facts are in," because all the facts will never be in. It is necessary, therefore, to make simplifying

---

21. Darlington, *op. cit.*, p. 337.

22. W. C. Allee, A. E. Emerson, O. Park, T. Park, and K. P. Schmidt, *Principles of Animal Ecology* (New York: Saunders, 1949), p. 666.

23. Dobzhansky, *op. cit.*, pp. 308-311.

24. Darlington, *op. cit.*, p. 322.

assumptions so that working hypotheses can be formed. As more data accumulate, some of the assumptions may be found inadequate. This is not a retreat but an advance, and revisions should thus be expected and welcomed. At the same time it may be added that the most helpful scientific contributions are those in which the assumptions and working principles are clearly identified.

How does the "marsupial story" relate to the Bible record? Mixter discusses the evidence that fossil and living kangaroos are found only in Australia. If kangaroos had been in the ark, one would expect to find fossil remains somewhere along the route to Australia. Mixter interprets this and other evidence to mean that kangaroos were not in the ark and that the flood was a local event. He further states that "a creationist may conclude that the first marsupials were created."[25] This would imply that all other marsupials developed from these first created forms. I am not aware of any specific Bible statement which would rule out the possibility of such an interpretation. It is clear, however, that on this basis a broad diversification must have occurred to account for the fossil and present species.

ADAPTATIONS

In the preceding discussion the adaptation of organisms to their environment has been mentioned. An "adaptation" has been defined as "a characteristic of an organism advantageous to it or to the conspecific group in which it lives."[26] Those animals which live in colder climates generally have longer and finer fur, are larger in size, and have shorter tails, ears, legs, and beaks than animals in warmer regions. All of these adaptations are thought to serve for the conservation of heat. Descriptions of many other types of adaptation may be found in biology textbooks.

Some scientists have criticized the concept of creation by pointing to the explanation of adaptations by "creationists."

> The origin of this apparent purposefulness of biological organization is a riddle which several generations of biologists have attempted to solve. Some have taken the easy way out by supposing that every living species is endowed by the Creator with those features which it needs in order to live in the habitats in which it is actually found. This is, however, a spurious solution; it implicitly blames the Creator also for all the imperfections and all the sufferings found in human and biological nature.[27]
>
> In St. Helena there is reason to believe that the naturalised plants and animals have nearly or quite exterminated many native productions. He who admits the doctrine of the creation of each separate species, will have to admit that a sufficient number of the best adapted plants and animals were

25. Mixter, *op. cit.*, p. 17.

26. George Gaylord Simpson, *The Major Features of Evolution* (New York: Columbia University Press, 1953), p. 160.

27. Dobzhansky, *op. cit.*, pp. 308-311.

not created for oceanic islands; for man has unintentionally stocked them far more fully and perfectly than did nature.[28]

Much of this criticism is not justified. There is considerable difference of opinion on specific details among the scholars who believe in a Creator. The generalized description of a "creationist" cannot be given in a few sentences any easier than that of the "evolutionist." The concept of creation is far more complex and sophisticated than is generally assumed. We might note also that a "creationist" concept of adaptation was held by scientists prior to Darwin as indicated by this statement attributed to Lamarck:

> Nature (or its Author) in creating animals has foreseen all possible sorts of circumstances in which they would be destined to live, and has given to each species a constant organization, as well as a form determined and invariable in its parts, which forces each species to live in the places and climates where it is found, and there to preserve the habits which we know belong to it.[29]

On the other hand, Christians (both laymen and ministers) should exercise considerable caution in interpreting God's relationship to his creation. An organism without essential adaptations simply would not survive or produce offspring. When the environment changes, the population of a species may be diminished, even to the point of extinction. Some species appear to have adaptations suiting them for environments in which they have not previously lived. In such considerations the effectiveness of natural selection in permitting and restricting variability should be acknowledged freely.

At the same time it must be remembered that natural selection is not the *source* of variability. Mutations of chromosomes and genes, and recombinations of these, are with minor qualifications the only known sources of hereditary changes.[30] The subsequent effects of natural selection upon these changes may be considered to have two aspects. "Stabilizing selection" keeps down the number of deleterious mutant genes and gene combinations. "Dynamic selection," on the other hand, permits the species to adapt to environmental changes and to seize new ecological opportunities.[31]

In addition, we must acknowledge that the careful study of adaptation involves considerable complexity. Simpson points out that a trait adaptive in one respect may not be so in another. For example, the development of armor is a frequent adaptation for defense, but

28. Darwin, *op. cit.*, II, 178.

29. In H. H. Newman, *Evolution Yesterday and Today* (Baltimore: Williams & Wilkins, 1932), p. 2.

30. Sewall Wright, "Adaptation and Selection" in *Genetics, Paleontology, and Evolution*, edited by Glenn L. Jepsen, Ernst Mayr, and George Gaylord Simpson (Princeton: Princeton University Press, 1949), p. 365.

31. I. I. Schmahlhauson, *Factors of Evolution* (New York: McGraw, 1949), pp. 73ff.

it also reduces the speed of movement which some other animals depend upon for defense. Furthermore, organisms are in one sense *in* the environment and in another sense *part of it*. "There is not simply a given environment to which organisms adapt. Their own activities change the environment and are part of the environment."[32]

The basic problem here seems to involve an opinion as to the amount of variability for which God is believed to be directly responsible. God's relationship to adaptations could, on the one hand, involve the extent of variability present in the original creation (or creations). On the other hand it could involve the further action of natural forces with which the earth and its organisms were endowed. This interpretation resembles Marsh's distinction between primary and secondary adaptations.[33] A more extensive and more adequate treatment of this problem would seem to be a very desirable addition to the evangelical Christian literature.

SUMMARY

In summarizing his observations concerning geographical distribution in *The Origin of Species,* Darwin stated:

> If the difficulties be not insuperable in admitting that in the long course of time all the individuals of the same species, and likewise of the several species belonging to the same genus, have proceeded from some one source; then all the grand leading facts of geographical distribution are explicable on the theory of migration, together with subsequent modification and the multiplication of new forms.[34]

It seems likely that this statement can be accepted by theologically conservative Christians without in any way violating fundamental doctrines of the historic faith. To be sure, Darwin later in the same book stated his belief that "animals are descended from at most only four or five progenitors, and plants from an equal or lesser number." However, he did not hold to this latter idea as an essential part of his argument. Most of Darwin's criticism of "creation" was directed against the concept of the absolute fixity of species. If one holds that created organisms can undergo species change, much of the force of Darwin's criticism is removed.

Evangelical Christians need a basic outlook which will permit them to view the growing body of scientific data and hypotheses without fear or hesitation, but with considerable interest and anticipation. This will be possible only as we continue to develop a comprehensive philosophy of science, a statement of the ways in which God is, and has been, related to the universe. In this undertaking we

32. Simpson, *The Major Features of Evolution,* p. 182.
33. Marsh, *op. cit.,* pp. 325-326.
34. Darwin, *op. cit.,* II, 198.

can learn much from writings of the past, such as this statement published shortly after Darwin's *Origin*:

> Only let us keep to the old Hebrew modes of thinking and speaking, and we need not be afraid of naturalism. It is God's nature that we read of in Genesis. If life is said to come from the waters, let us remember that it was upon these same waters the Spirit brooded in the first mysterious night of creation. If it is naturalism, it is the naturalism of the Bible; and the wonder is that such plain declarations of birth, growth, succession, law, generation — one thing coming out of another — should have been so much overlooked. It is because the Scripture doctrine of the Word, or Logos, in nature, has so fallen out of our theology, that we dread so much the appearance of naturalism. In proportion as we have lost that true Scriptural idea of supernaturalism, which sees no inconsistency in such blendings, are we driven to the dogmatic or arbitrary supernaturalism to defend our religious ideas from the equally dogmatic and arbitrary naturalism of modern science.[35]

35. Tayler Lewis, in *Genesis* by John Peter Lange; translated, with additions, by Tayler Lewis and A. Gosman (*A Commentary on the Holy Scriptures* by John Peter Lange; translated and edited, with additions, by Philip Schaff [New York: Scribner, 1871]), p. 147.

Chapter Eight

FOSSILS AND THEIR OCCURRENCE

By CORDELIA ERDMAN BARBER

DEFINITION

Some years ago a man brought a rock into one of the famous museums of our country and asked to have one of the scientists there examine it. Having been directed to the proper office, he at once laid his rock down on the desk and announced with pride, "I've got a fossil potato here."

The curator was accustomed to this sort of interruption of his work. He smiled, picked up the rock and expressed his regret that it was nothing more exciting than a brown and rounded chunk of a very common mineral. The owner was somewhat crestfallen, but after a further bit of conversation he thought of an argument which for him established his position and closed the case. "It must be a fossil potato," he insisted. "I found it right in my vegetable garden."

The man with his "potato" did not understand very much about the subject of paleontology, which is the study of fossils. For the benefit of those readers who wish to be better informed than he, the first portion of this chapter will be devoted to basic considerations of this subject.

The remains of, or the record made by, an ancient living thing constitutes a fossil. The catch in this definition is the word "ancient," which is a very flexible one. In this context it is generally conceded to mean "originating before the time of written history." The footprint of some prankster in a cement sidewalk is not a fossil, but the footprint of a dinosaur is.

CONDITIONS FAVORING FOSSILIZATION

Ordinarily, when an animal dies its flesh is eaten by scavengers, and its hide and bones crumble under the combined attack of sun, rain, bacteria, and chemicals. Dead plant material also decomposes and vanishes quickly. Under these conditions no fossil could form. But if the dead organism were to be protected from such thorough destruction, there would be the possibility that some record of it might remain through the ages. Quick burial in a favorable medium affords such protection. The sedentary clam living in an estuary and overwhelmed with mud during a spring flood; the hapless beast mired in an asphalt pool; the unwary insect trapped in a secretion of resin; all of these are potential fossils. Dry sand and cave deposits also may provide protective environments. Some fossils have been preserved in more rare media, such as ice and its opposite extreme, lava. This latter occurrence seems almost incredible, but it happened at least once: a rhinoceros engulfed in molten rock in the state of Washington left behind some charred bones and the imprint of its skin in the cavity which marks where it once lay.

Those animals which possess hard parts stand the best chance of leaving behind some documentation of their existence. Fossils of entirely soft-bodied creatures have been discovered, but it is more surprising that any such animals have escaped total destruction than that so few of them have been preserved.

CATEGORIES OF FOSSILIZATION

All fossils belong to one of two categories: they are either the direct remains, altered or unaltered, of once living things; or they are less direct evidence of their existence.

Remains. The great museums of natural history in our country display reconstructions of many historic animals. Often the animals have a setting which portrays the sort of environment in which they most probably lived. In order to make such scenes accurately it is necessary for scientists to study in detail every clue that the fossil record will yield. This is very painstaking work, and it would be a great convenience if more animals had been preserved in their natural condition. Unfortunately, actual remains are among the most rare of fossils. Perhaps the best known example is the hairy mammoths, ancient relatives of the elephant, which have been found in arctic countries with their very flesh perfectly preserved in ice and frozen soil.

By far the majority of fossils belong to the category of altered remains. These are the bones and shells which have been subjected to chemical processes in nature and have been slightly or entirely changed in composition. It is easiest to think of alteration as always involving either chemical addition or subtraction, or a combination of these. What happens in any given situation depends upon the particular chemicals which waters moving through the ground carry to the potential fossil.

Bones seem to be particularly susceptible to chemical addition. This means that spaces in the bone become filled in with new material so that the end product weighs considerably more than the original, which it may otherwise resemble closely.

Shells, like bones, may remain chemically intact. However, very often they are subject to "subtraction," which leaves a beautiful network of crystalline lace. Leaves and soft parts of animals, and sometimes even hard parts, may be subject to chemical subtraction which results in a thin film of carbon, often showing in faithful detail the structure of the original.

When subtraction and addition are combined, the resulting fossil is called a "replacement." The majority of direct remains exhibit some degree of this process. The end result may show forth the details of the original, but it is not uncommon for the details to become obscured or obliterated.

Evidences. A certain little-used trail in the Grand Canyon of Arizona leads the hiker across great sloping slabs of cream-colored sandstone. Here he discovers that he is not the first living thing to cross the area. His feet make no imprint on the long-hardened rock, but impressed distinctly into its surface there are footprints, tiny impressions made by scurrying four-footed animals when the sand was soft. Although the lizards responsible have long since vanished, so clear is the record of their presence here that one can almost imagine them hiding under a sheltering bush until the intruder passes by. Footprints, tracks, and trails, baked by the sun and buried beneath new layers of sand and mud, reveal important information about animals of bygone days.

Footprints are in reality a type of mold, an impression produced in some receptive material so as to correspond to the contours of a particular object. There are other sorts of molds, such as impressions of the inner or outer surfaces of a shell. Internal impressions are particularly valuable in conveying information about the soft parts of long extinct animals.

THE DISTRIBUTION OF FOSSILS

Fossils are not equally distributed throughout the rocks of all time. The very oldest rocks, belonging to what is called the first era of geologic time, have never yielded any fossils. Those of the second era have scarcely more to contribute. But from the opening of the third era and onward, the rocks bear testimony to the existence of abundant and diversified living things.

Fossils are found all over the world. Of course they are embedded for the most part in sandstone, shale, and limestone layers, since such rocks were once sediments favorable for burying the organisms. However, the density of fossil distribution varies greatly from place to place, even within the same layer, and some sedimentary layers contain few or no fossils. There is a thick formation of sandstone which has been traced from Wisconsin to Missouri and studied rather thoroughly by experts, and yet in all that volume of rock only a meagre handful of fossils has turned up.

HISTORIC ATTITUDES

Ancient and Middle Ages

Down through the centuries men have regarded fossils as objects of special interest and have speculated with much imagination as to their origin. The ancient Greeks often attributed them to some sort of inorganic "plastic" force which had produced them in the rocks. However, some minds were ahead of their times. As early as the sixth century B.C. the philosopher Xenophanes, having seen shells and fish skeletons in mountains and quarries of Mediterranean islands, came to the conclusion that there must have been former advances of the sea over the region. Other thinkers independently attributed sea shells found far inland to periods of oceanic flooding. It is plain that such men regarded fossils as of organic origin, but their reasoning seems to have made little impact on others.

The notion of a plastic force persisted down through the centuries and flourished during the Middle Ages when other similar ideas also gained favor. Many people thought that fossils were casualties of nature's struggle to produce living things by one method or another.

Renaissance

It was really Leonardo da Vinci, the artist and engineer, who touched off the great controversy whereby fossils came into their own. In the year 1500, while he was directing canal digging operations in northern Italy, he came across great quantities of ancient shells. These, he argued, must have belonged to animals once living there. Successive generations apparently had been overwhelmed by mud, and da Vinci described a process of replacement whereby the shells had been preserved. Perhaps because of the thorough consideration he gave these shells, the "organic theory" of fossils attracted attention as never before. Others began to write on the subject, and in 1565 a Swiss, Conrad Gesner, published what has been called "the first account of 'fossils' in essentially the modern sense,"[1] although he did include items which would not fall within the definition of that word today.[2]

The times were ripe for scientific advance, but the new science of paleontology met head-on with the accepted teaching that the earth was only a few thousand years old, a span of time which apparently left no room for this slow process of fossilization. Many people clung to the old beliefs or invented new ones. Perhaps "God, Himself, while learning the trade of creating, first made models out

---

[1]. Carey Croneis and William C. Krumbein, *Down to Earth* (Chicago: University of Chicago Press, 1937), p. 222.

[2]. George Gaylord Simpson, *Life of the Past* (New Haven: Yale University Press, 1953), p. 7.

of earth; those which satisfied Him were changed into living things and the rest, or sketches, became stony fossils."[3] Or perhaps fossils were the work of the Devil to delude man. At any rate, as late as 1696 a German medical faculty declared certain fossil bones to be merely a "freak of nature," and more than one hundred years later the same sort of opinion was being taken very seriously in the New World.

As further observations in geology and paleontology accumulated, the idea of attributing all fossils (and thus their enclosing rocks) to the great flood described in Genesis replaced earlier conjectures. This was a very acceptable proposition, for each fossil discovery could be hailed as confirmation of the Scriptures instead of as a threat to their integrity.

"Flood geology" has continued to find favor in some religious circles down to the present day, but it has long since been discarded by the great body of geologists, and the majority of students of Genesis regard it as unwarranted.

MODERN PERIOD

The century from 1758 to 1859 (Linnaeus to Darwin) was crucial in the development of paleontology. It was a time of rapid accumulation of biological data, without which there could be no real understanding of fossils.

Geology, too, was advancing rapidly during this period. A young English surveyor's assistant, later nicknamed "Strata Smith," made the observation that each fossil-bearing layer of rock contains a distinctive fossil assemblage. This at once cast doubt upon the traditional idea that one single chaotic period of flooding accounted for all fossils. In a practical way it meant that scattered outcrops of one layer of rock often could be recognized as belonging to that layer by their fossil content. In 1815 William Smith applied his observation in tracing and mapping the cross country appearances of certain English strata.

Smith also recognized the obvious fact that in an undisturbed sequence of rock layers the oldest is on the bottom, the youngest on the top. Thus it is possible to determine the relative ages of the contained fossils. With the studies made by Smith incorporating these ideas, fossils passed from their former status as relics of judgment to one as invaluable tools for building up the picture of earth history. In practice today geologists rely heavily upon fossils in assigning rocks of otherwise unknown age to their proper places in the geologic timetable.

3. Louis T. More, *The Dogma of Evolution* (Princeton: Princeton University Press, 1925), p. 132.

FOSSILS AND EVOLUTIONARY THEORY

EMERGENCE OF THE THEORY

The Fixity of Species Concept. Before the eighteenth century men were easily persuaded to believe in the frequent spontaneous generation of living things from nonliving. Another favored idea of the time was that offspring could be totally different in kind from the parental type. Not until scientific experimentation had advanced sufficiently to demonstrate, for example, that drops of water could not turn into "little green frogs" were such ideas overthrown. When it could no longer be doubted that plants and animals bred true to type, scientists rebounded to another extreme in their thinking and postulated that each of these types originally had come directly forth from the hands of God and had experienced no variation from that time to the present. This is the concept of fixity of species.

This doctrine seemed easily compatible with the Genesis record of creation, and it was thus in a position to receive ardent support from devout men of science. Accordingly it became very popular.

The Swedish botanist Linnaeus was one of the outstanding advocates of fixity of species. Recognizing that living things fall into groups-within-groups, he succeeded in developing a workable system of classification which proved to be equally applicable to fossil forms. However, although Linnaeus "constantly endeavored to strengthen this opinion [fixity of species] by his classification of fauna and flora, yet his work, in the end, had just the opposite effect."[4] Indeed, Linnaeus himself finally conceded that "new post-creation forms could arise through the crossing of the original ones, the offspring of this union forming new species."[5] For one thing, fossils generally did not fall into the same species as present-day life. This brought into focus the disconcerting fact of the rise and fall of species throughout geologic time. For another thing, as more and more plants and animals were collected in newly upspringing museums, students found it no simple matter to determine what actually constituted one definite species. Strong resemblances and intergradations were found to occur, frequently necessitating the drawing of arbitrary lines of separation. This did not lend support to the idea that all kinds of living things had been created distinct and had persisted without change to the present.

Undaunted by these difficulties, Baron Cuvier, a most capable and outstanding French zoologist, continued to affirm faith in the fixity of species. He was thoroughly familiar with the vertebrate animals, and although he could not deny that strong resemblances did exist among them, he refused to admit that resemblance was any

---

4. *Ibid.*, p. 134.
5. Richard S. Lull, *The Ways of Life* (New York: Harper, 1925), p. 305.

indication of physical relationship between groups. He preferred to regard them as variations on the theme by the Creator. Under his forceful leadership the concept of fixity was slow to die, even though more and more evidence was accumulating which made it a highly vulnerable position.

Such a divided state of affairs could not continue indefinitely. There was great need for the appearance of a unifying theory which might explain the intergradation of species as well as their rise and extinction with the passage of time. Some sort of evolutionary theory was inevitable.

The Role of Fossils in Evolutionary Theory. As applied to organisms the term "evolution" may have various shades of meaning. In its most general sense it refers to any descent with modification, any development of variations from an ancestral type. "Organic evolution may be defined as orderly change among organisms, both plants and animals."[6] In its most precise sense the term conveys the idea that "from some geologically remote, primitive form of life all the diverse kinds of plants and animals have developed . . . by gradual and orderly change. All creatures are genetically related. . . ."[7]

Since both of these definitions include a time element, it would seem that the natural starting point of the theory would have been the fossil record showing the changes which transpired from the past to the present. This was not the case, due to the fact that geologic sequence and the order in which new forms of life had appeared on earth were imperfectly known. Under these conditions the gradual change exhibited by fossil forms with the passing of time would have been much less obvious than the intergradation between living types. Nevertheless, we should not think that the records of ancient life did not influence the early evolutionists at all, because as Louis T. More has pointed out, "If we had not found fossils which were different from existing species, our argument for evolution would be academic, to say the least."[8]

The first really significant work on evolution was that of J. B. Lamarck, which reached the attention of the world in 1801. The monumental studies he carried out in seeking to apply the Linnaean classification to all the "animals without backbones" included fossils. Gradually there unfolded before him a panorama which led him to abandon his earlier view of fixity of species in favor of variations developing over long periods of time. But, "though he studied fossils and used them to support his evolutionary views, that development

---

6. William J. Miller, *An Introduction to Historical Geology* (New York: Van Nostrand, 1952), p. 25.

7. Carl O. Dunbar, *Historical Geology* (New York: Wiley, 1949), p. 58.

8. More, *op. cit.,* p. 13.

came late in his life and was a consequence rather than a cause of his advocacy of evolution."[9]

Charles Darwin likewise was aware of fossils, but in *The Origin of Species* "his discussion of them is introduced by a chapter entitled 'On the Imperfection of the Geological Record' which seems to indicate that he felt the contradictions offered by fossils to his theory more keenly than he felt their support."[10] Nevertheless, he believed wholeheartedly that descent with modification had gone on throughout geologic time, for he wrote, "Hereafter we shall be compelled to acknowledge that the only distinction between species and well-marked varieties is, that the latter are known, or believed, to be connected at the present day by intermediate gradations, whereas species were formerly thus connected."[11]

Intensive study of the fossil record during the past century has brought to light much new and more detailed information. There has been a corresponding increase in emphasis upon it as the most reliable evidence that evolution has actually taken place. For example, Julian Huxley comments, "Primary and direct evidence in favour of evolution can be furnished only by palaeontology."[12] One writer of a geology text has said, "Although the comparative study of living animals and plants may give very convincing circumstantial evidence, fossils provide the only historical, documentary evidence that life has evolved from simpler to more and more complex forms."[13]

THE FOSSIL RECORD

It is plain, then, that evolutionists feel that the fossil record validates their position. In order to evaluate this evolutionary position fairly it is necessary for one to be aware of the total picture presented by fossils. However, in this chapter we shall attempt to cite only sufficient data to illustrate the nature of the case which confronts both the evolutionist and the creationist.

Life assumes myriad forms upon the earth today. Nevertheless, it is possible, though not always easy, to fit these forms into groups, the members of which resemble one another more than they resemble the members of other groups. Thus we can discriminate between the plant and animal kingdoms, and within these kingdoms we can organize major subdivisions known as "phyla." The phyla in turn are composed of smaller groups, on down to the level of species and

9. A. Franklin Shull, *Evolution* (New York: McGraw, 1936), p. 43.

10. *Ibid.*, p. 43.

11. Julian Huxley, *The Living Thoughts of Darwin* (Philadelphia: David McKay Co., 1939), pp. 25, 26.

12. Huxley, "Discourses Biological and Geological," in Vol. VIII, *Collected Essays*, as quoted by Louis T. More, *op. cit.*, p. 00.

13. Dunbar, *op. cit.*, p. 52.

their subdivisions. Because of this grouping within groups any individual plant or animal is simultaneously a member of a species, a genus, a family, an order, a class, and a phylum.

The fossil record is the story of the rise and fall of species. Oldest known fossils are sketchy indications of sponges, worms, seaweeds and jellyfish, but beginning with the point in geologic time known as the Cambrian period (the opening of the third era) the aspect changes from one of scarcity to one of abundance. Not only have Cambrian rocks yielded a large number of individual specimens, but also they contain representatives of a great host of diverse groups. In fact, the majority of invertebrate animals and many of their classes make their first appearance there.

Successively younger rocks contain even more abundant fossils, but they are not identical with those of the Cambrian. Sometimes the differences are so great that the plant or animal is classified in a group not previously encountered in the record: it is a new species, introducing a new phylum or a major subdivision of an already existing phylum. Sometimes the differences are small enough that the new type can be regarded as a new species within an already existing genus.

Animals with backbones afford a simple illustration. Such creatures are as yet unknown among the fossils of Cambrian time, but in the rocks of the following period there are fragments of a peculiar type of fish. These fish constitute several species, but the possession of a type of backbone is so distinctive a characteristic that these species must be placed in a phylum separate from any previously encountered in the record. This is the phylum Vertebrata.

In rocks of later periods of time, species of other types of vertebrates are found and require the erection of new classes within the phylum: amphibians, reptiles, birds, and mammals, in that order. Although these classes have persisted from their time of origin to the present, there has been a procession of different species maintaining them and many species have become extinct subsequent to their appearance. Early forms such as dinosaurs and toothed birds seem bizarre when viewed from the standpoint of the familiar reptiles and birds of today. Sometimes even entire groups such as families or genera disappear from the record, but no phylum has been known to lose all of its constituent species.

For an example among the animals without backbones we shall consider a portion of the class Anthozoa of the phylum Coelenterata. To this class belongs the host of forms popularly called corals. Although other kinds of coelenterates are found in Cambrian rocks, corals do not appear in the fossil record until the period following. On the basis of their skeletal structure and manner of growth these early corals can be divided rather readily into two subclasses which persisted through numerous geologic periods until all of the species comprising one of them (the Tabulata, according to the classification by Raymond C. Moore) died out. The other subclass (Moore's Zoantharia) survived to the present time.

A study was made of certain of the corals (subclass Zoantharia) which were distributed through a thickness of 4,000 feet of ancient strata in Scotland.[14] Representative samples were taken from four successive horizons of the strata in order from older to younger. All of the corals studied belonged to one genus, but to four different species within that genus. For the sake of simplicity we shall refer to these species as I, II, III, and IV. (See Fig. 13. Roman numeral I refers to *Z. delanouei,* II to *Z. parallela,* III to *Z. constricta,* and IV to *Z. disjuncta.*)

In the lower or older layers, species I, II, and III were present. Sixty-nine per cent of the individuals were of species I and the rest were species II, except for one single specimen of species III. At the next horizon I was virtually absent, II had dropped to three per cent of the total individuals, III had risen to sixty-nine per cent, and IV made its first appearance with a strength of twenty-eight per cent of the total. At the third horizon I and II were insignificant, III dropped to twenty per cent, and IV was the dominant form. At the fourth horizon the proportion was about five per cent III to ninety-five per cent IV.

A living coral impresses its structure and configuration very distinctly upon its skeleton. As the animal grows, new skeletal deposits faithfully reflect the changes which occur. This means that by careful sectioning of the skeleton it is possible to reconstruct the stages through which any individual passed en route to maturity. Examination of the corals from the sequence we are citing shows that species II passed through early growth stages which correspond to the later and mature stages of species I. Species III passed through stages nearly identical to the mature forms of species I and II, in that order, before reaching its own distinctive mature stage. Likewise, species IV incorporated the mature forms of species II and III in its growth.

Here, then, is a series of adult corals which, with the exception of species II, succeed one another as dominant forms in a sequence of populations. Each successive form recapitulates in condensed form what has preceded it and then adds its own characteristic stage of development. It is quite possible that all of these should be assigned to one species instead of four. Modern paleontologic practice would emphasize that although "species" IV differs appreciably from

14. R. G. Carruthers, "On the Evolution of *Zaphrentis delanouei* in Lower Carboniferous Times," *Geological Society of London Quarterly Journal,* LXVI, 523-538.

"species" I, there is no real discontinuity from one to the other. "Species" II and III are simply arbitrary units that exist only because samples were taken from four horizons in the strata instead of having one continuous sample.[15] However, this is still a good example of the rise and fall of successive types such as is encountered repeatedly in the fossil record.

Similar, but on a larger scale, is the case of the order to which the corals just discussed belong. No new species of this order is known subsequent to the close of the third era of geologic time, nor was there any carry-over of the previously extant ones. The subclass to which the order belonged continued to be represented, but by entirely new species which must be placed in a new order.

INTERPRETATIONS OF THE EVIDENCE

It is in the light of such evidence that the question of whether or not evolution has occurred must be faced. There are three alternatives: either (1) all species and varieties, living and fossil, are totally unrelated to one another; or, (2) all species are related by descent from one ancestral form of life; or, (3) there is a limited amount of relationship among species because there has been more than one ancestral type. We will consider these alternatives in order.

Total lack of relationship. The idea that no species are or ever have been related to one another has already been mentioned as the fixity of species concept. The implication of this position is that each separate species was a direct creation of God and has maintained its identity from the beginning of the existence of life on the earth. A vast amount of misunderstanding has arisen from the association of the concepts "God" and "no variation" in this viewpoint. Many have thus presumed that any belief in a special or supernatural creation of life carries as a necessary corollary the fixity of species. It is the equating of creative activity on God's part with a strict lack of relationship among living things that has often led well-meaning Christians into positions of dogmatism and made them a needless target for ridicule. An example of this confusion is found in a standard textbook of geology, which reads, ". . . [Special] Creation assumes that each kind of animal and plant was 'molded from the dust of the Earth' and 'given the breath of life' in its present form, each being a 'special' and independent creation."[16] What the author has really defined is fixity of species. It is certainly possible to believe in a special creation without believing this.

It is easy to see that fixity of species is an unsatisfactory explanation of the fossil record on many counts. For example, as pointed

---

15. For a simplified discussion of this problem see Simpson, *op. cit.,* chap. 7.
16. Dunbar, *op. cit.,* p. 58.

out above, even those who held rigidly to it encountered difficulty in the attempt to recognize the supposedly distinct species. Shall corals I to IV be considered as four species or as one? The Linnaean practice was to classify plants and animals purely on the basis of similarities to and differences from an ideal (and generally non-existent) type. This would most probably favor the erection of four unrelated or "fixed" species at the cost of disregarding both the striking similarities of growth stages which all pass through and the progressive sequence exhibited by the dominant forms of the successive layers. The similarities and sequence must then be attributed to coincidence or the whim of God, neither of which is particularly credible.

If corals I to IV were regarded as one species, then it would be ridiculous to talk about fixity. The group would be exhibiting more internal variation than could be compatible with the idea of undeviating forms set forth from the hand of the Creator.

The origin of such a form as coral IV also presents a problem to proponents of fixity. Since IV was not found in the lowest layer of the series, it is necessary to say that it immigrated from elsewhere. Again, the fact that it arrived just in time to become the dominant form culminating a progressive sequence must have been merely fortuitous.

Invoking immigration to account for the appearance of new forms was the idea to which the learned Cuvier clung. His pupil, Louis Agassiz, recognized some of the difficulties inherent in it, and he proposed that new forms were direct creations of God which came into being subsequent to the original creation. Both of these men believed in cataclysmic floods as accounting for the extinction of any groups and thus preparing the way for immigration or re-creation.

Accumulation of geologic paleontologic data made it obvious that a fantastic number of cataclysms and re-creations would be required to account for the facts, and this school of extreme "catastrophism" fell into disrepute by the middle of the nineteenth century. Cuvier, Agassiz, and their followers were the last scientists who made any serious attempt to champion the cause of fixity of species.

Ultimate relationship of all living things. Diametrically opposed to the concept of fixity of species is the belief that all things which have ever lived have been related to one another through a meshwork of common ancestry. This is the most comprehensive form of evolutionary theory and is what is usually meant by that term.

It is easy to understand why so many students of paleontology feel that the ultimate conclusion urged upon them by the facts is that all things are related. Considering the sample case of the corals, even the most conservative person would have little hesitation about regarding members of species I to IV as close relatives. The strong resemblances and the carry-over from one population to the next in this and other examples implies that the successive species had much in common genetically, so much so that "to decide where in a graded series to draw a specific boundary is a vexing if not insoluble problem."[17]

The original Linnaean concept of classification was essentially devoid of any idea of relationship through descent. The modern concept is that members of a group are similar to one another because they are related. If this makes sense for a sequence such as the corals, how far shall the principle be extended? If all the species of a given genus are related, and all the genera of a given family are related, where or why shall a line be drawn to say "this group is totally unrelated to that one"?

The evolutionist feels that any such line drawing is artificial, even when it is not possible to demonstrate the intermediate forms whereby one group received its inheritance from another. Darwin wrote, "... I cannot doubt that the theory of descent with modification embraces all the members of the same great class or kingdom. I believe that animals are descended from at most only four or five progenitors, and plants from an equal or lesser number. Analogy would lead me one step farther, namely, to the belief that all animals and plants are descended from some one prototype."[18] Writing in 1951, G. G. Simpson states, "No one seriously doubts that the whole of life has factually been a continuum of populations when the whole sequence is considered, in spite of the innumerable discontinuities in the record."[19]

Limited relationship. In spite of Simpson's sweeping assertion, there are some who seriously doubt that the whole of life has been a continuum of populations. Since the fossil record opens with the majority of phyla already in existence, it is at least permissible to question the assumption that in earlier ages these phyla converged backward toward one primeval ancestor. Also, within the phyla there are many discontinuities among various groups of species. This is illustrated by the two orders of corals mentioned above, one becoming extinct at the close of the third era, the other appearing in the fourth era. The question then arises whether these groups had a common ancestor in Cambrian or Pre-Cambrian time and one group simply did not secrete skeletons capable of fossilization until late in its history; or whether species of the second group are descended from those of the first but the intermediate forms have not been found; or whether the two orders represent lineages which have

17. C. O. Dunbar, "The Species Concept," *Evolution,* IV (1950), 175.

18. Julian Huxley, *The Living Thoughts of Darwin* (Philadelphia: David McKay Co., 1939), p. 52.

19. Simpson, "The Species Concept," *Evolution,* V (1951), 292.

always been genetically distinct but within which there has been ample variation. This latter interpretation, of course, would fall under the heading of "limited relationship," the hypothesis that various groups arose independently of others and have undergone considerable internal modification.

Another example of discontinuity comes from the angiosperms or plants which bear covered seeds. This great group, which includes grasses, flowers, and hardwood trees, appears very suddenly in the fossil record, late in the fourth era. Its ancestry is a great puzzle. One recent student of the problem has commented, "Answers might be found more readily if the ancestral group or groups were known within the gymnosperms, or if, within the record of the angiosperms themselves there were fossils which pointed to these groups. But it is now generally conceded that no known type, fossil or living, can fill this key position."[20]

Such discontinuities or gaps are frequent at the level of orders, more frequent at the level of classes and almost invariable between phyla. The thorough-going evolutionist will frankly admit that on the higher levels, "transitional sequences are not merely rare, but are virtually absent," and that this absence "does require some attempt at special explanation."[21] The explanation takes the form that transitional types between major groups could not be expected as fossils, or at most would be very rare finds. This is attributed to the probability that transitional forms must have been few in number and undergoing very rapid change. Since fossilization is at best so fortuitous an event, it would be extremely unlikely that any but a very few of the transitional forms would have been preserved, and still more unlikely that any would be found today.

In speaking of those who emphasize the sudden appearance of new forms, Simpson writes, "We know as a fact that change often occurred gradually through successive populations overlapping in variation. We know that this is a *possible* explanation for all changes shown in the fossil record. We also know as a fact that abrupt change often did *not* occur. We do not know positively that it *ever* occurred. Is it logical to conclude that the latter process was usual or important in evolution?"[22] Although he has reference here to those evolutionists who do not agree with his conviction that life evolved always by gradual changes, his remarks also have pertinence for those who favor the concept of limited relationship.

20. Daniel I. Axelrod, "A Theory of Angiosperm Evolution," *Evolution*, VI (1952), 29.

21. Simpson, *Tempo and Mode in Evolution* (New York: Columbia University Press, 1944), p. 106.

22. Simpson, *Life of the Past* (New Haven: Yale University Press), p. 124.

The idea of limited relationship is not new. In the quotations given above, Darwin indicated his feeling that this is where the facts led and that further relationship could only be inferred by analogy. He then admitted, "but analogy may be a deceitful guide."[23] Nevertheless, this possible deception apparently did not worry him much!

It should be made clear that those who subscribe to this theory do not venture to say exactly how many original types there may have been. This is, after all, rather immaterial to the position.

WHAT DO FOSSILS PROVE?

We have seen that evolutionists regard the fossil record as a final court of appeal in substantiation of their theory. Whatever difficulties there may be in determining the how and why of evolution from the study of living things, always the evidence of the fossils stands to confirm the fact that multitudinous changes have occurred through the ages. It is in this light that fossils are often referred to as "the documents of evolution," as, for example, in the following quotation. "In the study of embryology and comparative anatomy we have only circumstantial evidence of evolution, but in the fossil remains of evolving series we have the actual documentary evidence that the changes have occurred."[24] The logical fallacy of this particular statement is apparent, for the thing to be proved is already assumed: you cannot appeal to "evolving series" of fossils as proof of evolution.

In all honesty it must be conceded that fossil series, too, are circumstantial evidence which permits an evolutionary interpretation — and many people feel even demands it — but cannot in and of itself close the issue. To a large extent the basic philosophy of an individual will enter into his consideration of fossils. As one evolutionary professor of paleontology remarked, "You can 'prove' almost anything you want to from fossils."

The paleontologist cannot experiment with his data as can the biologist. He is limited to observing that certain forms occurred at such a time and place, and subsequently they were joined or replaced by other similar or dissimilar forms. He can and does analyze populations of fossils statistically; he can examine fossil progressions in the light of modern genetic knowledge; he can study the relationship of newly appearing forms to the environment in which they flourished; he can decide what interpretations and conclusions seem most compatible with the data and most reasonable to him. But in the last analysis he is still dealing with probabilities, not with empirical evidence.

We turn to Shull, a modern defender of evolution, for an

23. Huxley, *op. cit.*, p. 52.
24. Dunbar, *op. cit.*, p. 63.

appraisal of the situation. He declares, after reviewing the fossil record for his readers, "Biologists have *assumed* genetic continuity because the alternative explanations have seemed incredible or impossible."[25] This is as frank a statement as one will find anywhere on this subject.

Fossils do not prove evolution. Neither do they disprove it. They strongly suggest that a considerable amount of descent with modification has transpired. They also exhibit a lack of transitional forms which may or may not be significant of limits of relationship.

FOSSILS AND SPECIAL REVELATION

It is commonplace in geologic and paleontologic literature for the authors to mention the supposed futility of seeking correlation between the fossil record and the scriptural record of life's origin. For them modern geologic knowledge has consigned all such investigation to the level of mediaeval thinking, and those who accept the biblical account are dismissed with sarcastic comment, or at best, pity.

It is safe to assert that the majority of those who thus scoff do so because they believe in evolution, and they erroneously regard Genesis as teaching the fixity of species which were created in six days some 6,000 years ago. Louis T. More in his critique of evolution says Genesis presents "an undoubted denial of the transmutation of species."[26]

A careful and unprejudiced study of Genesis 1 is essential to establish what is actually said, and equally important, what is *not* said, as it has bearing upon the fossil record.

On the positive side, Genesis primarily points out that God is the Initiator of the countless forms of life on earth in their original condition. The account of this activity of his is general, not specific. A few representative groups of plants and animals are mentioned. They are presented as appearing successively, not contemporaneously. There is progress from plant life to those forms of animal life which we regard as "higher," culminating in man. They are fashioned so as to reproduce "after their kind."

There are strong hints in the account that God's creative activity was a process involving time and materials. In the case of man, this is definitely indicated, but literal translation also points to it in the other phases of creation. In connection with plants the words say literally, "the earth caused to go forth grass of herbage," etc.[27] In connection with land animals we are shown the interaction of God's

25. Shull, *op. cit.*, p. 65. Italics mine.
26. More, *op. cit.*, p. 87.
27. P. J. Wiseman, *Creation Revealed in Six Days* (London: Marshall, Morgan & Scott, 1949), p. 122.

activity with the process which he ordained: "God said, 'The earth shall cause to go forth living soul' . . . and God made the beast of the earth."[28] These phrases taken in conjunction are doubtless highly significant. Certainly none of these positive points are at variance with the testimony of the fossils.

There is much left unsaid in the Genesis account. In its grand outlines we are not told how long ago God began his creative activity, but merely that it was "in the beginning."

The account does not state that the various groups mentioned appeared with their full complement of types and members, nor is any indication given of the time involved in attaining this complement. For example, although the "beasts of the earth" were caused to appear at some specific point in time, there is nothing which demands the belief that all types of animals which ever fit this general category appeared at that very time. Again, when God finished creating the group "mankind" there were only two individuals in it. The several races of mankind which exist today must have developed subsequently.

The possible degree of variation within the groups mentioned is not discussed, but the injunction to reproduce according to kind certainly need not indicate fixity of species because the word translated "kind" is a very broad one and is not the equivalent of the modern technical term.

The record does not even mention sea plants nor invertebrate animals. These striking omissions definitely indicate that Genesis 1 was not intended to be a comprehensive survey but only a suggestive outline.

On all of these points there is no lack of harmony between the fossil record and the sacred revelation. What is unequivocal in each can be accepted freely without undermining or detracting from the other. The points of friction between them are thus reduced to two considerations which can be presented in the form of questions: (1) What is the meaning of the six days mentioned in Genesis? Are they irreconcilable with the long period of time seemingly demanded by the fossils? (2) How much, if any, descent with modification is implicit in the phrase "after its kind"?

It is not within the scope of this chapter to discuss the already much-discussed word "day," with all of its possible meanings. Suffice it to point out that the Scripture does not say there were six immediately consecutive days on which instantaneous and complete creation occurred. Therefore there is no real conflict with the appearance of different fossil forms at different times throughout long ages. To the present author a plausible view is that the days in question

28. *Ibid.*, pp. 118, 122.

were literal ones upon which God revealed some phase of His creative activity to a particular individual who presented the information according to topic and in poetic form. Others deplore this viewpoint, and it is certainly not the only acceptable one.[29]

In connection with the phrase "after its kind" we have emphasized that this cannot refer to species as we regard them. Therefore it must describe some other sort of genetic boundary or law. We have no way of knowing how much variation was to be inherent in each "kind." Since the fossil record does contain profound and persistent gaps between otherwise reasonably complete sequences of forms, it is an easy step to equate the genetic boundaries of the "kinds" with these gaps or lack of transitional forms between groups. Scripture fully allows what fossils seemingly indicate, namely, considerable descent with modification but always within predetermined limits. This viewpoint is, of course, that of limited relationship mentioned above, expanded to include the creative activity of God in originating each of the several ancestral types with their genetic potentialities.[30] Whether or not this will be regarded as an evolutionary position will depend upon one's initial definition of evolution.

The chief objection to this view is that it is based on negative evidence, the absence of fossils. However, not even the most ardent evolutionary paleontologist anticipates that more than a few of the missing forms will ever be found. He crosses the gaps by faith in the principle of evolution because that seems a more realistic recourse to him than to invoke direct intervention from God. We can never be entirely certain just which gaps or discontinuities of record are real and which reflect the insufficiency of fossil collections. Likewise, one can never be dogmatic concerning just where the various groups of Genesis 1 may fit into modern classifications of plants and animals. Nevertheless, no apology needs to be made for this position.

In conclusion we may state that fossils give absolutely no ground for losing faith in the inspired character of the Genesis chronicle, for "without [God] was not anything made that was made" (John 1:3). Neither do fossils provide startling confirmation of the Scripture. Perhaps the most that can be said is that these two are complementary aspects of the same truths, both incompletely understood.

29. For a discussion of various interpretations, see Bernard Ramm, *The Christian View of Science and Scripture* (Grand Rapids: Eerdmans, 1954); and also Wiseman, *op. cit.*

30. For a pertinent discussion, see James L. Baldwin, *A New Answer to Darwinism* (Chicago: Mary E. Baldwin, 1957).

Chapter Nine

SIMILARITIES — THE IMPORTANCE OF THE OBVIOUS

By J. FRANK CASSEL

"No! You're superimposing your prejudice unnecessarily upon the facts. Animals and plants are not autos, dishes, or light bulbs. They mutate, they reproduce, they have offspring — this is sufficient. We need no other explanation of their similarities." I smile, concede his point as a possibility, and the seminar continues. Thus an internationally known biologist interprets to his complete satisfaction one of the most widespread phenomena of nature — the striking similarities between many distinct and well differentiated species.

It was these similarities, along with the geological and geographical distribution of animals, which first started Darwin musing about the formation of species and later gave rise to his monumental *The Origin of Species*. He says in his introduction:

> In considering the Origin of Species, it is quite conceivable that a naturalist, reflecting on the mutual affinities of organic beings, on their embryological relations, their geographical distribution, geological succession, and other such facts, might come to the conclusion that species had not been independently created, but had descended, like varieties, from other species.[1]

Wallace, too, was struck by the greater similarity of some animals in one region to each other than to those of another region. The implications of distribution for the theory of evolution have been discussed by Anderson in Chapter 7. The purpose of this chapter is to consider further the implications of similarities of animals for the overall theory. Previous chapters in this book have discussed the mechanisms whereby change can be established and transmitted in animal populations. Is there evidence that such change has been widespread? Mrs. Barber (Chapter 8) has shown some of its possible extent in the fossil record. In this chapter we will examine some of the evidence usually presented in support of the view that the theory of evolution is an adequate generalization to account for the development of all life that we know today from one or several primitive masses of protoplasm.

1. Charles Darwin, *The Origin of Species by Means of Natural Selection*, with additions and corrections from the 6th and last English edition, two vols. in one (New York: Appleton, 1905), I, 3.

Storer and Usinger define evolution as "that process by which living organisms have come to be what they are, structurally and functionally, complex forms being derived from simpler forms; hence descent with modification."[2] Most general biology and zoology texts allot considerable space to a discussion of data concerning this process under the headings "Comparative Morphology," "Comparative Embryology," and "Comparative Physiology." Some readers will recognize that there are advanced courses and texts in each of these fields, since biologists consider the "comparative approach" a very fruitful one. It has been found that what we learn concerning one animal can often be applied equally well to other somewhat similar animals. Studies on dogs, rabbits and monkeys, for instance, have contributed tremendously to the advancement of human medicine. As in other scientific disciplines, it is often possible to analyze what is known about a certain group of animals and predict what will be found concerning another member of that group or of a similar group not yet studied. Further study usually confirms a carefully made prediction.

The probing mind wonders why there should be this predictability in nature and realizes it must be due to some basic underlying principle or principles. Most biologists feel that evolution is an adequate concept or principle to account for this predictability. In fact, many consider the conception and development of the theory of organic evolution one of the greatest ideas yet conceived by man. Most basic texts discuss at some length the relation of comparative zoology to this concept. A few common examples will illustrate this method of analysis.

COMPARATIVE MORPHOLOGY

This body of data is often labelled simply "Comparative Anatomy." The broader term, "morphology," includes not only the gross structures usually studied in anatomy, but also the cellular and tissue structure as well. Frequently reference is made to the similarities in the basic structural elements in the forelimbs of vertebrates, even though these limbs may serve different functions such as grasping (man), digging (mole), swimming (seal), or flying (bat) (Fig. 14). Such similarities are termed homologies. Boyden points out that this term as originally proposed by Owen meant "an essential structural similarity."[3] Basic texts more often use it in the sense defined by Hubbs,

2. Tracy I. Storer and Robert L. Usinger, *General Zoology* (3rd ed., New York: McGraw-Hill, 1957), p. 621.
3. Alan Boyden, "Homology and Analogy: A critical review of the meanings and implications of these concepts in Biology." *American Midland Naturalist,* XXXVII (1947), 648-650.

"Homology has come to signify an agreement in evolutionary derivation and in embryonic developments."[4] (See below for a discussion of this concept.) Similarities of structure are more basic and hence of more importance in determining relationship than are similarities of function (analogy) such as can be observed in the wing of an insect, the wing of a bird, and the wing of a bat (Fig. 15). Although all are used for flying, the structural similarities (homology) of the bird and the bat show them to be more closely related to each other than either is to the insect, but not as closely as is the bat to the series listed above. Many series of similarities such as the forelimbs are found in the study of comparative morphology.

Sometimes a structure highly developed in most of the series will be very poorly developed in one. The poorly developed organ is then said to be vestigial. Key (Chapter 1) has suggested the historical role of the arguments from vestigial organs.

As pointed out by Bullock in Chapter 6, similarities and differences in structure (morphology) are some of the criteria used by the taxonomist in classifying and naming animals. Thus homology is a basic tool of the systematist.

Some textbooks present evidences from vestigial organs and from taxonomy separately from the evidences from morphology, but the same data are used in all three areas. As structure is highly important in taxonomy, so classification is highly important in recognizing the significance of the data in the following fields.

COMPARATIVE EMBRYOLOGY

The data from embryology are at once morphological and physiological as they show the way the various structures are developed. The developmental history of an individual organism from its origin until it reaches maturity is said to be its *ontogeny*. One of the catch phrases of biology for much of the past century has been "ontogeny recapitulates phylogeny," which means the history of the individual (his embryological development) reflects the history of the race (his evolutionary development). Although this concept is no longer deemed helpful[5] and is indeed directly refuted by some modern texts,[6] it is, unfortunately, one "law" which many students still remember ten years after their basic course.

To study the way an individual develops is, on the other hand,

4. Carl L. Hubbs, "Concepts of Homology and Analogy," *The American Naturalist*, LXXVIII (1944), p. 305.
5. Rainer Zangerl, "The Methods of Comparative Anatomy and its Contribution to the Study of Evolution," *Evolution*, II (1948), p. 372.
6. e.g., Mary J. Guthrie and John M. Anderson, *General Zoology*, (New York: Wiley, 1957), p. 634.

significant as an indication of some of the possibilities and limits of phylogenetic development. Although the methods whereby a single cell becomes a complex, multicellular organism may not be, step by step, those of an evolutionary sequence nor restricted by what has happened in the past, they may give us some idea of what *might* have happened. Thus we note that in a developing starfish or lancelet (amphioxus) one cell becomes two, two become four and so on according to a predictable pattern: a ball of many cells becomes hollow (blastula) as the number of cells increases, and layers are then formed (gastrulation) from which develop the various complex organs and systems which comprise the organism. It is interesting, too, as observed by von Baer many years ago and summarized by Zangerl that "those features of a larger group of animals that are mutually present among them develop earlier in the embryo than the particular character of the individual."[7] The Christian must face with interest and honesty the facts that, although man in his early development never actually has gill slits, he has much the same structure as a fish has when its gill slits are formed, or that at one time during his development a tail appears and then later disappears (Fig. 16). These interesting and unexpected patterns of development demand some sort of explanation. The developmental pattern of an organism aids the taxonomist in classification at times, but more often simply confirms the classification already made upon the basis of the structure of the adult. Thus the data from embryology usually support the data from morphology though derived by different methods.

COMPARATIVE PHYSIOLOGY

The methods of physiology differ markedly from those of morphology and embryology. While all have their observational elements, in physiology (and the physiological aspects of embryology) experimental techniques can also be fruitfully employed. When data derived from experiments confirm the observations made by morphological methods they give substantial support to the validity of the morphological observations. That physiochemical reactions and structures should parallel morphological structures shows an amazing unity not only within the individual organism, but within the taxonomic groups as well.

One demonstration of these phenomena is the precipitin test which is mentioned in most basic texts. Storer and Usinger recount it as follows:

7. *Op. cit.,* p. 368, n. 11.

The precipitin tests are reactions of the blood serum. In such tests human serum is least distinct from that of anthropoid apes (gorilla, chimpanzee, etc.), more so from other primates (monkeys), and still more distinct from that of other mammals. Sera of mammals, in turn, are more sharply distinguished from those of other vertebrates.[8]

Other physiological differences between animals often follow the same pattern.

On the other hand, an overall physiological unity in the animal kingdom is strikingly demonstrated by the similarity of protoplasmic components, the general pattern of protoplasmic organization, and the constancy of enzyme systems throughout the kingdom. This basic unity of all living things demands an explanation.

Darwin[9] looked at pigeons, for example. His reasoning was that if so many different kinds could be produced from known similar ancestors by *artificial* selection, why couldn't various groups of animals in nature, which differ no more than the kinds of pigeons, be produced in the same way by *natural* selection? This basic thesis is reflected in his full title, *On the Origin of Species by Means of Natural Selection, or the Preservation of Favoured Races in the Struggle for Life.*

To account for the unity or similarities observed in the animal kingdom, Darwin's approach has been reversed. The similarities in the various breeds of pigeons are due to the fact that they are all pigeons, derived from the same ancestor, the Rock Dove. Other similarities among animals whose ancestors are not known could be accounted for in the same fashion. So it is concluded that such similar animals have common ancestors also. Thus, by generalization, similarities of many magnitudes can be accounted for by having been passed down from an ancient progenitor. Set up as a syllogism the reasoning is as follows:

All animals having known common ancestors have certain similarities.
Some animals having unknown ancestors have equivalent similarities.
Therefore, these animals also have common ancestors.

And the usual reasoning implied in textbooks continues as follows:

Since animals having such similarities have been shown to have common ancestors,
And since the theory of evolution purports that all animals are derived from common ancestors,
Therefore such similarities in animals are evidence that evolution has occurred.

This is a reasonable explanation for the occurrence of similarities in animals, consistent with and in support of the theory of evolution.

---

8. *Op. cit.,* p. 209.
9. *Op. cit.,* pp. 18-25. All breeds of pigeons originated from the wild Rock Dove (*Columba livia*) of Mediterranean region.

But is the first conclusion demanded by or simply not excluded by the premises? Are there any other conclusions that might be valid? Are there any other possible explanations for the occurrence of similarities in animals whose pedigree we do not have?

The similarity between Icthyosaurus (an extinct aquatic reptile), the shark (a cartilaginous-skeletoned fish) and the dolphin or porpoise (a mammal) may be considered (Fig. 17). They have the same type of similarity as that illustrated by the wings of insects, birds, and bats mentioned above — a similarity adapting them for life under similar conditions. Their similarities, then, are analogous and not due to close common ancestry. But what about true homologies — actual similarities in essential structures (to use Owen's definition)?

HOMOLOGY

Perhaps it would be well here to re-examine the basic concept of homology because this concept is so fundamental to the reasoning validating the data from the areas of morphology, embryology and physiology. Hubbs,[10] Hyman,[11] Moore,[12] and many others feel that the presupposition of common origin and development (phylogeny and ontogeny) is valid and helpful when examining and interpreting natural phenomena having to do with similarities. Boyden,[13] Kalin,[14] and Zangerl[15] strongly oppose such a definition (or even connotation) of homology and such use of the concept as this view allows. They point out that this is actually arguing in circles.[16] Zangerl states, "The criterion of homology of organs or parts is said to be common phyletic origin of these structures whereby the supposed common origin itself is to be established by the very demonstration of their homology."[17] It is like saying that structural similarities in animals are due to and hence evidence for the common ancestry of these animals, which can be true only when we have a known pedigree which first validates the fact of common ancestry. In nature we have no such pedigree but rather are trying to establish it. Can we do so? Certainly homology could be due to common ancestry as

10. *Op. cit.,* pp. 289ff.

11. Libbie H. Hyman, *Comparative Vertebrate Anatomy* (Chicago: Univ. Chicago Press, 1942), p. 544.

12. John A. Moore, *Principles of Zoology* (New York: Oxford, 1957), p. 470.

13. *Op. cit.,* p. 657-659.

14. J. A. Kalin, "Die Homologie als Ausdruck ganzheitlicher Baupläne von Typen," *Bull. Soc. Fribourgeoise Sci. Nat.,* XXXVII (1945), 5-31, *fide* Zangerl, *op. cit.*

15. *Op. cit.,* pp. 351ff.

16. J. A. Kalin, *Ganzheitliche Morphologie und Homologie* (Freiburg [Schweiz] and Leipzig: Universitatsbuchhandlung, 1941) p. 6. *Fide* Zangerl, *op. cit.,* p. 363.

17. *Op. cit.,* p. 363.

in the case of pedigreed animals. Is there any other explanation possible for the occurrence of such similarities? Obviously Hubbs, Hyman, Moore and the many others who work with similar definitions do not think so. Boyden, Zangerl and others are particular about the proper use of terms because they wish to be sure of the validity of their conclusion. Zangerl has no doubt that "comparative morphological methodology" can make a "particular contribution ... to the overall discussion of problems relating to evolution."[18]

DESIGN IN NATURE

But what other explanation might there be for homologies? I think of the "homology" of dishes in a pottery shop, of automobiles, or of electric light bulbs. The similarity of structure and pattern in a set of dishes is very striking, but common ancestry does not account for such similarity. My wife can tell which sets are Lennox, which Spode, and which Franciscan (even though there are several different sets of each) because of basic similarities or "tell-tale" characteristics which identify their maker. Homology then can also be explained as basic design (a plan in the mind of the Creator) or, as it is more frequently designated, "Design in Nature." Such an explanation, however, my colleague in the seminar will not allow. We are dealing, he points out, with animate organisms rather than inanimate objects; and we have a good explanation of how changes can come about and similarities be maintained.

Simpson discusses "the problem of plan and purpose in Nature" and states that it is an unnecessary and unenlightening concept. "Of course an explanation might be metaphysical and nevertheless true," he says. "It is, however," he continues, "an obvious lesson from the history of scientific progress that in science one should never accept a metaphysical explanation if a physical explanation is possible or, indeed, conceivable."[19] Like many other scientists, Simpson seems to be presupposing that if there is a physical explanation there could not also be a metaphysical one. Natural systems, no matter how intricate, are assumed to be self-perpetuating. On the other hand, the Christian's presupposition is, "God created the heavens and the earth." In other words, he assumes God did it. The interest of the Christian biologist is in how God did it and in how God keeps it going. The amazing unity and consistency of creation is in keeping with the "master plan" of the Creator.

Simpson himself points out that the concept of basic design is

18. *Ibid.*, p. 372.
19. George Gaylord Simpson, "The Problem of Plan and Purpose in Nature," *The Scientific Monthly*, LXIV (1947), 487-488.

not incompatible with biological classification when he discusses the development of the principles of classification as follows:

> ... the evolutionists continued to group animals by the number and kind of characters that they have in common, but they explained the possession of these characters by community of inheritance, while the non-evolutionists explained them by a subjective pattern. By substituting "common ancestor" for "archetype" the same classification could be considered phylogenetic or not, at will. The common ancestor was at first, and in most cases, just as hypothetical as the archetype, and the methods of inference were much the same for both, so that classification continued to develop with no immediate evidence of revolution in principles.[20]

Moore uses the idea of "archetype" as part of the evolutionary inference. "If all chordates are related by descent from a common ancestor," he points out, "there should be indications of this in their structure. There should be a basic morphological plan, or *archetype,* from which all forms could be derived."[21]

Zangerl designates the concepts involved in this type of reasoning as "morphotype-structural plan," ideas basic to the morphological method.[22] Biologists, then, recognize and use the concept of design, but many feel that organic evolution is an adequate explanation for this design and fully accounts for the data observed. Their reasoning is illustrated by Moore's statement: "Any competent comparative anatomist would reach the conclusion that there are too many similarities between the alligator and pigeon *to be explained on a chance basis.*"[23]

A CHRISTIAN CORRELATION

Moore seems to say that "descent with modification" must rely on something more than mere chance. Yet Dobzhansky is eager to point out what such evidence does not mean.

> Homology does not prove evolution, in the sense that nobody has actually witnessed the gradual changes in the millions of consecutive generations which led from a common ancestor to a bird on one hand and to man on the other. But homology suggests evolution; the facts of homology make sense if they are supposed to be due to evolution of now different organisms from common stock. They do not make sense otherwise. To be sure, some die-hard anti-evolutionists still insist that homology means only that the Creator gratuitously chose to make homologous organs in quite unrelated organisms. This opinion may be said to be implicitly blasphemous: it actually accuses the Creator of

---

20. George Gaylord Simpson, "The Principles of Classification and the Classification of Mammals," *Bulletin of the American Museum of Natural History,* LXXXV (1945), p. 4.
21. *Op. cit.,* p. 360.
22. *Op. cit.,* pp. 355ff., 373.
23. *Op. cit.,* pp. 469-470. Italics mine.

arranging things so that they suggest evolution merely to mislead honest students of His works.[24]

It is not clear why Dobzhansky expects God to be any less consistent or logical than he himself would be in developing and executing ideas of form and structure. The Christian looks at the consistency of the biological world, the basic patterns of structure, the intricacies of the genetic mechanisms, the odd developmental sequences, the unity of physiological make-up as well as its variations consistent with morphology, the interesting geological and geographical distribution patterns of animals, and he is impressed, not that God is trying to fool him, but with the insight of Paul, who points out that God has made his truth quite plain in that "since the beginning of the world the invisible attributes of God, for example, his eternal power and divinity, have been plainly discernible through things which he has made and which are commonly seen and known...." (Rom. 1:19, 20, Phillips). In biological phenomena, as in the rest of the universe, we see the nature of God revealed.

It must be re-emphasized, lest we, too, be accused of falling into the vicious circle, that such things do not *prove* a Creator. Design does not necessarily demand a Designer (e.g., the Rorschach or ink blot test). Simpson concludes his discussion of plan and purpose in nature as follows:

> Adaptation by natural selection as a creative process and preadaptation in the special senses just explained are the answers of the synthetic theory of evolution to the problem of plan and purpose in nature. Of course much work remains to be done, many details to be filled in, and many parts of the process to be more clearly understood, but it seems to me and to many others that here, at last, is the basis for a complete and sound solution of this old and troublesome problem.
>
> Adaptation is real, and it is achieved by a progressive and directed process. This process is natural, and it is wholly mechanistic in its operation. This natural process achieves the aspect of purpose, without the intervention of a purposer, and it has produced a vast plan, without the concurrent action of a planner. It may be that the initiation of the process and physical laws under which it functions had a Purposer and that this mechanistic way of achieving a plan is the instrument of a Planner — of this still deeper problem the scientist cannot speak.[25]

Here, as in many other cases, the scientist must turn philosopher to probe beyond the limits of his observational or experimental data. To do so with Christian presuppositions is as intellectually and academically sound — if not as fashionable — as it is to do so with atheistic or agnostic assumptions. To postulate a Designer, a Planner, a

---

24. Theodosius Dobzhansky, *Evolution, Genetics and Man* (New York: Wiley, 1955), p. 227-228.
25. *Op. cit.*, p. 495.

Purposer from the nature, order, and cause and effect relationships in the universe or biological world is consistent not only with our basic assumption but also with our experience.

That an organic process provides design can certainly be demonstrated within certain limits (e.g., pigeons). But both the origin of the process and the limits within which it operates have yet to be explained. Neither the origin nor the limits can be delineated sharply on the basis of the data discussed in this chapter. Similarity can certainly be due to common ancestry. Similarity can certainly be due to planning. The data, then (i.e., similarity of structure, development, and function), beyond the limits of actual pedigree, support either common ancestry or design. Nor can we, in the absence of data, say that one is more or less likely than the other. Seldom considered is the possibility that common ancestry and design are not mutually exclusive possibilities. In other words, both could be true at once!

Thus, looking at the same data as does Simpson but with Christian presuppositions, we come to somewhat similar conclusions, with the exception that we believe that "natural processes" are God's processes and that the "Purposer" and "Planner" is also the Maintainer as well as the Power operating the universe. We do not hold God to be completely and only immanent as do the pantheists, but we do recognize his sustaining as well as his creative role.

I, personally, cannot agree with the inference of Simpson (above) nor with Hearn and Hendry (see Chap. 3 of this book) that "scientific investigations must always be mechanistic in their outlook, because it is only in this narrowed frame of reference that the scientific method can operate." If this is so, then no Christian can claim to use the scientific method because his "frame of reference" is not mechanistic in the usual sense of the term. Certainly we must realize, and make allowances for, our presuppositions when dealing with scientific data, but there is no excuse for a Christian to study God's creation with a non-Christian or an a-Christian bias. I have tried to show here that valid conclusions can often not be reached without valid primary assumptions. And no one, Christian or non-Christian, can approach any data without some basic assumptions. A Christian's assumptions or presuppositions must be Christian. There is no other approach to Truth, because God is Truth (John 14:6, 16:13, I John 5:6).

God works by "natural" means, since "natural" means are his means. To what extent he utilized natural descent in his creative process and to what extent other means were used is not clear from either biological or biblical data. We hold Christ to be "both the first principle and the upholding principle of the whole scheme of creation" (Col. 1:17, Phillips). We find biological data derived from the study of homology wholly compatible with this presupposition.

SUMMARY

That genetic variation in descent is one of the "upholding principles" of the biological world has been well documented by Robertson and Sinclair in Chapter 4 and Bullock in Chapter 6. Some of the limits observed for this process have been discussed by Mrs. Barber in Chapter 8. The data dealt with in this chapter, which are often designated as the "indirect" or "circumstantial" evidences for evolution, have been shown to be as applicable to and as much in support of the concept of a Creator's *design* as of *evolution* by descent from common ancestors. It is suggested that, on the basis of the data, these are not necessarily incompatible concepts. Determination of the limits of the Creator's use of "descent with modification" has to await the discovery of more data as well as more careful correlation and synthesis with other areas of investigation. The reasonable limits allowed by theological data are discussed by Henry in Chapter 11, where he assesses the biblical evidence relating to the problem of creation. Thus by carefully evaluating every available area of truth and by searching continually for new evidence in every area of knowledge, we learn more of God, the Truth.

Chapter Ten

A CREATIONIST INTERPRETATION
OF PREHISTORIC MAN[1]

By James O. Buswell, III

1859

Throughout its history, anthropology and the study of prehistoric man have been identified with the hypothesis of organic evolution. Indeed, evolution has been considered so fundamental a part of it that R. R. Marett, referring in 1911 to a brief, formal statement of the scope of anthropology, added:

> To put some body into it, however, it is necessary to breathe but a single word. That word is: Darwin.
> Anthropology is the child of Darwin. Darwinism makes it possible. Reject the Darwinian point of view, and you must reject anthropology also.[2]

This kind of association is, unfortunately, still held in the popular mind today. Thus it should be pointed out quite definitely to begin with, that a scholarly, objective, unprejudiced, yet *non-evolutionary* approach to the data of physical anthropology is not only possible, but will provide a more valid definition of the relation of such data to both evolutionary and creationist interpretations.

Despite the fact that today's anthropology is subject primarily to evolutionary interpretation, its relation to Darwin is hardly what Marett conceived it to be. Professor A. L. Kroeber has written that

> ...a designation of anthropology as "the child of Darwin" is misleading. Darwin's essential achievement was that he imagined, and substantiated by much indirect evidence, a mechanism through which organic evolution appeared to be taking place. The whole history of man, however, being much more than an organic matter, a merely or strictly Darwinian anthropology would be largely misapplied biology. One might almost as justly speak of a Copernican or a Newtonian anthropology.[3]

---

1. This chapter is an expanded and revised form of a paper presented before the graduate seminar of the Anthropology Department, University of Chicago, on February 18, 1957. Some material on physical anthropology and specific fossil forms published in the author's column "Anthropology" in the *Journal of the American Scientific Affiliation* for March, September, and December of 1954, and March, 1957, has been adapted for use in this chapter.
2. R. R. Marett, *Anthropology* (New York: Holt, 1912), p. 8.
3. A. L. Kroeber, *Anthropology* (New York: Harcourt, Brace, 1948), p. 6.

Thus it is evident that anthropological thought today need not retain any filial regard for a Darwinian paternity, in an over-all, theoretical sense. Kroeber points out one aspect of the explanation for this present association, as he adds:

> What has greatly influenced some of the earlier anthropology, mainly to its damage, has been not Darwinism, but the vague idea of progress, to the organic aspect of which Darwin happened incidentally to give such support and apparent substance that the whole group of evolutionistic ideas, sound and unsound, has luxuriated rankly ever since.[4]

In addition to the commemoration of the publication of Darwin's famous work, any discussion of prehistoric man would be incomplete if it omitted recognition of two other important events which took place in the year 1859 which together constituted a milestone in the course of prehistoric archaeology.

At Brixham Cave in England, excavations superintended by William Pengelly were begun in July 1858 lasting until the following summer. Here were found man-made flint tools in direct association with the bones of the mammoth and other animals long extinct in that part of the world. Overlying the artifacts was a layer of stalagmite from three to eight inches thick. Sir Charles Lyell reported to the Geology Section of the British Association at Aberdeen in 1859 his acceptance of the authenticity of this cave evidence.

Similarly, at Abbeville, France, the association of human artifacts with extinct animals was finally accepted as authentic in the same year. Jacques Boucher de Crêvecoeur de Perthes, after years of labor and continual rejection by the prevailing climate of opinion which denied man any prehistory whatever, was rewarded by the attention of a distinguished delegation of British scientists who accepted his claims and reported them to the important scientific bodies meeting the same year, 1859. The delegation which visited Boucher and examined his evidence constituted the kind of a team of specialists that would be demanded by any momentous discovery in our day. It included Hugh Falconer, paleontologist, Joseph Prestwich and Charles Lyell, geologists, John Evans, archeologist, and W. H. Flower, anatomist.

It is significant to note the parallel events surrounding the confirmation of man's association with extinct animals for the first time in the western hemisphere. Some of the leading anthropologists thought that man could not be older than perhaps five or six thousand years in America when, in 1926 at Folsom, New Mexico, J. D. Figgins discovered a projectile point embedded in a matrix which included the bones of an extinct species of bison. Archaeologists were not impressed with Figgins' claim. In the next field season,

4. *Ibid.*

another point was found still *in situ*. As H. M. Wormington describes it,

> Immediately, all work was stopped and telegrams were sent to leading institutions requesting that they send representatives to examine the new find.

Three of the most important institutions sent professional representatives who accepted the authenticity of the find. Elsewhere scepticism remained.

> The following year a third expedition was sent to the Folsom site.... Again, points flaked by man were found with the bones of extinct bison. Again, telegrams were sent announcing the discovery and this time numerous other specialists came to view the find. At last the evidence was considered conclusive.[5]

The acceptance of the discovery made by Figgins took only three years, revolutionizing the views held as to the antiquity of man in America. The acceptance seventy years earlier of the discoveries made by Boucher de Perthes, however, took over twenty years from the time of his first collections. The implications of his announcement were certainly much greater in the face of the prevailing opinions on man's antiquity. For the same reason scepticism still remains. This is due in part to a lack of accurate knowledge of the evidence, but chiefly, as Eiseley has noted with regard to the discovery of the first fossil remains of man, "the subject was one touching deeply upon human emotions, and it tended to become proportionately distorted."[6] Nevertheless, as Boule and Vallois have recently written:

> The announcement had a decisive effect on advanced scientific opinion throughout the world. The year 1859 stands as one of the turning points in the history of human thought: the high antiquity of man was established almost simultaneously with the publication of *The Origin of Species* by Charles Darwin.[7]

THEORIES AND TRENDS

Since that time, there has been a continuous controversy over the evidences for the antiquity of man. This controversy has been primarily between two systems of thought: on the one hand, there have been those who have taken for granted that any alleged evidence from science which seemed to conflict with their interpretations of Scripture were, together with the men and scientific discipline involved, automatically anti-biblical. On the other hand, there have been those scientists equally in error, who, largely due to the

5. H. M. Wormington, *Ancient Man in North America* (3rd ed.; Denver: The Denver Museum of Natural History, 1949), pp. 19-21.
6. L. Eiseley, *Darwin's Century* (New York: Doubleday, 1958), p. 257.
7. M. Boule and H. V. Vallois, *Fossil Men* (New York: Dryden, 1957), p. 2.

dogmatism of the first group's untenable positions on species, antiquity, geology, etc., but also due to their own ignorance of Scripture, took it for granted that anyone who held to biblical creationism was, together with the Bible itself, automatically anti- or non-scientific.

While the controversy has been continuous, it has by no means been uniform. For a long time each dogmatically defended positions of some truth mixed with considerable error, in violent and fruitless debate, whose brilliance was in many cases mostly oratorical or literary. As the factual and scientific aspects of the evolutionary position increased and became more widely accepted, however, the bases for the anti-evolutionary or creationist opposition remained comparatively constant, with the result that, while the anti-evolutionists continued to oppose actively the evolutionist position, their attacks were less and less frequently reciprocated. Finally the evolutionists' entanglements with anti-evolutionists dwindled to an occasional defense or debate, the last of which of any consequence in this country was the famous Scopes trial of 1925. Interaction still persists in the British Commonwealth, however, chiefly due to the seemingly tireless efforts of the Evolution Protest Movement, which has active branches in London, Australia, and New Zealand.

Quite another pattern also emerges from a general review of this question. It is quite evident that in the view each has taken, and still takes of the other, whether in opposition or reaction, there is a tremendous degree of ignorance as to progress made in the past hundred years. The creationist exhibits in almost all of his anti-evolutionary literature an antiquated, "moth-ball" conception of evolutionism reminiscent of the latter part of the nineteenth century, while the evolutionist on his part tends to identify all creationists with a position sometimes referred to as "hyperorthodox" or "hypertraditionalist."[8]

8. The term "hyperorthodox" has recently been brought into prominence by Bernard Ramm, *The Christian View of Science and Scripture* (Grand Rapids: Eerdmans, 1954), pp. 27-31, *passim*. Because of its relationship to the terms "fundamentalist" and "orthodox" and because of some objection to its use, it should be clearly defined and its usage clarified. The term "fundamentalist" is today the most widely known label in scientific circles for the Bible-believing creationist. It is important, however, to understand the crucial distinction between at least two meanings of this widely misused term: "Fundamentalism originally referred to the belief that there are certain great truths in Christianity, which, if changed, would dissolve Christianity. Each Christian is allowed personal conviction in respect to a great number of doctrines and interpretations but that personal liberty is hedged about by key infallible and eternal doctrines. This is the term in its historic and good sense. The movement included such stalwarts as James Orr, J. Gresham Machen, Benjamin Warfield, W. H. Green and the numerous contributors to the famous *Fundamentals* papers.

"In more recent years another movement has given the word an odious connotation. Men with much zeal, enthusiasm and conviction, yet lacking frequently

The complicating factor in all this is that while the anti-evolutionist is wrong in his usual appraisal of evolution today, the creationist position is still widely represented by the hypertraditionalist point of view, which is the most vocal expression of creationism. Thus it is not without reason that G. G. Simpson could dispense with a consideration of creationism in a public lecture in Philadelphia in 1950 with words to the effect that "creationists are found today only in non- or anti-scientific circles."

One of the chief drawbacks to the anti-evolutionists, from Darwin's early critics to the present day (familiar as some of their leaders are with the data), is that their activities and literature have been almost completely wrapped up in arguments over petty fragments of the record, assuming that to attack evolution as a total philosophy one must show the data upon which the assumptions are based to be untrue.

---

in education or cultural breadth, and many times highly individualistic, took to the stump to defend the faith. Many times they were dogmatic beyond evidence, or were intractable of disposition, or were obnoxiously anti-cultural, anti-educational, and anti-scientific. Hence the term came to mean one who was bigoted, an obscurantist, a fideist, a fighter, and an anti-intellectual." (Bernard Ramm, quoted in *United Evangelical Action*, Feb. 15, 1955, p. 13.)

The creationist position which this chapter attempts to advance is to be identified with the first, not the second meaning of "fundamentalist" as defined above. It is fully recognized, however, that all creationists who do not agree with this position are *not* automatically considered in the second category.

It is abundantly clear from his discussion of the matter that Ramm employs the term "hyperorthodox" to refer to this second brand of fundamentalism so as not to perpetuate the "odious connotation" with the term. His reason for so doing is that "we can sin to the right as well as to the left. Patriotism can degenerate into jingoism and enthusiasm into fanaticism and virtue into prudishness. It is possible not only to have slack theological views, but also to have views far more rigid and dogmatic than Scripture itself. Hyperorthodoxy in trying to be loyal to the Bible has developed an exaggerated sense of what loyalty to the Bible means" (*Christian View*, p. 29).

He evidently got the term from J. W. Dawson who, he points out (p. 28), referred to "pedantic hyperorthodoxy" in evangelical apologetics in 1877.

Certain objections to its use have been raised, however, chiefly upon the basis of a possible misidentification of this position with sound, theological orthodoxy. Thus the alternatives "distorted orthodoxy" and "blind orthodoxy" have been suggested. Even more significant, perhaps, is the objection to the form of the term itself. Thus, the Reverend John Buswell, my brother, wrote me: "Can anyone be hyperorthodox? Is not orthodoxy an ultimate — in one sphere, anyway? In other words, many would regard 'hyper-orthodox' as they would 'hyper-straight' or 'hyper-sterilized.' "

Since these and other objections seem to have some value, I have chosen to use instead the term "hypertraditionalist" suggested by my colleague, Dr. Joseph Free. The term seems to refer more precisely to those who, being bound by tradition, prefer to retain the peripheral, relative, and changeable interpretations with the fundamental truths, without being able to distinguish the difference.

A popular misconception of evolution held by creationists is this "vague idea of progress" mentioned by Kroeber in another context above. The common objection that evolution claims man is climbing "ever onward, ever upward" does not apply today. G. G. Simpson wrote ten years ago that

> Examination of the actual record of life and of the evolutionary processes as these are now known raises such serious doubts regarding the oversimple and metaphysical concept of a pervasive perfection principle that we must reject it altogether....
>
> In sober enquiry, we have no real reason to assume, without other standards, that evolution, over-all or in any particular case, has been either for better or for worse. Progress can be identified and studied in the history of life only if we first postulate a criterion of progress or can find such a criterion in that history itself.[9]

Evolution involves change, not progress, necessarily; and physical anthropology today is increasingly interested in the processes involved. Such things as growth patterns, bone-muscle formative relationships, processes of population genetics, the role of mutations and other genetic alterations, processes of geology and prehistoric ecological change, and many other related interests claim the attention of what S. L. Washburn has called "the new physical anthropology."[10]

Having passed through its "initial descriptive phase," physical anthropology is now entering its "analytic stage," stimulated by recent advances in evolutionary theory, and by focusing of genetic and other sampling and measurement techniques upon problems of process and cause rather than upon those of description and classification only.

"For many years," Washburn points out, "physical anthropology changed little and was easy to define. Physical anthropologists were those scientists, interested in human evolution and variation, who used measurements as their primary technique. The main training of a physical anthropologist consisted in learning to make a small number of measurements accurately.... The assumption seems to have been that description (whether morphological or metrical), if accurate enough and in sufficient quantity, could solve problems of process, pattern, and interpretation....

"During the last fifty years, although excellent descriptive data were added, techniques improved, and problems clarified and defined, little progress was made in understanding the process and pattern of human evolution. The strategy of physical anthropology yielded

9. G. G. Simpson, *The Meaning of Evolution* (New Haven: Yale University Press, 1949), p. 241.

10. S. L. Washburn, "The New Physical Anthropology," *Transactions of the New York Academy of Sciences*, Series II, XIII (1951), 298-304.

diminishing returns, and, finally, application of the traditional method *by experts* gave contradictory results. After more than a century of intensive fact-finding, there is less agreement among informed scientists on the relation of man to other primates than there was in the latter part of the nineteenth century.... With regard to race, agreement is no greater...."[11]

The transition is more graphically portrayed in a table which analyzes the old and the new physical anthropology under the headings of Purpose, Theory, Technique, and Interpretation.[12]

PURPOSE OF THE OLD
  a. Primarily classification.
  b. Problems solved by classification and correlation.
  c. Description of difference enough.

PURPOSE OF THE NEW
  a. Understanding process.
  b. Classification a minor part, and the *cause* of differences critical.

THEORY OF THE OLD
  Relatively little and unimportant; facts speak for themselves.

THEORY OF THE NEW
  Theory is critical, and the development of consistent, experimentally verified hypotheses a major objective.

TECHNIQUE OF THE OLD
  Anthropometry 80 per cent, aided by morphological comparison.

TECHNIQUE OF THE NEW
  Measurement perhaps 20 per cent, supplemented by a wide variety of techniques adapted to the solution of particular problems.

INTERPRETATION OF THE OLD
  Speculation.

INTERPRETATION OF THE NEW
  The primary objective of the research is to prove which hypotheses are correct; the major task begins where the old left off.

Washburn has injected a caution, however, lest such an itemized table lead one to infer that the change is one with a clear and definite beginning and a sharp abandoning of the old methods. He makes it plain that the differences are "in degree only," maintaining a very real continuity in the over-all trend. But it is a great trend and is taking place swiftly. "Actually," he observed, "the physical anthropology of 1950 will seem much more like that of 1900 than it will like that of 1960."[13]

What implications may creationists draw from this advance in physical anthropology? It seems that there is every reason to survey

11. S. L. Washburn, "The Strategy of Physical Anthropology," in A. L. Kroeber (ed.), *Anthropology Today*, (Chicago: University of Chicago Press, 1953), pp. 714-715.

12. *Ibid.*, p. 716.

13. *Ibid.*, p. 715.

the trend as one in the direction of a much more objective and less prejudiced study of the data at hand. For example, Washburn contrasts the old and new ways of evaluating superorbital ridges:

> As viewed traditionally, if one was interested in brow ridges, the procedure was to classify the structures and then to draw conclusions on the interrelations of races or fossil men. That is, the classification gave a tool to be used in the analysis of evolution and variation. It was, in this sense, final knowledge. But in a different sense, the classification merely outlined the problems to be investigated. No description of the types of brow ridges gives understanding of the reasons for any of them. The classifications show what kinds exist, under what circumstances they are found, and so pose a series of problems which need investigation. To traditional physical anthropology, classification was an end, something to be used. To the new physical anthropology, classifications merely pose problems, and methods must be devised to solve them.14

This is just an indication of the way in which more and more of the problems of man's variations and prehistory are being handled. Partly responsible is the increased realization that the various divisions of anthropology must co-operate in order to progress. Washburn points out that "one of the main implications of the new point of view is that there is a far more detailed interrelationship between the different parts of anthropology than under the old strategy. A dynamic analysis of the form of the jaw will illuminate problems of evolution, fossil man, race, growth, constitution, and medical application. . . . By its very nature, the investigation of process and behavior has a generality which is lacking in purely descriptive studies."15

Similarly, William Howells has observed that "a physical anthropologist, instead of yawning at the preoccupations of archeologists with minutiae which he cannot understand, can only be impressed more and more every year by how necessary to him is the information from archeology which alone can keep him from going completely off the track at certain points in problems dealing with human paleontology, or with early population spreads and movements, which might in turn be important to the understanding of the genetics and evolutionary processes of human populations in general."16

This is all indicative of a changed attitude from that of scientific generalizers of fifty to seventy-five years ago. The cocksure solution, though cropping up in elementary and popular treatments, is seldom in evidence in the scholarly journals and summaries which have seriously come to grips with the problems. Such attitudes of honest and objective inquiry, although truly enough biased by evolutionary preconceptions, give the creationist a real opportunity to contribute

14. *Ibid.*, p. 717.
15. *Ibid.*, p. 726.
16. W. W. Howells, "The Study of Anthropology," *American Anthropologist*, LIV (1952), 2.

to his field with equal authority, supernaturalist preconceptions notwithstanding, if he is willing to come to grips similarly with the same bodies of data.

THE EVIDENCE FOR PREHISTORIC MAN

The evidence for the existence of prehistoric man consists of the artifacts which were part of his material culture, and his own fossilized bones. The latter are far fewer in number than the cultural remains.

Complete evaluation of any fossil find or site of discovery involves at least four special lines of interpretation: archaeological, geological, paleontological, and morphological. The archaeologist studies the cultural artifacts and sequences; the geologist, the stratigraphy; the paleontologist, the associated plants and animals; and the physical anthropologist, the morphology of the human fossils themselves.

The days of morphological dating, judging the antiquity of a fossil by its differences from modern forms, are past. The present view is expressed in the words of Le Gros Clark as he explains that in a fossil series, the "lines of development can be finally determined only by the demonstration of an actual temporal sequence, and the latter can be established only if geological dating is secure."[17] Geological dating includes not only stratigraphic correlations but geochemical analyses, such as fluorine content and radiocarbon tests, whenever possible. The corroboration of archaeological and paleontological correlations is also necessary wherever there are found cultural remains or associated plants and animals. Any contradictory evidence necessitates a thorough re-examination of the entire site.

One of the most dramatic indications of progress in methodology, after nearly a century of holding sacred the morphology of human fossils, was the final exposure of the famous Piltdown Man in 1953. For more than forty years the controversy over Piltdown centered primarily upon the perplexing morphological contradiction of a fairly modern human cranium found with an ape-like jaw. This, together with the relative uncertainty of the stratigraphic and archaeological associations as compared with the results of modern painstaking techniques of excavation, prevented any conclusive interpretation of the find.

While many conceived of Piltdown as the "first Englishman" and the most ancient of European fossils, there were others who believed all along that the jaw was that of an ape form in the same deposit with a human skull, and, on morphological grounds, refused to accept

17. W. E. Le Gros Clark, *The Fossil Evidence for Human Evolution* (Chicago: University of Chicago Press, 1955), p. 37.

the conclusion that the whole thing was human. Kroeber,[18] never one to jump to conclusions anyway, decided that "the claim that the Piltdown skull belongs to a distinct genus *Eoanthropus* is to be viewed with reserve. That the jaw and teeth pertain to an early human form seems equally doubtful. Miller[19] in 1915, Saller[20] and Hrdlicka[21] independently in 1930, Frederichs[22] in 1932, have all denied that the skull and the jaw can have come out of the same body."

Weidenreich in 1946 was of the opinion that the mandible was "without any doubt, the jaw of an anthropoid." He concluded that "both skeletal elements cannot belong to the same skull. All that has been known of early man since the discovery of the Piltdown fossils proves that man cannot have had an ancestor with a lower jaw of a completely simian character."[23]

Even recent texts published before the exposure tended to agree with this opinion. Beals and Hoijer stated that "the skull fragments must be regarded as those of a relatively late *Homo sapiens* form, accidentally associated with the jaw of an older chimpanzee-like animal."[24]

Thus there can be little certainty and much controversy over a find which doesn't seem to square with the rest of the fossil picture, particularly when the find is an isolated one like Piltdown. It is essential to realize that the authenticity and antiquity of most of the important prehistoric human remains are established by the very corroboration of numbers. The skull cap of the famous Java man, *Pithecanthropus erectus,* discovered by Dubois in 1891 was subsequently corroborated by the discovery in 1937, 1938, and 1939, of three more skull fragments and in 1936 and 1939 by portions of the dentition which indicate without question a distinctly hominid morphology.[25] Furthermore the thigh bone of *Pithecanthropus erectus* which, because of its marked modern appearance, was thought by many not to belong to the same race and period as the skull, is now

18. Kroeber, *op. cit.*, p. 90.

19. G. S. Miller, Jr., "The Jaw of Piltdown Man," *Smithsonian Miscellaneous Collections*, Vol. LXV (1915).

20. K. Saller, *Leitfaden der Anthropologie* (Berlin, 1930).

21. A. Hrdlicka, "The Skeletal Remains of Early Man," *Smithsonian Miscellaneous Collections*, Vol. LXXXIII (1930).

22. H. F. Frederichs, "Schadel und Unterkiefer von Piltdown" in neuer Untersuchung. *Zeitschrift Fur Anatomie Und Entwicklungsgeschichte,* XCVIII (1932), 199-262.

23. F. Weidenreich, *Apes, Giants, and Man* (Chicago: University of Chicago Press, 1946), pp. 22-23.

24. R. Beals and H. Hoijer, *An Introduction to Anthropology* (New York: Macmillan, 1953), p. 138.

25. Le Gros Clark, *op. cit.*, p. 93.

fully accepted as such. This acceptance has been the result of at least four different lines of evidence. According to Le Gros Clark,

> In the first place, there seems little doubt that the femur was actually found in situ in the Trinil beds (and, according to Hooijer,[26] the field notes kept by Dubois show that his excavations were carried out systematically and accurately). Second, it has recently been reported by Bergman and Karsten[27] that the fluorine content of the femur is equivalent to that of the calvaria and also of other representatives of the Trinil fauna, an observation which is in conformity with the geologic evidence that they were contemporaneous. Third, remains of five other femora of similar type in the Leiden Museum have been found among fossils collected from Trinil deposits (three of them were described by Dubois,[28] in 1932), and these also show a fluorine content which is compatible with a Middle Pleistocene date. Thus they confirm that at this early time there existed in Java hominids with a type of femur indistinguishable from that of H. sapiens, though all the cranial remains so far found emphasize the extraordinarily primitive characters of the skull and dentition. Finally, portions of seven femora of Pithecanthropus from Choukoutien show that in the Chinese representatives of this genus a femur of modern human type was also associated with the same primitive features of the skull and dentition.[29]

Of course the "Chinese representatives"[30] in themselves serve to corroborate the whole Pithecanthropus picture since there were remains of over forty individuals, which gives adequate skeletal material for complete reconstruction of the type.

Similarly, the Neandertal[31] race is known from the comparatively

---

26. D. A. Hooijer, "The Geological Age of *Pithecanthropus, Meganthropus, and Gigantopithecus,*" *American Journal of Physical Anthropology*, IX (1951), 265.

27. R. A. M. Bergman and Karsten, "The Fluorine content of *Pithecanthropus. . . .*" *Proceedings Koninklijke Nederlandse Akademie Van Wetenschappen*, L (1952), 151.

28. E. Dubois, "The Distinct Organization of *Pithecanthropus erectus* Now Confirmed from Other Individuals of the Described Species," *Proceedings Koninklijke Nederlandse Akademie Van Wetenschappen*, XXXV (1932), 716.

29. Le Gros Clark, *op. cit.*, p. 82.

30. It has become customary to classify *Sinanthropus pekinensis*, the Peking Man, in the same genus with the Java Man, *Pithecanthropus*, owing to their morphological similarity.

31. On the spelling of "Neandertal" Dr. E. A. Hoebel, in the latest edition of his text *Man in the Primitive World* (New York: McGraw-Hill, 1958 [p. 62]) has this to say: "The original spelling of this word was *Neanderthal*, but just before the First World War an Imperial Commission of Philologists with authority to streamline the German language in the interests of Teutonic efficiency recommended that since German is quite consistently spelled as it is pronounced, the unsounded *h* should be dropped from all *th* combinations except in *der Throne*. For a group of professors to tamper with the seat of the emperor would be lese majesty. Less respectful German wags said it was because of fear that the throne might collapse if the *h* were removed. Be that as it may, physical anthropologists are not philologists and most of them still leave the *h* in Neandertal. Lately, however, the clarion has sounded to call them up to date: See H. Vallois, 'Neanderthal-Neandertal?' *L'Anthropologie*, LV (1952), 557-558."

profuse remains found in more than ten major sites over a period of a hundred years.

NEANDERTAL STRAIGHTENS UP

Although not as sensational as the solution of the Piltdown problem, Neandertal man himself has undergone a critical reappraisal at the hands of modern science. Professor William L. Straus, Jr., of Johns Hopkins University, at the commemoration of the one hundredth anniversary of the discovery of Neandertal at the type site, Neandertal Cave, near Düsseldorf, Germany, presented a report of great significance.[32] It concerned a re-examination of one of the better-known Neandertal finds, that discovered at La Chapelle-aux-Saints in 1908, "the most complete and best preserved Mousterian human fossil known up to that time."[33] In the burial were found the skull, twenty-one vertebrae, about twenty ribs, one collar bone, arm bones, leg and foot bones, and other fragments. The bones were sent to Professor Marcellin Boule, then Director of the French Institute of Human Paleontology, who during 1911-1913 studied, interpreted, and reconstructed the skeleton. It was upon Boule's interpretation and reconstruction of the La Chapelle skeleton that the long-famous posture of the classic Neandertal man was based. Stooped, with head thrust forward, Neandertal man has been posing for countless textbooks and museum displays ever since. From the examination of the vertebrae, it was believed that there was

> in the cervical region of the vertebral column either a complete absence of curves, or a slight curve, in a direction opposite to that in modern Man, prolonging the dorsal curve, as occurs in anthropoid apes, such as the Chimpanzee.[34]

The vertebrae themselves were shown to be "much more like those of a Chimpanzee than those of a man."[35]

Another argument for the classic posture of Neandertal was derived from the idea that the occipital foramen, the hole in the base of the skull at which point the vertebral column joins the skull, lies more to the rear than in modern man, thus indicating that the head would have to hang forward a little instead of being straight up as in the present human form.

Straus reported, however, that after a recent re-examination of the original bones, there was abundant evidence of advanced osteo-

---

32. This report has been extended and revised by Dr. Straus in cooperation with A. J. E. Cleave and appears as "Pathology and the Posture of Neanderthal Man" in *The Quarterly Review of Biology*, XXXII (1957), 348-363.

33. Boule and Vallois, *op. cit.*, p. 202.

34. *Ibid.*, p. 232.

35. *Ibid.*

arthritis in the La Chapelle mandible and throughout the post-cranial skeleton. The vertebrae not only reveal marked "lipping" and deformation, but indicate as well, significantly faulty repair on the part of the earlier investigators. He pointed out that recently Aramburg and Schultz have seriously questioned the "naturalness of semi-erect posture in an habitually bipedal stance." Furthermore, Aramburg has shown that modern man has frequently the same form of vertebrae as La Chapelle, proving that it was not a simian feature as Boule had thought.

Earlier, Franz Weidenreich had pointed out that

> In the case of the Neanderthalians Boule (1911), using Topinard's method to determine the position of the occipital foramen of the skull of La Chapelle-aux-Saints, came to the conclusion that the foramen occupies a more backward position than is found in any case of modern man. But this is erroneous, for despite the fact that in this skull the *opisthion* lies fairly well to the rear, it does not fall beyond the range of modern man.[36]

Professor Straus concluded his centennial report by saying that "there is nothing about Neandertal man that would necessarily cause him to walk any differently than ourselves."

SHAPES AND LABELS

Now a word must be said about the distinctive morphology of prehistoric man and its taxonomic implications. Frequently creationists have been guilty of denying that there are any characteristics of prehistoric races which are not found in modern man. The popular expressions that one can "find Neandertal man on almost any New York subway" or "dig him up in any graveyard" are simply the result of a general impression of the physical reconstructions of prehistoric man, museum variety, which could hardly be held to by anyone who is willing to examine the skeletal details. It is almost overemphasizing the obvious, but still necessary to point out, that the skeletal details, proportions, and indices with which the physical anthropologist works are not always able to be observed in the living man due to the overlay of flesh. It is almost unbelievable how much is made in anti-evolutionary literature of such examples as Lafayette's profile to show a slanting forehead and lack of chin eminence; of the wrestler "the Angel" as a Neandertal type; or even of Darwin's deep-set eyes and shaggy eyebrows to indicate a supraorbital ridge! The typical supraorbital ridge of Neandertal and Pithecanthropus is a massive development of bone lying above the eyes with a marked

36. F. Weidenreich, "The Skull of *Sinanthropus pekinensis*," *Palaeontologia Sinica*, No. 127 (1943), p. 131.

constriction immediately behind on either side between the bony ridge and the cranium itself. This is combined with a cranial formation called platycephaly or flattening of the skull as if mashed downward by a giant hand. Consequently the occipital or rearmost area of the skull extends backward beyond the limits of modern man, and, particularly in Pithecanthropus, the points of greatest width of the skull are quite low, in the temporal region just above the ears, whereas in modern man the greatest width is well up in the parietal region. The angle of the forehead, of course, is simply a part of the whole morphological pattern of platycephally. Despite this distinct morphological difference from modern man, the Neandertal cranial capacity averages somewhat more than that of modern man, or from 1,300-1,600 c.c.

Thus it can be easily demonstrated that certain prehistoric races in their "total morphological pattern,"[37] even though not in many individual features, are quite different from all modern races. But it must be recognized that these differences have only taxonomic significance and nothing more. Taxonomy, or biological classification, need have no derivative implications. Only within an evolutionary framework need morphological similarities imply phylogenetic relationship. Despite the claim on the part of evolutionists that relationship implied by similarity is "a fundamental principle of taxonomy,"[38] it is only a principle in the evolutionary interpretation of taxonomy. A non-evolutionary interpretation of taxonomy views it as purely a comparison and classification of similarities and differences. Thus, the anatomist can look at Pithecanthropus and modern man, and conclude that they legitimately belong to different genera on the logical basis that "the cranial and dental differences ... appear to be as well marked as those which are commonly accepted as justifying a generic distinction between the gorilla and the chimpanzee."[39] Similarly, with respect to Neandertal, "the skeletal differences from H. sapiens are of much the same order as those which have been accepted as valid evidence of specific distinction in other groups of Primates."[40]

Yet, even the specialists are not agreed upon the best taxonomic

37. It is not widely understood in creationist circles how important this is in modern anthropology. Le Gros Clark points out that "it seems desirable to stress this concept of pattern rather strongly because the assessment of the phylogenetic and taxonomic status of fossil hominoid remains must be based, not on the comparison of individual characters in isolation one by one, but on a consideration of the *total pattern* which they present in combination." *Op. cit.*, p. 15.

38. Le Gros Clark, *op. cit.*, p. 17.

39. *Ibid.*, p. 106.

40. *Ibid.*, p. 60.

interpretation of these morphological differences. Le Gros Clark points out, for example, that

> Even the generic term *Pithecanthropus* is not to be accepted as a final assessment of the taxonomic status of these Far Eastern fossil hominids, for some authorities (e.g. Mayr) take the view that their morphological characters are not so divergent as to justify a generic distinction from *Homo*.[41]

Franz Weidenreich went even further when he claimed, upon the basis of the evident continuity of the gradual human change, that "not only the living forms of mankind but also the past forms — at least those whose remains have been recovered — must be included in the same species."[42]

Now any proper creationist interpretation of taxonomy should recognize, just as much as the evolutionary interpretation should, that the morphological data alone do not demand nor prove creation or evolution. Both interpretations are wholly dependent upon the philosophical presuppositions, and the one is just as legitimate, scientifically, as the other, so long as no violence is done to the factual body of data.

A CREATIONIST INTERPRETATION

There are four particular areas of God's creative activity which are held by most creationists to be essential. They are (a) the origin of matter; (b) the origin of life; (c) the origin of the major "kinds" of plants and animals; and (d) the origin of man.

The consideration of these areas is not simply a question of whether "evolution" or "creation" is the exclusive explanation. Organic evolution is so inclusive and so complex a system that it must be broken down into its constituent elements. This may be attempted on various levels of abstraction. One of the most obvious and important steps which can be taken is a separation of the consideration of *origins* from the consideration of *process*. I have the impression that British evolutionists are perhaps oftener involved in considerations of origins than are American evolutionists. The American, at least in anthropological circles, tends to leave questions of the origin of the earth and of life to the astronomers, physicists, and biologists on the one hand, or to the philosophers on the other. William Howells has stated the position thus:

> We are totally bewildered, of course, about the beginnings of life and the reasons for our existence, and these are questions which have been grist to the mills of philosophers and myth-makers alike. But we know, roughly, what happened along the way, and that is the story of human evolution.[43]

41. *Ibid.*, p. 82.
42. Weidenreich, *op. cit.*, p. 3.
43. W. W. Howells, *Mankind So Far* (New York: Doubleday, 1944), p. 3.

Considerations of process, as we have pointed out above, make up the major concerns of the physical anthropologist, and they also constitute the fundamental area of concentration of evolutionists today. Therefore let us postpone the consideration of origins to another context.

I find Simpson's three "modes" or aspects of evolution extremely useful for purposes of analysis and comparison with the creationist position. The first of these is speciation or "splitting," which, as Simpson points out, "is almost the only mode accessible for experimental biology, neozoology, and genetics. It embraces almost all the dynamic evolutionary phenomena subject to direct experimental attack."[44] This is simply the hereditary mechanism for the production of variety in nature.

The second mode Simpson calls "phyletic" evolution, which "involves the sustained, directional (but not necessarily rectilinear) shift of the average characters of populations. It is not primarily the splitting up of a population, but the change of the population as a whole."[45] This mode could be thought of as the process of speciation going on throughout vast periods of geological time.

While speciation may explain the formation of races, species, and sometimes genera, Simpson points out that the phyletic mode "is typically related to middle taxonomic levels, usually genera, subfamilies, and families." He also observes that "nine-tenths of the pertinent data of paleontology fall into patterns of the phyletic mode."[46]

Thus, although evolution does not consist of wholly distinct processes, and a fossil series, for example, can exhibit speciation, or splitting, in a phyletic pattern through geological time, nevertheless the well documented data of natural selection on these levels — the genetic and geological processes — may be abstracted from the overall theory of organic evolution. *The creationist may accept all of the facts within these two areas of consideration.* Thus he need have no quarrel with the transmutation of species or other taxonomic categories, and may fully accept the genetic explanation for variation. Similarly he may accept the evidence of the "evolution" of the horse, and other such well-documented paleontological series, upon the basis of the adaptive, dynamic interaction of genetic and environmental change called natural selection.

Turning to more anthropological matters, the creationist may

44. G. G. Simpson, *Tempo and Mode in Evolution* (New York: Columbia University Press, 1944), p. 202.
45. *Ibid.*
46. *Ibid.*, p. 203.

accept the evidence for the age of prehistoric man and his culture. He need have no quarrel with an antiquity of hundreds of thousands of years; there is nothing in the Bible to indicate how long ago man was created. The date of 4004 B. C., which has been an item of ridicule by evolutionists and a rallying point for the hypertraditionalists, now finds itself a cultural survival, firmly ensconced in the notes on Page 1 of certain editions of the Bible, but without a valid function in either modern Christian theology or chronology.

Neither need the creationist have any quarrel with morphological features of ancient man. The Bible, which is the creationist's basis of belief and life, simply says nothing about what Adam looked like. And, although the creationist, Protestant and Catholic alike, must of necessity hold to the belief (which will be further discussed below) that there was a "first man," it is of no consequence whether he looked like a Pithecanthropoid or a Caucasoid. Furthermore, if anthropological opinion swings in favor of calling some prehistoric types by separate specific or generic names, and calls other types *Homo sapiens* with modern man, this is of relatively little consequence. For the creationist recognizes the arbitrary and non-qualitative nature of taxonomic categories and is not bound to equate any one of them with the "kind" spoken of in Genesis 1.

Thus the creationist may look on with the same interest, or relief, as any anthropologist, when a classic Neanderthaloid posture is straightened up, or a Piltdown forgery exposed. Here, of course, is a characteristic difference from the hypertraditionalist reaction. When the Piltdown news hit the press early in 1954 the anti-evolutionist and many religious journals were full of "I told you so's" and exclamations that "another major pillar of evolution had fallen!" One creationist, on the other hand, simply expressed "relief that one of the more perplexing riddles of man's prehistory is finally solved." Presumably the same sort of reactions can be expected once Professor Straus's re-analysis of the La Chappele bones gains wider circulation.

With the consideration of Simpson's third mode, we introduce the principal theoretical area of disagreement between evolution and creationism. Essentially it boils down to a matter of facts vs. theory, data vs. interpretation, or a matter of attitudes and presuppositions.

Despite the factual basis of speciation and phyletic evolution, there are what Simpson refers to as "major discontinuities of the record" existing in the paleontology of the larger taxonomic groups between which there is no fossil evidence of relationship. The origins of these larger groups are attributed to "a particular set of evolutionary events" that are "changes of adaptive zones such that transitional forms between the old zone and the new cannot, or at any rate do not, persist."[47] After showing in some detail how this applies to the perissodactyls, or horse group, Simpson concluded in 1944 that

> This regular absence of transitional forms is not confined to mammals, but is an almost universal phenomenon, as has long been noted by paleontologists. It is true of almost all orders of all classes of animals, both vertebrate and invertebrate. *A fortiori*, it is also true of the classes, themselves, and of the major animal phyla, and it is apparently also true of analogous categories of plants.[48]

Now Simpson's third mode, called "quantum" evolution, purports to be the explanation for the jumping of these gaps. In his words, quantum evolution is "applied to the relatively rapid shift of a biotic population in disequilibrium, to an equilibrium distinctly unlike an ancestral condition.... It is ... believed to be the dominant and most essential process in the origin of taxonomic units of relatively high rank, such as families, orders, and classes. It is believed to include circumstances that explain the mystery that hovers over the origin of such major groups."[49]

Simpson candidly admits that this is a "controversial and hypothetical" attempt to establish the existence of an "inferred phenomenon." He points out that "major incidents of quantum evolution have systematically poor records, for reasons discussed [above]. Nevertheless, we do have many partial records of quantum evolution, even at high levels (e.g. origin of classes), which can be completed by sound and unequivocal inference."[50]

Of course, Simpson does not necessarily represent all evolutionists, but his threefold breakdown is, *de facto*, applicable to organic evolution in its present-day form. Thus we conclude that it is at this point — quantum evolution — that the creationist and the evolutionist must part company. How will "creation" as an alternative to the

47. G. G. Simpson, *The Major Features of Evolution* (New York: Columbia University Press, 1953), p. 389.

48. Simpson, *Tempo and Mode*, p. 107.

49. *Ibid.*, p. 206.

50. Simpson, *The Major Features*, p. 389. It should be added that Dr. Simpson points out the following as "the most important point about this mode of evolution and one of the reasons for its separate designation and special study." "Quantum evolution may lead to a new group at any taxonomic level. It is probable that species, either genetic or phyletic, often arise in this way. Certainly genera and all higher categories may do so. The phenomenon naturally becomes clearer and more readily definable when the change in adaptation and structure is relatively large, and such changes commonly eventuate in the development of higher categories. There is no level at which clear-cut quantum evolution is the only mode of origin of new groups, but at high levels some element of quantum evolution is usually involved" *(Ibid.)*.

quantum interpretation still fit the facts? As mentioned above, it becomes a matter of presupposition: for the creationist, super-naturalism; for the evolutionist, naturalism. I propose, then, that since in a percentage of *orders,* major gaps appear between them, perhaps the *order* is as near to being what Genesis 1 means by the term "kind" as any single taxonomic category can be. This proposal implies simply that God created the orders, and natural selection took it from there. Of course this cannot be maintained consistently as far as *orders* are concerned, since in some cases classes or even phyla could be applied, and obviously in the case of man, a much lower category, perhaps genus, would apply.[51] In other words, "an honest creationist will ask the paleontologist what he knows of the time of origin of animals, and draw his conclusions from the data."[52]

The fact that the evolutionary hypothesis as a total explanation for all major transitions is so firmly established in our scientific and educational system is due to at least three important factors. (1) Based upon the experimental knowledge of genetics, the sequen-tial data of paleontology, and the logical consistency of the processes of adaptation and natural selection as presently conceived, this major jumping of gaps, in Simpson's words, "has a probable mech-anism and would be expected under given conditions."[53] (2) The only alternative, creation, or the allowance of a supernaturalistic presupposition in the tradition of science, has been considered as

51. Mixter arrived at a similar conclusion (*Creation and Evolution,* ASA Mono-graph No. 2 [West Lafayette, Ind.: American Scientific Affiliation, 1953]), suggesting that the order is at present a reasonable approximation of "kind." The obvious fact that "kind" cannot be equated consistently with any one taxonomic group is also explained as follows: "Because marsupials are separated by structural gaps un-bridged by intermediate forms from other orders of mammals, a creationist may conclude that the first marsupials were specially created. If there are gaps between families or genera within the order of marsupials, he may believe that such families also had separately created beginnings. Whenever a gap is filled then a revision of the idea of what are the special creations should be made" (p. 17).

Despite this clear statement, when Mixter expressed the feeling in a paper in 1957 at the 12th annual convention of the American Scientific Affiliation, that, in view of Simpson's revised treatment of the gaps in the fossil record between certain orders (Simpson, *The Major Features of Evolution*), it might be necessary to assume that one order did evolve from another and that the gap between them perhaps was not as wide or meaningful as formerly believed to be, so that at this point a phylogenetic continuity might indeed be presumed to exist, he was widely misunderstood by creationists as "completely reversing his position," "capitu-lating to evolution," and theistic evolutionists present lauded the position with expressions to the effect that "we wondered how long it would take him!" Both failed to realize that this was not a reversal but only "a revision of the idea of what are the special creations" which he had allowed for all the time.

52. *Ibid.,* p. 18.

53. Simpson, *Tempo and Mode,* p. 207.

clearly "incredible."[54] (3) The creationists, due to their own peculiar tradition of fending off the advances of science, have failed to formulate this alternative in a scientifically respectable manner.

The primary point of difference, then, between evolutionism and creationism is not a matter of accepting or rejecting facts. *There are no data as such that conflict with the Genesis account of creation as interpreted in the context of the author's language and culture.* The primary point of difference is on the level of mechanistic vs. supernatural presuppositions. Most evolutionists claim with G. S. Carter that

> Man is an animal, and, however greatly his present state differs from that of the rest of the animal kingdom, we must accept that he arose from subhuman ancestors by a process of evolution.[55]

And, despite their acknowledgment that man is a wholly unique, or culture-bearing animal, most would tend to agree with Simpson that

> Man is the result of a purposeless and materialistic process that did not have him in mind. He was not planned. He is a state of matter, a form of life, a sort of animal, and a species of the Order Primates, akin nearly or remotely to all of life and indeed to all that is material.[56]

The creationist claims that man is more than a unique animal, and that he was both planned and created by God.

In summary on these three modes of evolutionary process, the creationist may well hold, with Professor Mixter, the following conclusions:

(1) Speciation. "Whenever geneticists can show common genes, they are entitled to infer common ancestry."[57]

(2) Phyletic evolution. "When animals are traceable to other animals by a closely graded series of transitional forms, [the paleontologist is entitled to infer that] the early forms have given rise to the later ones."[58]

---

54. "Evolution itself is accepted by zoologists ... because no alternative explanation is credible" — D. M. S. Watson in *Nature*, Aug. 10, 1929. "The only alternative [to evolution] is the doctrine of special creation which may be true but is irrational" — L. T. More in *The Dogma of Evolution* (Princeton: Princeton University Press, 1925), p. 22. "If Darwin's hypothesis be rejected, there is, it must be frankly admitted, no satisfactory alternative to take its place" — W. B. Scott, *The Theory of Evolution* (New York: Macmillan, 1917), p. 26. (I am indebted to Dr. John R. Howitt, Supt., Ontario Hospital, Port Arthur, Ontario, for these three quotations.)

55. G. S. Carter, "The Theory of Evolution and the Evolution of Man," in A. L. Kroeber (ed.), *Anthropology Today* (Chicago: University of Chicago Press, 1953), p. 327.

56. G. G. Simpson, *The Meaning of Evolution*, pp. 344-345.

57. Mixter, *op. cit.*, pp. 10-11.

58. *Ibid.*, p. 23.

(3) Quantum evolution. "When a group of animals is separated from another group by an unbridged gap, then until bridges are found, one may hold that the groups so separated have arisen from independently created kinds."[59]

THEISTIC EVOLUTION

The crux of the whole matter lies in the question of origins. The creationist, while he may fully accept the facts of genetics and the fossil record, believes that God created life, and man, and that man did not arise from a previously existing organism. This position is frequently, but erroneously, called "theistic evolution," because it allows for some process in God's creative activity instead of necessitating an instantaneous creation. But while genetics and paleontology have played a big part in the expression of organic evolution, *they neither singly nor in combination constitute evolution*. One might as logically call the creationist a "theistic speciationist" or a believer in "theistic Mendelism" or "theistic stratigraphy" because he grants that God has instituted the hereditary process of genetics and the geological dynamics of prehistory. Or one might call a Bible-believing weather forecaster a "theistic meteorologist" simply because he believes that the laws which God instituted at creation, are believed and relied upon by non-Christian observers as well!

The theistic evolutionist, however, while believing that God is operating the process, also accepts the possibility that man could have arisen from a non-human creature, and that God merely endowed him with a soul which act constituted the "creation of man," culturally, mentally, and spiritually. This position of theistic evolution is typically, but not exclusively, that of the Roman Catholics who only specify their opposition to "materialistic" evolution. Dr. J. F. Ewing, in a recent issue of the Catholic *Anthropological Quarterly*, summarizing "The Present Catholic Attitude Towards Evolution," admits that "God may indeed have used a body prepared for the soul as far as possible by evolution . . .," that "there is no defined doctrine which opposes a theory of the evolution of Man's body . . .," and that "the possibility that there were true men before Adam and Eve, men whose line became extinct (in other words, Pre-Adamites), is allowable."[60]

This I find, at present, impossible to accept, on theological as well as on anthropological grounds. Theologically, the fundamental doctrines of the original perfection and subsequent fall of man and his consequent need of redemption; and the role of the Saviour,

59. *Ibid.*
60. J. F. Ewing, "The Present Catholic Attitude Towards Evolution," *Anthropological Quarterly*, XXIX, 134, 138.

Jesus Christ, the Son of God in dying on the cross to pay the penalty for the fall, for all who will accept him, are seriously jeopardized by a first man having descended organically from pre-human parents. Now theistic evolutionists likewise acknowledge the necessity of retaining this doctrine of original sin. It is inextricably tied up with the necessity of having all mankind arise from *one* man. The Catholic statement on this from the Encyclical "Humani Generis" quoted by Ewing, is as follows:

> No Catholic can hold that after Adam there existed on this earth true men who did not take their origin through natural generation from him as from the first parent of all, or that Adam is merely a symbol for a number of first parents. For it is unintelligible how such an opinion can be squared with what the sources of revealed truth and the documents of the Magisterium of the Church teach on original sin, which proceeds from sin actually committed by an individual Adam, and which, passed on to all by way of generation, is in everyone as his own.[61]

Thus the theistic evolutionist, if he allows man to have arisen from a non-human form, is obliged to inject some creative action or other upon his physical body in addition to giving him a soul, in order to make that body perfect and not subject to death. To me this is simply an additional and unnecessary complication of hypotheses to which Occam's razor[62] could well be applied.

A much more important indication of man's creation can be gained very easily from the Genesis creation account itself. Genesis 1:21 states that God created every "living creature" *(nephesh hayah)* which the waters brought forth, and verse 24 states that "God said, Let the earth bring forth the living creature" *(nephesh hayah)* "...of the earth." Then Genesis 2:7 states, "And the Lord God formed man...and man became a living soul" *(nephesh hayah)* presumably for the *first time.* So it would certainly seem from this that man was not derived from any pre-existing line of *nephesh hayah,* or living creatures.

Anthropologically, the theistic evolutionary explanation for the origin of man seems to run counter to what we have become accustomed to expect of the cultural assemblages in association with fossil man. The pre-Adamic theory would seem to imply that there were beings morphologically human but *without culture.* The evidence of human paleontology seems to argue otherwise. There is no consistent indication anywhere of fossil man without definite indications of his material culture associated with the fossil bones. In fact, as has been mentioned above, the material cultural remains of the

61. A. C. Cotter, *The Encyclical "Humani Generis" with a Commentary* (Weston: Weston College Press, 1951), p. 43.

62. *Essentia non sunt multiplicanda praeter necessitatem* (entities must not be unnecessarily multiplied).

most ancient men are far more abundant than the remains of his bones.

Of course we are at once faced with the question, What is morphologically human? I believe that the question of human or non-human cannot be answered categorically upon morphological grounds. The question must be answered on spiritual grounds, which I presume are only indicated by cultural remains.

The problem of the interpretation of the Australopithecines, the famous South African "ape-men," immediately arises. So far no definite indication of any cultural assemblage has been identified.[63] I readily accept the facts of the unique Australopithecine morphology, the marked humanoid conformation of the dentition, the ilium, and other features indicative of an upright posture. Nevertheless, until such time as the chronological problem of Australopithecine's antiquity in relation to the hominids is resolved, and some identifiable cultural assemblage is discovered, I prefer to class them as an extinct family of anthropoids. I consider Mayr's designation of Homo transvaalensis premature, and cannot yet see Robinson's inclusion of Meganthropus in the same genus as Paranthropus without more remains of the former.[64] But should such a cultural assemblage be identified for the Australopithecines, it will necessitate perhaps a drastic revision of what we are used to considering "human" but nothing more as far as the creationist position is concerned.

By way of summarizing similarities and differences between the theistic evolutionary view and the creationist view, we may itemize (a) the following points which we hold in common (adapted from Ewing) :[65]

(1) The body of data and the processes of speciation and the paleontological record are accepted without reservation.

(2) "We know of Adam and Eve only from revelation, and a belief in an original pair is not in conflict with any real scientific evidence."

(3) "All men (and hence the first man) are endowed by God with spiritual souls."

(4) The first man was constituted a human being "by the direct

---

63. There are many bone tools or weapons which appear to have been made and used by Australopithecus. These are lengths of bone of the natural conformation of a short club with the "handle" end crudely sharpened. However, there are no other indications such as hearths, stone tools, or cultural tradition usually referred to as an archaeological "assemblage."

64. E. Mayr, "Taxonomic Categories in Fossil Hominids," *Cold Spring Harbor Symposium on Quantitative Biology,* XV (1950), 109-118. J. T. Robinson, "The Genera and Species of the Australopithecinae," *American Journal of Physical Anthropology,* XII (1954), 181-200.

65. Ewing, *op. cit.*

and immediate action of God, an action that affected both soul and body."

(b) The differences lie in the question of origins which may be summarized as follows:

(1) The evolutionary origin of the major taxonomic groups, or of paleontological series between which there is only inferential evidence of connection, sometimes referred to as "quantum" or "macro-" evolution, is *accepted implicitly* by the theistic evolutionist but is rejected by the creationist.

(2) The evolutionary origin of man from some pre-human form is *allowed* by the theistic evolutionist but is rejected by the creationist.

CONCLUSION

The past century has witnessed a tremendous variety of both evolutionary and anti-evolutionary positions on the origin and development of man and the universe. The principal positions which have consistently opposed the theory of evolution have been based upon supernaturalistic presuppositions.

Today, one hundred years after the work of men like Darwin and Boucher de Perthes, we can identify three major groups in this category: first, there are creationists whom we have called hyper-traditionalists, bound to certain rigid interpretations of Scripture, who are loath to accept any new facts which seem to contradict their interpretations, since these are seen not as interpretations but as the literal teachings of Scripture itself.

Second, there are creationists, many of whom have specialized in one field of science or another, or else, as theologians, have either taken pains to keep abreast in some measure with scientific advance, or else have sought the council of those who have, who constantly allow their interpretations to be open to the acceptance of newly discovered facts, so that the reintegration of their position has been free from the contradiction of embracing one body of facts, whether from Scripture or from nature, and excluding the other. These creationists have been given different labels of varying degrees of consistency. Carnell[66] has called the position "threshold evolution"; Ramm,[67] "progressive creationism"; others, "micro-evolution" and even "theistic evolution." Since it is not strictly an evolutionary position at all, perhaps a more appropriate name would be, simply, scientific creationism.

As for the third supernaturalistic position, Roman Catholic theo-

66. E. J. Carnell, *An Introduction to Christian Apologetics* (Grand Rapids: Eerdmans, 1956).

67. B. Ramm, *The Christian View of Science and Scripture* (Grand Rapids: Eerdmans, 1954).

logians, although generally considered creationists, have with many Protestant scholars, found it necessary to accept more of evolutionary theory than the facts seem to demand. Thus, with theistic pre-suppositions postulated, their position is most accurately described as theistic evolution.

In presenting to the secular world of science an alternative to the evolutionary explanation of origins, it would seem that the best position must be one which is equally objective and non-contradictory in facing the facts of the natural world, and the facts of biblical truth. Such an alternative is best found in a position of scientific creationism.

Chapter Eleven

THEOLOGY AND EVOLUTION

By Carl F. H. Henry

Theology is the science of God; evolution, the doctrine of change. How theology and evolution intersect remains among the anxious questions of our disturbed generation. The answer involves fundamental issues determinative both for individual and cultural well-being. The fate of the West, of modern civilization itself, has a stake in the conclusion.

Can the convictions linking the West with fixed Hebrew-Christian values any longer be upheld? Or must we defer to the current theory of all-inclusive development? Is disregard for scientific claims the only avenue to renewed modern respect for revealed religion? Is confinement of science and religion to separate compartments their only hope of peaceful coexistence? Is it even possible a century after Darwin to coordinate theology and science with fresh confidence and conviction?

To adjust the respective claims of biblical theology and of modern philosophies of science by a mere semantic shift is obviously futile. Swift solutions, whether exalting change as a veritable divinity or debasing deity into a process, have slumped in stature. Fortunately, a more wholesome respect for the history of ideas undergirds today's concerns of theology and evolution. Few scholars any longer consider the issue squarely met by dignifying Evolution with a capital vowel, or by introducing god with an impersonal consonant.

The basic tension is still between the concept of a personal Creator-God and that of an impersonal chance process. To resolve that debate delineates, in truth, the very destiny of our century.

Perhaps to Darwin more than to any other man, unless it be Herbert Spencer, the modern world owes its confused understanding of evolution. Caught in the backwash of speculative debate, our generation has focused its thought easily to a blurred sense of evolution's meaning and scope. Eager to correlate the pressing cultural concerns of the age, modern scholars constantly explore the compatibility of the compound term God-evolution. They carefully minimize each suggestion of God and evolution as competitive ultimates — that is, of an unchanging Creator of the changing world *over against* a universe simply evolving from some unthinking first principle.

The classic Greek philosophers distrusted the evolutionary concept of reality as a development of simpler processes. To them deity and process clearly were alternative ultimate principles rather than interchangeable concepts. The central issue in ancient philosophy was whether reality is to be interpreted in terms of Being or Becoming. Even when the great Greek thinkers invoked both principles, they shunned the combinations and commutations of Being-Becoming characteristic of recent modern thought.

It was Darwin's researches and writings that catapulted evolution to recognition as the prevailing scientific conception of nature. Although he deferred to the existence of God in an agnostic sort of way, he nonetheless assigned the practical lordship in the world of nature to the principle of change. By allowing a possible divine origination of the primal protozoa from which all other forms assertedly took their rise, Darwin paid token respect to the inherited religious tradition of the West. To gradual change, however, he traced all the kinds of life. According to Darwin, therefore, the later and more complex forms owe their existence to chance variation and natural selection, while the first protozoa were perhaps indebted to God.

The conjunction God-evolution is found only in this fleeting moment in Darwin's theory. Yet for the past century this conjunction has supplied the major tension of intellectual life. Fresh inquiry into the relationship of Christian theology and evolution therefore is not only appropriate but is quite inevitable during the centennial of Darwin's *The Origin of Species*.

THE MODERN FAITH IN EVOLUTION

Evolution as an established scientific fact is a ruling tenet of our generation. While today's world may divide over the reality of the supernatural, East and West unhesitatingly merge in popular acknowledgment of evolution. One swift century of our scientific age sufficed to yield pre-eminence to the evolutionary description of the forces through which the complex world of life arose. While midnineteenth century evolution was admittedly but speculation, hypothesis and theory, today's concept both assumes and presumes that all life and being must somehow be integrated into this reigning principle. For over a generation the majority of schools in the Occident, including many Christian institutions, have taught evolution as fact. Some, longer than others, resisted the tide of evolutionary thought, but today the majority of classrooms no longer waver ambiguously between probability and certainty touching this issue.

Already a quarter-century ago scientific scholarship fidgeted over reservations. H. H. Newman in 1932 was among the more cautious of his contemporaries: "There is a strong undercurrent of steady increasing knowledge of the facts, and a steadily strengthening conviction that the general principle of evolution is sound."[1] But the very next year evidenced his unmistakable movement: "Scientists the world over agree that the validity of the principle has been amply demonstrated.... Let us rest assured that the truth of evolution is demonstrated."[2]

Whatever scholarship was vocal was firmly evolutionary. "We do not know of any competent naturalist who has any hesitation in accepting the general doctrine.... No one has any hesitation in regard to the fact."[3] So wrote J. Arthur Thomson just before inception of the century's second quarter. President of Oglethorpe University, Thornwell Jacobs, said: "Master minds from all the fields of discovery, astronomy, geology, biology, palaeontology, embryology, and from many others, are united in their confession of faith which is embraced in that superb generalization called 'evolution.'"[4] Smithsonian Institute proffered the following: "Regarding the general proposition [of evolutionary process] there is nearly unanimous consent."[5] Augusta Gaskell summarized the virtual concurrence of scientific thought: "It is a fact that perhaps never before in the history of human thought has there been more complete unanimity of opinion on a debated question than the unanimity of men of science concerning the general idea of evolution."[6]

In the list of ruling dogmas of the past generation, assuredly none is so firmly established as belief in evolution as an indisputable fact. J. S. Huxley's pithy statement in *Encyclopedia Britannica,* 14th edition, reads: "We are not in the least doubt as to the *fact* of evolution. Among those who have gone into the evidence, there is not a single one who is not convinced that evolution has occurred and is occurring."[7] Writing in *Scientific Monthly,* E. W. Berry

1. H. H. Newman, *Evolution Yesterday and Today* (Baltimore: Williams and Wilkins, 1932), p. 170.

2. H. H. Newman, *The Nature of the World and of Man* (New York: Garden City Publishing Co., 1933), p. 381.

3. J. Arthur Thomson, *Concerning Evolution* (New Haven: Yale University Press, 1925), p. 53.

4. Thornwell Jacobs, *The New Science and the Old Religion* (2nd ed.; Georgia: Oglethorpe University Press, 1935), p. 471.

5. Charles Greeley Abbot, *Smithsonian Scientific Series* (New York: Smithsonian Institute Series, Inc., 1934), VII, 21.

6. Augusta Gaskell, *What is Life?* (Springfield, Ill.: Charles C. Thomas, 1928), p. 213.

7. J. S. Huxley, "Evolution," *Encyclopedia Britannica,* 14th ed., Vol. VIII (1930), p. 916.

stressed that "evolution is not a theory of origins, nor an article of scientific faith, but an indisputable fact."[8] John M. Coulter, of the University of Chicago, gave the same verdict: "Such an enormous mass of evidence has by this time been accumulated that, in scientific circles, evolution is regarded no longer as a mere theory, but as an established fact."[9] The Columbia University zoologist Theodosius Dobzhansky states: "The fact remains that among the present generation no informed person entertains any doubt of the validity of the evolution theory in the sense that evolution has occurred. . . . Evolution as an historical fact is established as thoroughly as science can establish a fact witnessed by no human eye."[10] The classic brevity of W. H. Werkmeister, then at the University of Nebraska, portrays succinctly this ruling theme of science: "Evolution is a fact."[11]

In the twentieth century, therefore, evolution took its place as a cosmic law whose scientific status the academic mind scarcely disposed to question. "Evolution in some form," wrote S. J. Holmes, "has now come to be as much a part of the prevailing scientific conception of nature as the Copernican system of astronomy or Newton's laws of motion."[12] Geoffrey Parsons agreed: "It has attained, in part at least (as it relates to living things), the status of scientific law, like the law of gravitation."[13] In H. H. Newman's words, many scientists "go so far as to rank evolution as a law of nature and assign it to a rank equal to that of the law of gravitation, the Copernican theory, the atomic theory, and other great scientific generalizations."[14]

In the opinion of some scholars, evolution is now so firmly entrenched that to set it aside would threaten science itself, would, in fact, nullify the comprehension of the universe. Julian Huxley states in *Encyclopedia Britannica*: "Modern psychology recognizes that the human mind is unintelligible without an evolutionary background."[15] Speaking of zoology, Parker and Haswell assert that "evolution has to be looked upon as in many respects a guiding principle in the study

8. E. W. Berry, "Selected Articles on Evolution" (E. M. Phelps, compiler), *Scientific Monthly*, August, 1922, p. 34.

9. John M. Coulter, *Where Evolution and Religion Meet* (New York: Macmillan, 1926), p. 14.

10. Theodosius Dobzhansky, *Genetics and The Origin of Species* (New York: Columbia University Press, 1941), p. 8.

11. W. H. Werkmeister, *A Philosophy of Science* (New York: Harper, 1940), p. 502.

12. S. J. Holmes, *An Introduction to General Biology* (New York: Harcourt, Brace, 1926), p. 327.

13. Geoffrey Parsons, *The Streams of History* (New York: Scribner, 1929), p. 110.

14. H. H. Newman, *The Nature of the World and of Man*, p. 381.

15. J. S. Huxley, *loc. cit.*

of our science."[16] Sir Arthur Keith even insists that "the botanist and zoologist cannot breathe or move at his work unless you permit him to be an evolutionist."[17] W. H. Werkmeister contends that "the principle of evolution is the only principle that integrates all relevant data."[18] And Henshaw Ward goes so far as to say that the theory of evolution "is now an integral part of all general education and culture. To suppose that it may some day be abandoned is to live in intellectual barbarism."[19]

Whoever in the mid-twentieth century aligns himself against the evolutionary principle faces contradiction, therefore, by virtually all modern science and philosophy. Whatever doubts at times may plague the modern mind, it treasures the evolutionary concept above all others. Twentieth-century scholarship chafes most irritably under any questioning of evolution. Especially this rationale is a credential of creative scientific competence. Doubt over its factuality seems to reflect on the very integrity of science. And when religion dares to voice its unbelief, it does so today at the cost of a marked loss of intellectual respect.

INDECISION OVER THE MECHANICS OF EVOLUTION

Nonetheless, a significant number of scientists readily acknowledge spheres of doubt in relation to the evolutionary concept. To dogmatic assertions of the fact of evolution they append at the same time the widest disagreement over the cause, the method, and even the extent of evolution. Louis T. More speaks to the troublesome question of causes, for example: "In contrast to the unity of opinion on the law of evolution is the wide diversity of opinion on the causes of evolution. In fact, the causes of the evolution of life are as mysterious as the law of evolution is certain."[20] Durant Drake states: "What is in doubt among scientists is not the fact of evolution . . . but the causes and method of evolution."[21] J. S. Huxley stresses that "we need not deny the fact because we have not discovered the machinery."[22] In the areas of uncertainty, scientific studies have given priority to questions of evolutionary method rather than to the more intricate questions of causation. Science has concentrated

16. T. J. Parker and W. A. Haswell, *A Textbook of Zoology* (4th ed.; London: Macmillan, 1928), p. 630.

17. Sir Arthur Keith, *Concerning Man's Origin* (New York: Putnam, 1928), p. v.

18. Werkmeister, *op. cit.*, p. 502.

19. Henshaw Ward, *Evolution for John* (London: Arrowsmith, 1926), p. 12.

20. Louis T. More, *The Dogma of Evolution* (Princeton: Princeton University Press, 1925), p. 26.

21. Durant Drake, *Invitation to Philosophy* (New York: Houghton Mifflin, 1933), p. 294.

22. J. S. Huxley, *loc. cit.*

to unravel the order of change in nature, thereby hoping subsequently to isolate the factors occasioning that change. Arthur W. Lindsey voices the high optimism of science that the fact of evolution being assured, the techniques would soon be laid bare: "The fact of evolution is so well established that we may expect confidently to solve the riddles of evolutionary method in the future."[23] Controversy there may be, but Lindsey hastens to mark its limits: "The controversy deals with details of evolutionary processes."[24] In a recent issue of *Science*, Dobzhansky writes that "the occurrence of the evolution of life in the history of the earth is established about as well as events not witnessed by human observers can be.... The most pressing problems of evolutionary biology seem at present to belong to two groups — those concerned with the mechanics of evolution and those dealing with the biological uniqueness of man."[25]

The speculative possibility of detaching evolution as a fact from the vitally related questions of method, extent and cause is an important issue. The disjunction of fact and method is, in fact, an extremely vulnerable element in the modern delineation of evolution. Can divorce of fact from method be granted without thereby sacrificing all need of empirical verification? Would not evolution thus dangle from purely speculative considerations? Does virtual scientific unanimity in and of itself remove the necessity for supportive empirical considerations? Some writers seem to imply this. Richard S. Lull writes: "All scientists and most other thinking men are now convinced of the truth of evolution.... For our purpose, then, the fact of evolution is taken *ab initio*, without argument...."[26] Professor Lull even states that no doctrine "is conceivable" that reconciles so well with the phenomena of the present and with the records of the past as this doctrine of continuity and of gradual change.[27] Despite such proclamations, scientists nonetheless today remain at variance over gradual or sudden change as the methodology of evolution.

Whatever one's subjective inclinations, an objective approach should detect the circular logic of the familiar argument: No one acquainted with the facts doubts that evolution has occurred; therefore, evolution is a fact. While the empirical facts themselves, in terms of scientific evidence, are difficult to organize (or, although the major and minor premises are still in process of construction),

---

23. Arthur W. Lindsey, *Textbook of Evolution and Genetics* (New York: Macmillan, 1929), p. 443.

24. Arthur W. Lindsey, *The Science of Animal Life* (New York: Harcourt, Brace, 1937), p. 482.

25. Theodosius Dobzhansky, "Evolution at Work," *Science*, CXXVII (1958), 1092.

26. Richard S. Lull, *Organic Evolution* (New York: Macmillan, 1938), p. 83.

27. Richard S. Lull, *The Ways of Life* (New York: Harper, 1925), p. 338.

we need not on that account doubt the conclusion of the fact of evolution itself. This kind of presentation is not uncommon in the texts of the day. Only an occasional lonely voice laments the capitulation of our educational enterprise to the dogmatic promulgation of evolution. Only infrequently does one find a cautious appraisal: "Today the fact of evolution is commonly accepted, and hardly ever discussed, although this position seems to be somewhat rash and premature. The main discussions are on the modes and factors of evolution."[28] Despite doubt and disagreement over the particulars supportive of evolution, modern thought nevertheless pronounces certainty over the generalization.

Presumably Darwin's confidence in evolution as a fact stemmed from his conviction that a particular methodology accounted best for relationships of change in nature. Through meticulous observation that presumably yielded specific evidence for natural selection, he endeavored to lift evolutionary speculation to the status of scientific generalization. Thus he claimed to vindicate the emergence of all living forms by minute variation through natural law. Apart from the validity of this causal explanation in terms of natural selection, would not logic have driven Darwin to the acknowledgment of the theory's collapse? The breakdown of Darwin's formula, namely that *through slow change* all higher forms come from lower, might have cast doubt on the broader premise that all higher forms come from lower. But a progress-minded generation, without any longer disputing the fact of evolution, confined its questions to the method of evolution. Some scientists remained content that Darwin's idea of small changes as a mechanism for evolution was not superseded in all respects. For others, the sole preoccupation and passion became the finding of an alternative methodology to unqualified slow change. A possibly transposed formula of *lower* forms springing from *higher* forms, either supernaturally by way of creation or naturally by way of retrogression, seemed to the modern mind obviously unworthy of consideration. For the searching, churning scientific mind, abandonment of Darwin's methodology presented no threat to the general theory of evolution itself. To account for the complex world of nature and of life, concentration simply turned from the method of repetitive evolution to the doctrine of the sudden emergence of new and higher forms, without seriously raising the question of the supernatural. Understandably enough, therefore, today's debate in evolutionary circles revolves around alternative claims of the repetitive and emergent theories. To borrow Will Durant's words, "Among the present generation no informed person entertains any doubt of

28. Charles A. Dubray, *Introduction to Philosophy* (New York: Longmans, Green, 1923), p. 123.

the validity of the evolution theory in the sense that evolution has occurred, and yet nobody is audacious enough to believe himself in the possession of the knowledge of the actual mechanics of evolution."[29]

DEFINITION OF THE EVOLUTIONARY FACT

Closer definition of this well-nigh universally admitted *fact* of evolution is therefore of singularly imperative importance, if that factuality is to be preserved in the face of undermining disagreement and doubt attaching to its cause and method and if its consequent significance and serviceability are to survive.

Does merely the presence of change in nature constitute the assumed fact of evolution? Obviously not, for in all ages influential philosophers have depicted the space-time world as a realm of change, and not every theory of change is evolutionary. By the fact of evolution so-called are we to understand simply that there is development in nature through such factors as natural selection, inherited characteristics and mutation, and that over a period of time some new and often more complex forms of life have appeared? This interpretation would fully satisfy evangelical Christians who insist upon divinely graded *kinds* of being, but do not invoke special creation to account for all the multiform *species*. If evolutionists had derived all life forms from supernaturally fixed classes, orders and families consistently with the biblical emphasis that "there is one flesh of men, and another flesh of beasts, and another flesh of birds, and another of fishes" (I Cor. 15:40), each reproducing "after its kind" (Gen. 1:21,24ff., etc.), Christianity could have found an immediate basis for friendly discussion with evolutionary science. As interpreted today, however, "the fact of evolution" obviously implies something more.

What then is intended by the term?

The history of philosophy defines evolution as an immanent process whereby the whole universe of being and life has evolved through the self-differentiation of lower into higher forms. The ancient Greek philosophers of change favored this meaning; from the principle of "becoming" they sought to derive the whole of reality. Fixed in the long history of ideas, this interpretation of evolution is incompatible with supernaturalistic theism, since it derives men and all things from lower forms of being. To the philosophers of antiquity the term designated the supposed derivation of all existence from simpler elements through temporal factors only.

29. Will Durant, *The Mansions of Philosophy* (New York: Simon & Schuster, 1929), p. 70.

This comprehensive understanding of the word continued into early modern expositions of evolutionary theory. Did not Diderot's *Pensées sur l'interpretation de la nature* (1754) assert: "Even if Revelation teaches us that species left the hands of the Creator as they are now, the philosopher who gives himself up to conjecture comes to the conclusion that life has always had its elements scattered in the mass of inorganic matter; that it finally came about that these elements united; that the embryo formed of this union has passed through an infinitude of organization and development; that it has acquired in succession, movement, sensation, ideas, thought, reflection, conscience, emotions, signs, gestures, articulation, language, laws, and finally the sciences and arts; that millions of years have elapsed during each of these phases of development, and that there are still new developments to be taken which are as yet unknown to us"?[30] Conformably to this naturalistic understanding of the term, Ernst Haeckel's *The Riddle of the Universe* turned the evolutionary thesis against supernatural religion in sixteen languages, and became one of the major influences for atheism in twentieth century Europe.[31]

Indeed, some of the most influential thinkers of the day still understand "the fact of evolution" in this unrestricted sense. The Communist philosophy of dialectical materialism propounds this broad definition. Many scholars in the non-Communist world, as well, insist upon assigning the whole of things to ultimate process or "becoming," in specific opposition to a superior supernatural principle. All humanists and naturalists in the Western world thus delineate evolution — not only on the Continent but also in the Anglo-Saxon world — continually etching their communication of "the evolutionary fact" upon the younger generation. John Dewey was such an exponent, whose philosophy has been — and even continues to be — the most controlling in American education.

G. G. Simpson affirms that wholehearted acceptance of evolution is inconsistent with belief in the activity of God in the universe.[32] He proclaims it "already evident that all the objective phenomena of the history of life can be explained by purely materialistic factors."[33] Oscar Riddle is intolerant of "the cults of supernaturalism" as imposing a "leash on thought." He therefore hails the Soviet restraint

30. Cited by H. F. Osborn, *From the Greeks to Darwin* (New York: Macmillan, 1894), p. 116.

31. Ernst Haeckel, *The Riddle of the Universe*, transl. J. McCabe (London: Watts, 1929).

32. G. G. Simpson, *The Meaning of Evolution* (New Haven: Yale University Press, 1949), p. 230.

33. *Ibid.* (4th ed., 1950), p. 343.

on religion[34] in the same spirit as Freud, Dewey and Reichenbach.[35] "To this writer, it seems entirely probable that past and present attitudes of Soviet Russia toward Western nations are far more antagonistic and dangerous than would have been the case if other nations had dethroned the personal God before Russia did."[36] "Never again can a majority of the best-informed minds of any advanced culture give support or countenance to a belief in the supernatural."[37] Riddle designates "fundamentalism and supernaturalism" alike as "more formidable and more durable enemies of science and society than Nazism and Communism."[38] "The age of firm belief in the supernatural was the prescientific age. Practically all of the scientific age is still ahead of us, and there is insufficient reason to assume that belief in the supernatural can long survive that age."[39] "Always incomplete, science has now advanced far enough," Riddle would assure us, "to make any imaginable view of the supernatural unacceptable to a high proportion of the best-informed minds."[40] Over against supernaturalism in any form, Riddle pleads for "unmitigated evolution," for development not rendered "flat and innocuous" through the introduction of ideas of divinity. Dobzhansky asserts that "evolution is not striving to achieve some foreordained goal; it is not the unfolding of predetermined episodes and situations. . . . Man was not programmed in biological evolution. In one sense, man . . . and all other forms of life are evolutionary accidents. If slightly different environmental opportunities had been offered . . . quite different creatures might have arisen as a result of evolutionary transformations."[41] Infected by this all-inclusive understanding of evolution but unready to banish altogether the idea of divinity, other scholars join Samuel Alexander in placing alongside the premise that space-time is the source of all things, the notion that even God is a creature of ever-changing content.

Whatever their attitude toward biblical theism, many readers will hardly complete the previous paragraph before protesting: but evolution need not be understood as anti-supernaturalistic! Did not even Darwin's *The Origin of Species* come to this sensational ending: "There is grandeur in this view of life, with its several powers, having been originally breathed by the Creator into a few forms or

34. Oscar Riddle, *The Unleashing of Evolutionary Thought* (New York: Vantage Press, 1954), p. xvi.

35. *Ibid.*, p. xxi.

36. *Ibid.*, p. 310.

37. *Ibid.*, p. 401.

38. *Ibid.*, p. 396.

39. *Ibid.*, p. 406.

40. *Ibid.*, p. 388.

41. Dobzhansky, "Evolution at Work," *loc. cit.*

into one; and that, while this planet has gone cycling on according to the fixed law of gravity, from so simple a beginning endless forms most beautiful and most wonderful have been, and are being evolved."[42] And, before Darwin, did not Hegel (who was not a biological evolutionist) and the idealistic philosophers in general join supernaturalism and evolution? Stated another way: the admission of evolutionary process does not imply the ultimacy of that process, nor that the whole of reality is a free-floating chaos.

The blurred structure of the widely acknowledged "fact of evolution" is evidenced by the sharp division among modern thinkers over whether evolution is an ultimate or limited explanatory principle. Without a primary interest in this issue, discussion of evolutionary theory deteriorates from a testing of central defenses to a mere intellectual foray on the outposts of contemporary thought. Any discussion of theology and evolution first of all must always bring into clear focus the question of competitive ultimates. A Christian view of man and the universe must always oppose any system of thought, ancient or modern, that deserts God in its devotion to process. In discussing the "fact of evolution," Christian theology is impelled to delineate as well the monstrous consequence of unqualified change. Is the asserted "fact of evolution" the speculative underside of the assumed "fact of not-God"? If not, then what are its actual limits?

Even tolerance of God as a kind of "honorary First Cause" of evolutionary process grapples inadequately with this crucial theological question. By demoting God to merely First Cause, Darwin cancelled the principle of a personal divine government and providence in nature, and deferred completely to the mechanical principle of natural selection. In his *New York Herald Tribune* (April 3, 1955) review of *Apes, Angels and Victorians* by William Irvine, Joseph Wood Krutch remarks that Darwin's theory "was anti-religious, not merely in the sectarian sense, but absolutely and completely. It banished not only God but whatever might be called Godlike in man himself. . . . Perhaps the religionists were nearer right than the evolutionists in their estimate of what the consequences would be of accepting this documentation as final." Darwin snubbed the historical revelation of the Hebrew-Christian religion, with its declaration of man's role in the universe, and appealed instead to speculations contingent on the fossil remains of nature. His suppositions strangled the religion of a once-for-all divine incarnation: "Judging from the past, we may safely infer that not one living species will transmit its

42. Charles Darwin, *The Origin of Species by Means of Natural Selection,* with additions and corrections from the 6th and last English edition, two vols. in one (New York: Appleton, 1905), II, 305f.

unaltered likeness to a distant futurity."[43] For, if Darwin were right, an incarnation of the Logos on the assumption of the permanence of human nature would be ludicrous.

Does the "fact of evolution" mean, as influential evolutionists on both sides of the Atlantic suggest, that all existence (including matter, life, consciousness and reason) has one primitive unendowed source? If so, the question of evidences is crucial. When speaking of evolution, do or do not the scientists intend a demonstrable fact? Gamertsfelder and Evans inform us that "no scientific generalization is more strongly supported by thoroughly tested evidences than is that of organic evolution."[44] Canon Raven, in his Gifford Lectures, declares that "evolution as a demonstrable and omnipresent characteristic of life on the earth stands secure."[45] S. A. McDowall states emphatically: "Of the fact of evolution there is no possible shadow of doubt,"[46] thus implying that the evidence is incontrovertible. Robert A. Millikan affirmed: "We have found evidence of progression, evidence of a continuous movement from the lower up to the higher forms."[47] Edwin G. Conklin asserts that "year by year it [evolution] has received increasing confirmation, so that now it is almost universally accepted by scientists and is opposed only by those who reject the methods and results of science."[48] J. E. Boodin writes: "The existence of law in the evolution of life is no longer a matter of opinion but of observation."[49] To quote H. E. Crampton: "Evolution is a science, and it meets all the criteria of sure knowledge.... It is really an interpretation of the past in terms of actual experience at the present time and experience is verifiable fact."[50] Thomas Barbour, in the *Atlantic Monthly,* March, 1943, writing on "Tests of Evolution," says: "No one who thinks and has had a real chance to study modern palaeontological material doubts the fact of evolution. Science has been the evidence where evolution has run riot."

Alongside these affirmations, however, other quotations may be adduced which, instead of supporting the case for evolution by an appeal to observed or experienced events, emphasize evolution as an "inferred event," i.e., an interpretive explanation of a given phenom-

43. *Ibid.,* p. 304.

44. W. S. Gamertsfelder and D. L. Evans, *Fundamentals of Philosophy* (New York: Phentice-Hall, 1930), p. 235.

45. Charles E. Raven, *Natural Religion and Christian Theology* (Cambridge: University Press, 1953), II, 130.

46. S. A. McDowall, *Biology and Mankind* (New York: Macmillan, 1931), p. 5.

47. Robert A. Millikan, *Evolution in Science and Religion* (New Haven: Yale University Press, 1929), p. 81.

48. Edwin G. Conklin, *Man Real and Ideal* (New York: Scribner, 1943), p. 147.

49. J. E. Boodin, *Cosmic Evolution* (New York: Macmillan, 1925), p. 24.

50. H. E. Crampton, *The Coming and Evolution of Life* (New York: The University Society, Inc., 1931), p. 18.

enon or set of phenomena. Sometimes the improbability of extensive confirmation by direct observation is conceded. Thomas H. Morgan appeals to circumstantial evidence and probability, rather than to direct observation: "This theory of descent has so much circumstantial evidence in its favor, and its probability is so great, that I do not believe it would be profitable to go over again what is contained in hundreds of available books...."[51] J. Arthur Thomson writes: "Biologists remain in thick mist as regards most of the 'big lifts' in organic evolution. The formulae of 'mutation,' 'heredity,' 'selection,' 'isolation,' and the like can, no doubt, be applied, but they do not as yet scatter the clouds.... Lloyd Morgan has done good service in frankly admitting that we cannot at present analyse these 'creative syntheses' or 'emergences.' "[52] Thomson again writes: "Evolution itself is accepted by zoologists, not because it has been observed to occur or is supported by logically coherent arguments, but because it does fit all the facts of taxonomy, of palaeontology, and of geographic distribution...."[53] Schuchert and Dunbar say: "Although the comparative study of living animals and plants may give very convincing circumstantial evidence, fossils provide the only historical, documentary evidence that life has evolved from simpler to more and more complex forms."[54] (This way of affirming evolution gains importance in view of many recent scientific studies, in which the claim that paleontology demonstrates that all forms of life are fluid is softened if not suppressed.)

For the great mass of people, acceptance of evolution is not a personal judgment rising from evidence, any more than scientific beliefs generally are; rather, popular acceptance represents a deference to scientific authorities. This is acknowledged by James H. McGregor: "Practically all enlightened people have come to accept the idea of man's origin by descent from lower animals, even though they may be quite ignorant of the evidence for it or the stages in the slow progression from simple beginnings to mankind's present estate."[55]

Today there is increasing awareness of the major role of scientific interpretation, and the minor role of direct observation, in constructing the case for evolution. Scholarly writers less frequently

51. Thomas H. Morgan, *The Scientific Basis of Evolution* (New York: Norton, 1935), p. 15.

52. J. Arthur Thomson, "A Biologist's Philosophy," in *Contemporary British Philosophy*, Second Series, ed. J. H. Muirhead (2nd ed., New York: Macmillan, 1953), p. 332.

53. J. Arthur Thomson, *Biology for Everyman* (New York: Dutton, 1935), II, 1003.

54. Charles Schuchert and C. O. Dunbar, *Outlines of Historical Geology* (3rd ed., New York: Wiley, 1937), p. 18.

55. In *General Anthropology*, F. Boas, ed. (New York: Heath, 1938), p. 21.

construe evolution as a scientific explanation wholly free of speculative elements; they are less disposed to repudiate a creation doctrine
as speculative, and instead to urge the view of primal evolution as
unadulterated science. G. Mead, for example, quite naively declared:
"Our biology, until evolution set it free, was bound up in meta-
physics. It could explain species only in terms of creation. But an
evolution which explains the development of form is free from such
a metaphysical statement."[56] Far nearer the actualities is Conklin's
candid recognition of the postulational and metaphysical factor in
evolutionary explanation: "The concept of organic evolution is very
highly prized by biologists, for many of whom it is an object of
genuinely religious devotion, because they regard it as a supreme
integrative principle. This is probably the reason why severe meth-
odological criticism employed in other departments of biology has
not yet been brought to bear against evolutionary speculation."[57]
The governing influence of the world view with which the interpreter
already approaches the data is recognized more and more as a significant factor in scientific theory.

This brief survey of scientific opinion confirms our contention
that "the evolutionary fact," while conceded virtually everywhere
today, means a variety of things to those who concede it. A most
vexing task for the remaining half of the twentieth century will be a
critical analysis of this "phantom fact" so uniformly accepted during
the first half.

That all space-time phenomena — life, consciousness, human reflection and conscience — are emergents of living from non-living
entities by immanent causes, each stage comprising but a more
complex organization of previous forces and forms, has been strenuously urged for a century. Naturalistic evolutionists were not alone
in making this exorbitant claim. Both deistic evolutionists who
classified God as mere First Cause of a process that continues differentiation under its own momentum and pantheistic evolutionists
who pictured all life as a development of a single cell through
immanent (non-miraculous) activity supported this concept. Admittedly the naturalists in their denial of an original Divine Reason
manifested the widest departure of all from the inherited religious
tradition. But in their practical consequences, the deistic and pantheistic views also were far removed from the Christian view; they no
longer enforced the uniqueness of human reason and morality on the
basis of the created image of God, but referred both rather to a
development from bestial origins. Either God was regarded simply

56. George H. Mead, *Movements of Thought in the 19th Century* (Chicago:
University of Chicago Press, 1936), p. 451.
57. Conklin, *loc. cit.*

as the causative antecedent of the first shadows of the universe, or the world was viewed solely as the evolving product of immanent Divine Intelligence, which transcended the law of continuity, if at all, only at the original creation. The latter could be summarized by the lines from William Herbert Caruth's poem "Each in His Own Tongue": "Some call it Evolution, and others call it God." By the second quarter of the twentieth century adherents were content simply to call it evolution.

Critics of such unmitigated evolution called continually for facts to support this comprehensive claim. Failure by exponents to produce such conclusive, convincing scientific evidence, their increasing recourse instead to speculative considerations, progressively weakened the assertion of total evolution. Again and again, therefore, all attempts to unravel the mystery of beginnings have impelled a return to the acknowledgment of the origin of matter, the origin of life, the origin of graded orders or kinds of life, the origin of man, as enigmatic gaps in the scientific search for continuities.

DEBATE OVER THE FIXITY OF SPECIES

The religio-scientific conflict over orders of life flared into violence mainly because both sides propounded excessive assertions. Darwin's conclusion that "species are not immutable" need not have disturbed the careful reader of Genesis, which affirms only the fixity of major "kinds" of life. As already noted, his controlling assumption, of course, shattered the permanence of all forms of life. On the other hand, champions of biblical theology overstepped the requisites of Genesis by interpreting the revealed "fact of creation" to mean that all species of life in the modern biological sense were created originally as they now appear. This presupposes an absolutely constant relationship between all the historical species of life, and hence also a direct continuity between modern and primitive forms. Evangelical theology, interestingly enough, had emphasized striking variations within the unity of the human species; human nature ranged from unfallen Adam through fallen man, from the newly or immaturely or even carnally regenerate believer to the perfect God-man. Nonetheless, discussion of life settled into a unilateral view of the biblical declaration of reproduction; "after its *kind*" became confined to species only. Not Moses, however, but the English biologist John Ray (1628-1705) spoke first of species originating simultaneously at the beginning of a divine act of creation. Karl Linnaeus (1707-1778) defined plant and animal species as forms which God established by creation, thereby supporting the idea of a definite creative act for each species: "There are as many species as the Infinite Being created as diverse forms from the beginning ... just as there are now no more species than there have been from the beginning."[58] Subsequent research prompted him to speak of the constancy of genera rather than of species. But it must not be thought that even in Darwin's time a century ago religious thinkers were at odds with scientific circles in affirming the constancy of species. That is far from the fact. Historically, the fixity of species was no article of Christian doctrine. The early theorizing of modern scientists, often men of Christian piety, presumed to find in observational science a basis for the doctrine of the constancy of species, and this was then supported — by scientists and theologians alike — by appeal to the authority of the biblical creation narrative. R. E. D. Clark decisively scores this point, that the dogma of the fixity of species passed into Christian circles because of an indebtedness to early modern scientific speculations.[59]

Awareness grew, however, that this conception of species understates the dynamic potential of certain created forms of life. Three developments, particularly, challenged this doctrine of the fixity of species, with which fundamentalist Christianity unfortunately identified itself. First, fossils of great extinct monsters disputed a one-to-one continuity of the created and existing forms of life. Further, the modern "multiplication of species" introduced an even more disquieting complication; classifications of living forms tended increasingly to catalogue varieties (especially in botany) as species. Moreover, by artificial mutation and the development of hybrids, research could even produce new forms. But the scientific data most disconcerting was the evidence of morphology and paleontology; this indicated a developmental link between certain species not hitherto related in terms of descent, e.g., between *eohippus* and the modern horse.

True, scientists often used hasty generalizations to explain the appearance of such new species; they appealed exclusively either to natural selection, to genetics, to mutation or to various combinations of these factors, so that to this day only elemental suggestions of the mechanism of origin and development have been attained.[60] Nevertheless, the extreme theory of absolute fixity of species which funda-

58. Karl Linnaeus, *Genera Plantarum*, 1737.

59. Cf. his survey of the mediaeval doctrine of origins in *Darwin: Before and After* (Grand Rapids: Grand Rapids International Publications, rev. ed., 1958), p. 34. In mediaeval times the doctrine of spontaneous generation was held even alongside the philosophical emphasis on the constancy of universals.

60. The problem of chronology and ancestral stages of many living species is confused today; anatomists' attempts to pyramid species in an "order of complexity" on the assumption that the simpler forms are earlier types are vulnerable. The difficulty is threefold: that of devising definitive criteria of complexity; the fact that paleontology has reversed some of the postulated sequences; and the acknowledgment of the "reversibility of evolution," or, that acquired characteristics may be lost and the direction of evolution reversed.

mentalism espoused has been driven into retreat. The Genesis narrative, however, does not teach that all species of life were specially created; neither does it exclude the antiquity of the earth, nor the appearance of intermediary forms of life by secondary means. To identify biblical creationism exclusively with a six-day week wherein all the known species of life were divinely created without any interdependence overstates the facts. By the criteria of the essential identity of individuals and of the ability of opposite sexes to produce fertile offspring, living things can be classified into almost a million different species. Such an interpretation of the "kinds" of life obviously cannot be retained in understanding the Noahic account of the ark which sheltered the diverse forms of life from flood waters.[61] The biblical account, significantly, emphasizes creation on the basis not of similarities but of major dissimilarities. At the same time, the widespread confusion in scientific circles today over the definition of species — a debate in which advocates of a descriptive-systematic, phylogenetic, and genetic approach are ranged in disagreement — is so extensive that Jan Lever, professor of zoology at Free University, Amsterdam, senses a threat to unity not only in systematic biological thinking, but in the conception of the essence of living structures.[62]

Modern thought is virtually agreed that the "kinds" are broader than species. But are they broader than genera? If so, how much broader? Does "kind" designate "order," and does it embrace men, apes, monkeys and lemurs in one such grouping? Does "kind" refer to "class," including in one category primates, carnivores, insectivores, rodents? Is it coextensive with "kingdom," including all animals?

If fundamentalists erroneously asserted the absolute fixity of species, evolutionists, on the other hand, by claiming that all living forms come from one primal form of life, assailably asserted the fluidity of all forms or kinds of life. E. S. Goodrich of Oxford, in *Encyclopedia Britannica* (14th ed.), reflected the scientific drift toward monophyletic evolution in this fashion: "It is now universally held by competent biologists that all organisms living or extinct have arisen from remote common ancestors by a process of gradual change or evolution."[63] J. Arthur Thomson remarked in *Biology for Everyman*: "Whatever we think about living creatures, we must include in our thought the fact that all have evolved from very

---

61. Russell L. Mixter contends that if a hybrid can be produced by crossing species, the species themselves may have arisen by differentiation of an earlier unitary form. Such crossing obviously is confined to compatible groups; reptiles and birds, for example, cannot be crossed.

62. Jan Lever, *Creation and Evolution* (Grand Rapids: Grand Rapids International Publications, 1958), pp. 125ff.

63. VIII, 917.

simple forms of life. Flowering plants evolved from flowerless plants, and backboned animals from backboneless animals, and many-celled creatures from one-celled creatures."[64] The myth of monophyletic origin rallied an almost religious devotion from many scientists. Their appeal to anatomical similarities as indubitable evidence of the common physical descent of earthly forms implied that special divine activity was tenable only if God created types of life each wholly dissimilar in structure from every other.

In 1800, even before Darwin, Lamarck asserted on the basis of finds near Paris that living creatures had developed successively and interdependently. Cuvier blunted the force of Lamarck's evolutionary views, however, by explaining fossil remains in terms of successive catastrophes in nature, especially that of the flood. Both men agreed, nevertheless, in questioning the recency of the earth and the then prevailing doctrine of the contemporaneous creation of species.

The Bridgewater Treatises of 1829 represented attempts to allay the growing sense of conflict between the Hebrew-Christian revelation and the new views. In his Gifford Lectures, Canon Raven called the claim that new species arise by accumulating minute and successful variation an assumption that Darwin "could not prove and which in fact has not yet been conclusively demonstrated."[65] The strain on evolutionary theory was first apparent by its uncertain fluctuation between speculations intended to account for changes in form. The choice between heredity and environment to explain major changes; growing acknowledgment of missing necessary links in the geological record; rejection by Dobzhansky of the gene-mutation doctrine to account for sudden new species, are representative uncertainties. While Weismann's theory of sexual selection has little contemporary support, natural selection to improve and to yield new species today enjoys greater support of zoologists than of botanists and biologists. The latter tend to regard the notion as a contributory cause of novelty rather than as an adequate explanation of species.

Notwithstanding, evolutionists for several generations appealed confidently to paleontology in support of their thesis. These very data, however, caused the theory its greatest embarrassment. Oswald Spengler stated the matter plainly enough: "There is no more conclusive refutation of Darwinism than that furnished by palaeontology. Simple probability indicates that fossil hoards can only be test samples. Each sample, then, would represent a different stage of evolution, and there ought to be merely 'transitional' types, no definition and no species. Instead of this we find perfectly stable and unaltered forms persevering through long ages, forms that have not

64. Thomson, *Biology for Everyman* (1934 ed.), p. 7.
65. Raven, *op. cit.*, I, 179.

developed themselves on the fitness principle, but *appear suddenly and at once in their definitive shape;* that do not thereafter evolve towards better adaptation, but become rarer and finally disappear, while quite different forms crop up again. What unfolds itself, in ever-increasing richness of form, is the great classes and kinds of living beings which *exist aboriginally and exist still, without transition types,* in the grouping of today."[66]

Acknowledgment that major groupings of life existed from the beginning as fixed patterns has come from others as well. Austin H. Clark referred to the "entire lack of any intermediates between the major groups of animals — as for instance between the backboned animals or vertebrates, the echinoderms, the mollusks and the arthropods," using these blunt words: "If we are willing to accept the facts, we must believe that there never were such intermediates, or, in other words, that these major groups have from the very first borne the same relation to each other that they have today."[67] G. G. Simpson conceded that each of the thirty-two known orders of mammals appears suddenly in the paleontological record: "The earliest and most primitive known members of every order already have the basic ordinal characters, and in no case is an approximately continuous sequence from one order to another known."[68] He indicates that missing links, or rather, "deficiencies of record," exist between the zoological orders — between marsupials (opossums), insectivores (moles), rodents (rats), carnivores (cats), and so on. Some fossil discoveries since suggested as median forms appear to have narrowed but not to have eliminated these gaps; actually, modern scientific philosophy tends to discount the likelihood of finding transition forms. In fact, the absence of transitional forms between orders, classes and phyla is conceded equally among vertebrates, invertebrates and plants. The twenty-two orders of the class Insecta, for example, derive from a common ancestor, and this class, together with five parallel classes, forms the phylum Arthropoda. No transition form is known between Arthropoda and other phyla. Some botanists acknowledge unbridgeable gaps in plant life itself, and reject the idea that all plants (not to mention animals) derive from one form.

According to present datings, the animal fossil record goes back 550 million years (to the Cambrian period).[69] All major phyla

66. Oswald Spengler, *The Decline of the West* (New York: Knopf, 1932), II, 32.

67. Austin H. Clark, *The New Evolution* (Baltimore: Williams and Wilkins, 1930), p. 189.

68. G. G. Simpson, *Tempo and Mode in Evolution* (New York: Columbia University Press, 1944), p. 106.

69. No animal remnants are dated earlier. The existence of fossil algae in pre-Cambrian layers militates against the notion that earlier animal fossil remains were destroyed because of intervening changes in rock formations.

existed at the outset of the Cambrian period, or came into existence rather abruptly: one-celled animals, sponges, sea-nettles, segmented worms, the jointed limbed Arthropoda, shellfish, and the arm-footed Brachiopoda. No paleontological data for their interrelationship are known. Fossils of vertebrates are found only after the Cambrian period; no fossil ancestors have been discovered. Those who argue for evolutionary descent of these forms, do so despite the lack of paleontological evidence, appealing to anatomical and embryological considerations which have often led interpreters to postulate rival theories. The Dutch zoologist Jan Lever has asserted candidly: "Nothing is known about the origin of the chief groups of organisms, the phyla. . . . For various . . . subgroups the same thing holds true as for the phyla."[70] The German zoologist O. Kuhn likewise remarks: "We can indeed speak of a descent within the types, but not about a descent of the types."[71] For 400 million years no new phyla of animals have appeared, nor has any major type become extinct.

Scientists have classified all life into ten to twenty phyla. While some (non-major types) are extinct, no transitional forms have been found between these ten to fifteen major types, despite the fact that within the phyla transitional forms are numerous. (Variations are great, with a general progression from simple to complex.) This persistence of constant forms in the long paleontological record inflicts death to Darwin's theory that all species arise by slow, gradual, almost imperceptible modification of simpler forms. Likewise, the swiftly reproducing species known to modern science invest no support to the theory. Under favorable conditions, for example, bacteria will produce a new generation in approximately twenty minutes. This could mean 20,000 generations in a single year. Science has confirming evidence, furthermore, from the diseased conditions of fossils, that some of these bacteria have continued to reproduce without any perceptible change since the time of the ancient Egyptians.

Richard B. Goldschmidt reminds us that "nobody thus far has produced a new species or genus, etc., by macro-mutation. It is equally true that nobody has produced even a species by the selection of micro-mutations. In the best known organisms, like Drosophila, innumerable mutants are known. If we were able to combine a thousand or more of such mutants in a single individual, this still would have no resemblance whatsoever to any type known as a species in nature."[72] In view of such statements, recent expositions that ask

70. Lever, *op. cit.*, p. 80.

71. Cited by Lever, *ibid.*, p. 84.

72. Richard B. Goldschmidt, "Evolution as Viewed by One Scientist," *American Scientist*, XL (1952), 94.

Christian apologetics to defend only the special creation of the broad *orders* of life, including the human form, would seem premature and needlessly concessive. Evangelical theologians today concur with Russell L. Mixter's statement that "the ancestors of the orders were created," but many are not ready to concede without further evidence the broad statement that "the families, genera and species within the orders are the result of descent with variation."[73] The question here does not concern what is *de fide,* since the Genesis narrative does not explicitly define the primal "kinds"; it is, rather, a matter of the scientific necessity for this concession.

Disclosure of the highly organized scheme of creature-life in the beginning of the fossil record spurred science to a new deduction cognizant both of the sudden actualization of diverse kinds and of their relative constancy throughout the fossil record. A divine origination of graded forms of life now once again became a relevant option. Those who abhorred any recourse to theological considerations clung to the development theory, however, and turned to a doctrine of emergence as the speculative alternative to creationism.[74] This transition from the Lyell-Darwin doctrine of unlimited continuity to that of emergent evolution was cushioned to avoid the appearance of an obvious return to the "catastrophism" of Cuvier's day, reflecting an unmistakable bias against supernaturalism, especially against miracle. C. Lloyd Morgan's Gifford Lectures, *Emergent Evolution* (1923) and *Life, Mind, and Spirit* (1925) stated the emergent theory in terms of pantheistic divine immanence; Samuel Alexander's Gifford Lectures, *Space, Time, and Deity* (1920), in terms of naturalism.

Both Morgan and Alexander, therefore, share in the revolt against fiat creation and miraculous divine origin. Similarly, Burnham and Wheelwright assert the irrelevance of biblical theism: "Today comparatively few educated people accept literally the account [of origin] in Genesis. This change is not due wholly to the strength of the factual evidence against Genesis, but in some measure to a weakening of general belief in Divine Revelation. . . . Science does not admit this belief. . . ."[75] J. Arthur Thomson reflects the same mood. Giving a variety of arguments for evolution, he assures his readers that "evolution . . . is accepted . . . because no alternative explanation

---

73. Mixter, "Creation or Evolution," in *The Witness* (1949), a periodical.

74. A new era of semantic confusion is dawning through the current tendency, even of non-supernaturalists, to speak of the creative aspect of biological evolution when all they intend is the formation of novel and harmonious genetic features that enable the carriers to survive in certain environments; while the vocabulary of creation is substituted for that of emergence, supernaturalism and purposive development are excluded.

75. James Burnham and P. E. Wheelwright, *Introduction to Philosophical Analysis* (New York: Holt, 1932), p. 287.

is credible."[76] In this exposure, the problem of the sudden appearance of fixed forms inevitably led to a theory of non-miraculous emergence. R. Goldschmidt pleads the cause of macro-evolution (evolution by big jumps) this way: "There is no such category as incipient species. Species and the higher categories originate in single macro-evolutionary steps as completely new genetic systems."[77]

The theory, however, that dramatic new forms arise by chance is more incredible, and leaves the future distressingly more unpredictable, than explanation through the act of a superior intelligence. In seeking a natural basis to understand the sudden appearance of a new fossil species, Ernst Mayr explained it as a geographical rather than an evolutionary event, since instantaneous speciation is an "exceptional process." But recent evolutionary thought's frustration in the debate over the origination of the forms of life actually gives a new relevance to the theological doctrine of the origin of graded levels of being by divine creation. Supposition of *abrupt emergence* falls outside the field of scientific analysis just as fully as the appeal to supernatural creative forces. Scientific emphasis on an orderly universe challenges the speculation that man and the world evolved by pure chance. A. C. Garnett, professor of philosophy in the University of Wisconsin, rejects the thesis of the evolution of life from the non-living, and postulates that life has always existed.[78] Lecomte du Noüy in *Human Destiny* offers the laws of mathematical probability as strong arguments against an accidental origin for man, and for the single-jump emergence of the universe and life.[79]

LIFE AND INANIMATE MATTER

The subject of the origin of life has held a speculative fascination for great minds in many ages. Ranging from the ancient assertion of spontaneous generation to the more recent view of sudden emergence, secular attempts to penetrate this mystery reflect a curious evolution of opinion. Aristotle (384-233 B.C.) supported the theory of spontaneous generation; Roman and Neo-Platonic thinkers likewise accepted it. The Brussels physician Van Helmont (1577-1644), known for very critical experimentation in plant nutrition, as recently as the seventeenth century gave a formula for creating mice from grain. The formula: a dirty shirt, a pile of grain, and an interval of

76. Thomson, *Biology for Everyman*, II, 1003.
77. Richard B. Goldschmidt, *The Material Basis of Evolution* (New Haven: Yale University Press, 1940), p. 397.
78. A. C. Garnett, "Scientific Method and the Concept of Emergence," *Journal of Philosophy*, XXXIX (1942).
79. Pierre Lecomte du Noüy, *Human Destiny* (New York, London: Longmans, Green, 1947).

twenty-one days for the combined vapors to generate mice. The Tuscan physician Redi (1626-1697) disproved spontaneous generation of worms in meat by showing them to be fly maggots. His experiments, however, were limited to organisms visible to the naked eye. By their conclusive proof that bacteria come from other bacteria, the famous experiments of Louis Pasteur in 1862 finally removed all doubt about micro-organisms.

To achieve generation of living from non-living would be an even greater marvel than the development of simple into complex forms of life. The expectation that science in fact will eliminate this gulf between the inanimate and the animate worlds has spurred today's belief in the unlimited transformation of species. Infusion of life into the non-living world would add to the hope of bridging these realms on a naturalistic basis, yet it would not actually eliminate the staggering gulf between subrational and submoral beings on the one hand, and rational and moral beings on the other, nor would it scientifically validate the assumption that the one emerged from the other. The biblical view ascribes to special acts of divine intelligence and will the existence of both non-living and living forms, as well as of animal and human levels of life. To derive the living from the non-living by a purely natural operation would therefore cast a question over the whole.

Recently, scientists have produced new strains of micro-organisms by mutation. This they achieved by using X-rays to alter suddenly the environment of the organism, by exposing it to radioactive rays, and by changing its nutrient. For the most part, these mutants are weaker than the original strain, and less capable of reproducing.

About the development of life in micro-organisms, George A. Baitsell tells us that "even at the present time the scientist has nothing definite to offer as to when or where or how protoplasm and the associated living phenomena originated, and comparatively little as to the basic features of the complex chemistry of metabolism essential to life."[80] He says, further, that "they [virus] reproduce, they adapt themselves to certain variations in different types of living cells, exhibit 'heritable' permanent changes or mutations, and are destroyed by certain conditions fatal to living cells." But, he finally asks, "can it be established that the virus protein molecule is the ultimate and indivisible unit of life?"

H. Fraenkel-Conrat and Robert C. Williams have succeeded both in separating the tobacco mosaic virus into its protein and nucleic acid components and in reconstituting the virus. This reconstituted virus exhibited the same infective properties as the original intact

80. George A. Baitsell, "The Cell as a Structural Unit," American Scientist, XLIII (1955), 133.

virus.[81] If the virus is considered the unit of life, such reconstitution of a virus could mean that life was restored in a test tube, but hardly that it was "created."

Since all living organisms contain protein, and since proteins are composed of amino acids, some scholars have postulated that under a reducing atmosphere of primitive earth conditions, amino acids and certain other organic compounds could be produced.[82] Stanly L. Miller has recently demonstrated such synthesis.[83] In his research on the origin of life, Melvin Calvin has devised ways to synthesize nucleic acids. Thus, synthesis in the test tube of both proteins and nucleic acids seems possible. Does this mean that life can be created in the test tube? In his address on "Chemical Evolution and the Origin of Life,"[84] he remarks: "This is not to say that I believe or am convinced that an answer can be found within the scope of science — a complete answer — it may not be." Yet, to explain the origin of life, he reckons especially on the time factor, even as scientific theory on the origin of species once appealed to this as the decisive consideration, but in vain. Calvin writes: "We have plenty of time to do this [to explain life within the scope of modern science] — 2½ billion years. Although every one of the processes that I have described is probable — there is no great improbable event that I have required — the selection amongst the random probable events of a particular sequence is a highly improbable thing and has required the billion years or so that it took to do it." No comment is necessary, perhaps, other than the obvious one that, in a professedly scientific account of origins, no amount of time and speculative probability ever compensates for lack of evidence and verification.

Erwin Schrödinger points to the great influence of the chromosome upon man's development.[85] That one unique isolated chromosome can yield the orderly establishment of an individual possessing a combination of 10^{14} chromosomes must occasion wonder and awe at the miracle of the initial group of atoms. Schrödinger continues: "It needs no poetical imagination but only clear and sober scientific reflection to recognize that we are here obviously faced with events

81. H. Fraenkel-Conrat and Robert C. Williams, *Proceedings of National Academy of Sciences*, XLI (1955), 690-698.

82. Cf. A. I. Oparin, *The Origin of Life* (New York: Dover, 1953); J. D. Bernal, *The Physical Basis of Life* (London: Rutledge, 1951); H. C. Urey, *Proceedings National Academy of Sciences*, XXXVIII (1952), 351, and *The Planets* (New Haven: Yale University Press, 1952). See also Chapter 3 of this book.

83. Cf. *Science*, CXVII (1953), 528ff., and *Journal of the American Chemical Society*, LXXVII (1955), 2351-2361.

84. *American Scientist*, XLIV (1956), 248-273.

85. Erwin Schrödinger, *What is Life?* (Cambridge: Cambridge University Press, 1945).

whose regular and lawful unfolding is guided by a 'mechanism' entirely different from the 'probability mechanism' of physics. For it is simply a fact of observation that the guiding principle in every cell is embodied in a single atomic association existing only in one (or sometimes two) copy — and a fact of observation that it results in producing events which are a paragon of orderliness. Whether we find it astonishing or whether we find it quite plausible, that a small but highly organized group of atoms be capable of acting in this manner, the situation is unprecedented, it is unknown anywhere else except in living matter."[86]

Since science is based on experimentation and observation, its truth is always on trial, always subject to revision, and never fully assured. Where both experimentation and observation are impossible, the scientist makes an intelligent guess, or hypothesis. Such hypothesis may become a "law" if it can endure all the critical tests. Nevertheless, failure in even one relevant test discredits the hypothesis. Under certain circumstances, however, it is extremely inconvenient or virtually impossible to test an hypothesis. In such cases it is called a working hypothesis, since it can be used as a crutch. If deductions rest upon working hypotheses, however, the risks of speculation are increased extensively. Especially in the discussion of the origin of life, the unknown suspends like an impenetrable darkness over the field of modern scientific knowledge. Men of science have found nothing to erase the relevance of the Genesis account with respect to the origin of life. If anything, the biblical account offers our scientific age a noteworthy alternative to its speculations of a swift or slow spontaneous generation.

Inescapable barriers confront any attempt to prove the thesis of spontaneous origination of living from non-living, that is, from inanimate, forms. Since present-day science obviously cannot observe past origins, the possibility of direct scientific proof or disproof does not exist. Nonetheless, laboratory demonstration bearing on the problem of the origin of life cannot be wholly discounted simply because it provides no direct verification of primitive origins. Such demonstration will at least deflate if not destroy dogmatic assertions of impossibility. While the further step need not follow logically, laboratory findings might perhaps even engender, in the thinking of present opponents, acknowledgment of the possibility that life originated from the non-living by this mechanics, so that the dogmatic affirmation of creationism would need to be conformed to this development. An important consideration should be noted here. Even if the twentieth century scientist succeeds in evolving life from the non-living, he must concede that his own experiments were

86. *Ibid.*, pp. 79ff.

controlled by an intelligence superior to the elements under control. This acknowledgment should confront him with the Hebrew-Christian insistence that the original combination of finite life and matter issued from the operation of an infinite Mind and Will. Because a finite mind like that of the scientist can correlate the inanimate and animate worlds does not disprove the fact that an infinite mind was active in superimposing life on matter. Indeed, the one development may even strengthen the other. To answer instead that the finite mind is bringing together what originally came together by chance is to assume what needs to be proved. At any rate, today's experimental knowledge about the origin of life grants science no support for the thesis of radical transformism, whether in linking the broad orders of life or in explaining the origin of particular kinds of being.

THE HUMAN SPECIES

If alongside the "fact of evolution" the present scientific inability to deduce life from inanimate matter must be admitted, as also its inability to trace a convincing number and sequence of transitional forms for the major kinds of life, the situation with particular regard to the origin of man likewise perpetuates the relevance of the Hebrew-Christian view of origins. Today science more frankly acknowledges the constancy of the human form, a concept to which Spengler already had called attention: "As for mankind, discoveries of the Diluvial age indicate more and more pointedly that the man-forms existing then correspond to those living now; there is not the slightest trace of evolution towards a race of greater utilitarian 'fitness.' And the continued failure to find man in the Tertiary discoveries indicates more and more clearly that the human life-form, like every other, originates in a sudden mutation (Wandlung) of which the 'whence,' 'how,' and 'why' remain an impenetrable secret."[87]

Alongside this recognition, however, scientific belief in the evolution of man remains prevalent. William F. Quillian, Jr., doubtless overstates the case, but his emphasis on the pro-evolutionary bias in contemporary thought is pertinent: "Among competent scholars there is no longer any serious questioning of the evolutionary development of man."[88] While the existence of various humanlike forms from the Pleistocene epoch is undoubted, the fact that no undisputed anthropoid fossils occur in the prior Pliocene epoch contributes a period of 10 to 15 million years of enigmatic silence about a human animal ancestry. Moreover, Jan Lever, who in principle is not opposed to

---

87. Oswald Spengler, op. cit., II, 32.
88. William F. Quillian, Jr., "Evolution and Moral Theory in America," Evolutionary Thought in America, Stow Persons, ed. (New Haven: Yale University Press, 1950), p. 416.

the derivation of all forms of life (including man) through the mechanism of evolution as a supernaturally directed process, reminds us nonetheless that "the opinion expressed at times, that it has been *proved* that man descended from anthropoids, lacks a scientific basis."[89] While man shows a strong anatomical and physiological resemblance to the anthropoids, we must take into account, as F. Weidenreich admonishes, not only "the congruities between the organization of man and the great apes, but their most characteristic differences."[90] Furthermore, Lever notes that "investigators are becoming more and more convinced that upon the basis of the remnants of skeletons of these old forms it is not possible to decide whether a being is man or animal."[91] In other words, the criterion of humanity is not simply anatomical but functional and cultural. This fact lifts into new relevance the emphasis of the Genesis narrative on the *imago Dei* as the distinguishing human characteristic.

THE HARMONY OF SCIENCE AND RELIGION

As already noted, needless tension between science and faith through excessive claims on both sides has marked the attempt to unravel the mystery of origins. One group paraded speculation under the cloak of science, the other under the cloak of revelation. In view of the stalemate to which scientific endeavor has come, the time is propitious for re-examination of the Hebrew-Christian view of nature and man.

The dispute over the limits of evolution is being pressed today not only by theologians but also by scientists, who are more aware than a generation ago of the wide role of inference and theoretical choice in their conclusions. In this second half of the twentieth century many scientists, due to the limitations of scientific method, understand more clearly that the results are nevertheless not beyond amending. Not a theologian but a research specialist, Professor William E. Ritter of the University of California, detected already a generation ago "signs that the whole battleground of evolution will have to be fought over again; this time not so much between scientists and theologians, as among scientists themselves."[92] Today his prophecy is finding at least a partial fulfillment; the debate extends beyond the causo-mechanics of evolution.

Bernhard Bavink emphasizes the futility of ecclesiastical opposition to genuine scientific concerns: "We may safely describe the fight

---

89. Lever, *op. cit.*, p. 157.

90. Franz Weidenreich, *Apes, Giants and Man* (4th ed., Chicago: University of Chicago Press, 1948), p. 5.

91. Lever, *op. cit.*, p. 158.

92. William E. Ritter, in *Science*, April 14, 1922.

against the doctrine of evolution as the greatest of all follies of which the church has been guilty in the course of its history; even the struggle against the Copernican system had no such disastrous results, since only small circles of the learned really participated in it."[93] But to secure Christian enthusiasm for the evolutionary claim, must not scientists first provide a formulation of scientific agreements and disagreements, and a clear recognition of the role of evidence and verification in establishing such agreements? No less than Robert A. Millikan insisted that science must assume its share of the blame for the controversy with religion, "for science is just as often misrepresented as is religion by men of little vision, of no appreciation of its limitations, and of imperfect comprehension of the real role it plays in human life— by men who lose sight of all spiritual values and therefore exert an influence which is unsettling, irreligious, and sometimes unmoral."[94] The Christian ideal makes scientific research not a purely speculative probing of reality but a vehicle of learning subordinated to higher spiritual and moral ends. This involves no minimizing of research, but rather a horror of its secularization and paganization. The Christian ideal hopes for a concentration on nature that leads not away from but toward nature's God.

Most scholarly circles today dismiss anyone venturing to question the "fact of evolution" as unacademic. Whoever dares to challenge "the fact" is marked for the reproach of "fundamentalist" or "obscurantist." For some of this reaction, fundamentalism is alone to blame: its apologetics has met the "problem of science," unfortunately, with a coupling of invective, or of ridicule, and a "stop-gap" exegesis. Distinguished scientists, consequently, shrug off religious carping which rails at hypotheses irrespective of their tentative laboratory success as the negative prating of small-minded men. Science has also chafed often under the zeal of popular apologists. Without pretense of being scientific, they confidently explore any experimental pronouncement offering an orthodox alliance with the Christian faith, even exploiting such data for evangelistic purposes. Most devastating of all is hasty "popularization" of the newest scientific evaluations by those who neither define nor support either science or theology, but who emotionalize them for newspaper and magazine feature sections.

The doctrine of special creation withstood all doubts until Darwin's popularization of the evolutionary idea. This evolutionary speculation challenged not only the dignity of man on the basis of

93. Bernhard Bavink, Science and God (New York: Reynal & Hitchcock, 1934), p. 169.
94. Robert A. Millikan, "Science and Religion," in Bulletin, California Institute of Technology, March, 1922, pp. 5ff.

creation; it challenged also the fact of his fall and sinfulness. For both these conceptions, evolutionary philosophy substituted the dogma of human progress and perfectibility. Hence it eliminated the doctrine of man's need for supernatural redemption. The intellectual movement of the past century portrays a loss of faith in the Apostles' Creed simultaneous with a rise of faith in the evolutionary creed. The new importance of change whetted the destructive assault on Holy Scripture as a divinely given revelation, and on Jesus Christ as an absolute divine incarnation.

Today, acknowledgment comes more readily that "the evolutionary fact," whereby biblical realities were openly challenged and scorned, lacked proper scientific basis for doubting the cardinal doctrines of Christian faith. The evolutionary faith misled the sophisticated twentieth century into advocating some of the crudest class, race, and nationalist myths of all times, e.g., the Nazi notion of the *Herrenvolk* or master-race; the Marxist hatred for the bourgeoisie; and tyrannical subordination of the worth of the individual to the state.

The collapse of this century's dogma of inevitable progress struck the first major blow at the theory of unmitigated development. While Genesis had withstood any myth that space-time processes inherently imply moral and social progress, the twentieth century championed, virtually as solidly as the doctrine of evolution itself, the notion that mental and moral forces automatically propel the natural world to a high destiny. This notion of moral and cultural evolution is in discard today. World history ironically identifies the greatest human progress in moral and spiritual achievement with those eras of Christian history when the evolutionary thesis was not determinative. Triumph of the evolutionary philosophy actually engendered one of the most staggering moral declensions in the history of the world. Deterioration reached its widest extremes with the speculative dogma that man is an animal only, and with the application of the ancient Greek doctrine of change to all fields of study, religion included. The readiness of theologians to join philosophers in mediating theories of theistic evolution preserved a kind of speculative truce between the interests of theology and science.

This effort failed, however, to answer many of the deeper questions that still attach to the evolutionary debate. Since Darwin's day the emphasis has rested on the similarities between man and the animals, turning the resultant difficulties against the Christian view A new day may now be in prospect when emphasis will center on dissimilarities, calling speculative evolution, in turn, to sober account. At any rate, the strange infatuation with the term "evolution" is at long last being questioned. An age which holds a tongue-in-cheek reception for magic and myth could do well to free itself from magical and mythical overtones in all areas. A generation confused by generalities and clichés — "evolution," "the evolution of matter," "the evolution of life," "the evolution of man," "the evolution of history," "the evolution of theology," "the evolution of immortality," indeed, the evolution of anything and everything — faces now a candid sobering confession about "the evolution of evolution." While man is lost in his theories and hurtling toward the twenty-first century, God is still on his throne.

Scientists today are increasingly less dogmatic, and increasingly unsure not only about the method of evolution, but about the sense in which the term evolution itself is to be understood. The "fact of evolution," however, is still strenuously maintained. The contemporary scientist may admit that Darwin's hypothesis was too simple, may confess that we are still far removed from an adequate interpretation of the data of nature, but he is still inclined to defend evolution as a scientifically-established fact, and to insist on agreement at this point before he will discuss the case for theism. Thus the fact of evolution is presupposed, while theism is reduced to a theory.

But generalities gain precision only in the light of specifics. That the meaning of evolution is more debated in this generation than in the last can scarcely be questioned. Some scholars proclaim that "evolution is an indisputable fact" and that "evolution is demonstrable," but behind this curtain of words the only universally accepted meaning is an undefined transition from unorganized simplicity to organized complexity. If by the evolutionary fact is meant that the universe is billions of years old, and that millions of years were required for the development of all the various species of plant and animal life, and that the antiquity of the human race is somewhat greater than the brief span of six thousand years assigned by scientists and theologians alike a few centuries ago, then warfare between science and Christianity is at an end. Theologians today reflect a fresh determination to let the biblical account of origins speak for itself, rather than to standardize some prevailing interpretation of the Genesis narrative.

For most Western scholars — though assuredly not for all — evolution requires no disbelief in the supernatural. For increasing numbers of scientists, evolution is consistent with a belief in primal creation. For many it does not imply the transformation of all kinds of life. For others, evolution requires no surrender of confidence in a unique creation of man's soul, nor for some, of his body also. Whoever refutes these beliefs does so not by an appeal to contrary evidence but rather because of unbelief in the biblical revelation of a supernatural Creator of man and the universe, and because of rejection of the witness of conscience, nature, and history to the reality of God.

In fact, the victory of the new theory of sudden emergence over the older theory of gradual transformation unwittingly involves evolution in defending itself apart from demonstrable causes.

What Christian thinkers unfortunately have failed to do is to elaborate a schematic philosophy of science based on revealed theism, from which standpoint forceful questions can be levelled at the competitive secular philosophy of science. In the raising of ultimate questions, no contempt of science, no prejudice against its achievements and methodology, need be implied. In fact, all who are identified with the deepest burdens of science must keep such issues in the forefront. The established dogmas have always been called in question. The real issue concerns conclusive evidence; on this, in the mid-twentieth century, a literate Christian population and a disciplined scientific temper should not find agreement impossible. What is needed today is charity and restraint in the face of earnest inquiry and discussion. The evolutionary concept dominates the thought of our century. Unless its application to nature and life, to man and his destiny, and to morality and religion, is matched by a challenging alternative, in which the reality of God and his claim is convincingly related to the whole of experience, the task of devout scientific effort is only partly done. A world convinced only of what it must not believe is still threatened by the penalties of minoring in major issues and majoring in minor.

The great truths of the revealed narrative of creation retain their pointed relevance to the scientific discussions of our decade. It may not be amiss to quote, in this connection, something recently noted in another symposium, "That a sovereign, personal, ethical God is the voluntary creator of the space-time universe; that God created *ex nihilo* by divine fiat; that the stages of creation reflect an orderly rational sequence; that there are divinely graded levels of life; that man is distinguished from the animals by a superior origin and dignity; that the human race is a unity in Adam; that man was divinely assigned the vocation of conforming the created world to the service of the will of God; that the whole creation is a providential and teleological order: the whole front of theology finds these irreducible truths of revelation in the Genesis creation account. That the word of creation is no mere instrumental word, but rather a personal Word, the Logos, who is the divine agent in creation; that this Logos permanently assumed human nature in Jesus Christ; that the God of creation and of revelation and of redemption and of sanctification and of judgment is one and the same God: these staggering truths evangelical theology unanimously supports on the basis of the larger New Testament disclosure."[95]

95. Carl F. H. Henry, "Science and Religion," in *Contemporary Evangelical Thought"* (Great Neck, N. Y.: Channel Press, 1957), pp. 258ff.

The various contributors to this present volume are engaged in the task of showing the compatibility of these convictions with the best knowledge that contemporary science affords; hence, their major role is that of removing objections to Christian belief, or at least of exposing the fact that such objections rest really upon spiritual unbelief rather than upon solid rational supports. In an elementary way the contributors also indicate rays of light by which these great affirmations illuminate the obscure dilemmas confronting scientists at the contemporary crossroads of decision. They do not — except here and there — carry the argument on to indicate that scientific decision — even in the physics laboratory or astronomy observatory — always involves a decision for or against the Logos. It was the scientists' failure to understand the universe in relation to personal categories, to ethico-rational will, that betrayed the scientific enterprise into the charting of reality only in terms of weight, measurement, and mathematical relations. And the rejection of the Logos in nature, history, and conscience is but the first step to the rejection of the Logos come in the flesh, Jesus Christ.

This volume, therefore, looks to a sequel, in which the reality of divine revelation in the cosmos and in Scripture is coordinated, and in which Jesus Christ, and not evolutionary process, is seen as the only adequate index to cosmic activity and purpose. If the vast range of modern scientific interests, so conspicuously departmentalized and even fragmented today, is once again to be integrated, it will be through the recovery of the Logos as the key to creation, revelation, redemption, sanctification, and judgment — in other words, as the center of reference for science, philosophy, religion, ethics, and history. If the men of science who are men of faith can carry forward the commendable venture represented by this volume, to elaborate an evangelical philosophy of science, they shall have come to the world for an hour like this. This is the age of power. The world needs to be reassured that the power that awes the astronomer and that intrigues the physicist is the power disclosed in Jesus Christ as the power of righteousness and love.

SHORT INDEX OF PRINCIPAL SUBJECTS

Adaptation, 126ff., 162; *see also* Natural selection
Anthropology, 165-189

Cambrian Period, 144, 208, 209
Catastrophism, 16, 30, 147, 207, 210
Cells, 25, 62, 63, 65, 73, 74, 76f., 80, 82, 96, 98, 100, 101
Common ancestry, 14, 18, 119, 147f., 158, 163
Creation, Christian doctrine of; creationism; *see* Evolution and the Christian faith.

Darwin, Charles Robert, 11-32, 53, 54, 55, 56, 71, 89, 93f., 96, 107, 110, 114, 119, 123ff., 126, 134, 143, 148, 150, 154, 158, 165, 190, 191, 196, 200, 201, 204, 209
Distribution of animals, 123-135; mammals, 127, 130ff.

Earth, 35ff., 45ff., 64ff.
Ecology, 19f.
Embryology, 15, 16, 156f.
Evolution and the Christian faith, 16, 17, 18, 20-22, 27, 29-32, 34f., 47-52, 67-70, 89-91, 103, 107, 109f., 114, 121-122, 129, 132, 133-135, 141, 146-150, 151-153, 157, 160-164, 168, 179-189, 190-221
Evolution, definition of, 20-32, 121f., 128f., 142, 155, 180, 185ff., 190, 197-204

Finches, Darwin's, 126-129
Fossils, 16ff., 121, 130, 131, 136-153, 173ff., 180, 181, 185, 186, 200, 202, 205, 207, 208, 209, 210, 211, 215
Fruit fly, 26, 73, 84f., 87, 88, 93, 209

Galapagos Islands, 126ff.
Genetics (chromosomes, genes, mutations), 24, 25, 26, 27, 59, 60, 70-91, 93, 94, 96, 98, 100, 101, 102, 133, 180, 183, 185, 205, 212, 213

Homologies, 12, 154ff.
Hybridization, 92-106, 111, 112, 118
Lamarckism, 14, 22ff., 72
Life, origin of, 14, 53-70, 141, 203, 211-215; chemical analysis of, 58ff.
Man, origin of, 215f.; prehistoric, 17, 165-189, 215f.
Morphology, 110f., 155f., 173, 177, 181, 186, 205
Natural selection, 12, 14, 19, 23, 25, 26, 27, 57, 66, 71, 78, 79, 81, 89, 93, 94, 114, 119, 124, 128, 132, 158, 162, 180, 183, 191, 196, 200, 205, 207
Origin of Species, The, 11, 14, 15, 24, 53, 54, 71, 107, 124, 126, 134, 143, 154, 158, 167, 191, 199
Paleontology 16ff., 25, 136-153, 173, 180, 181, 182, 183, 185, 186, 187, 201 202, 205, 207, 209
Physiology, 11-15, 157ff.
Sexual selection, 23f., 26
Similarities, 154-164
Species, definition of, 94f., 109ff., 126, fixity of, 94ff., 109f., 129, 132ff., 141ff., 152, 204-211; origin of, 17, 18, 23-28, 71ff., 107-122, 127ff., 144ff., 180, 181, 182, 184, 187, 204-211
Spontaneous generation, 14, 16, 53ff., 141, 211, 214
Taxonomy, 18, 92f., 107-122, 141, 143ff., 156, 157, 177-170, 180, 181, 182
Universe, origin and nature of, 33-52
Variation in animals, non-genetic, 113-118; *see also* Genetics
Variation of Animals and Plants Under Domestication, The, 94, 114
Vestigial organs, 12, 13, 14, 23, 156
Viruses, 63f., 212f.
Vitalism, 12, 14, 15, 55f.
Zoogeography, 123-135

THE CONTRIBUTORS

V. ELVING ANDERSON received the B.A., M.S., and Ph.D. degrees from the University of Minnesota. He is chairman of the Department of Biology at Bethel College, St. Paul, and Assistant Director of the Dight Institute for Human Genetics at the University of Minnesota.

CORDELIA ERDMAN BARBER received the B. S. degree from Wheaton College and the M.A. degree from Columbia University. She taught geology at Wheaton from 1949 to 1954 and was a Park Ranger Naturalist at Grand Canyon, Arizona, in the summers of 1951, 1952, and 1953. After marriage she moved to California with her husband, who is also a geologist.

WILBUR L. BULLOCK received the B.S. degree from Queens College and the M.S. and Ph.D. degrees from the University of Illinois. He is Associate Professor of Zoology at the University of New Hampshire. He has done research in parasitology at the University of New Hampshire and Rice Institute as well as at several biological stations. He is the author of numerous technical papers.

JAMES O. BUSWELL III received the B.A. degree from Wheaton College and the M.A. degree from the University of Pennsylvania. From 1948 to 1954 he taught anthropology at Shelton College. He is now Assistant Professor of Anthropology at Wheaton.

J. FRANK CASSEL received the B.S. degree from Wheaton College, the M.S. degree from Cornell University, and the Ph.D. degree from the University of Colorado. He is Chairman of the Department of Zoology at North Dakota Agricultural College.

WALTER R. HEARN received the B.A. degree from Rice Institute and the Ph.D. degree from the University of Illinois. Thereafter he served on the biochemistry faculties of Yale University School of Medicine and Baylor University College of Medicine. He is now Assistant Professor of Chemistry at Iowa State University at Ames.

RICHARD A. HENDRY received the B.A. degree from the University of California at Santa Barbara, the M.A. degree from the College of the Pacific, and the Ph.D. degree from Baylor University College of Medicine. Subsequently he did research at the University of Illinois and at Iowa State College. He is now Associate Professor of Chemistry at Westminster College, New Wilmington, Pennsylvania.

CARL F. H. HENRY received the B.A. and M.A. degrees from Wheaton College, the B.D. and Th.D. degrees from Northern Baptist Theological Seminary, and the Ph.D. degree from Boston University. He also studied at the University of Edinburgh. He is the author of several books, among which are: *Remaking the Modern Mind, Fifty Years of Protestant Theology, The Drift of Western Thought, Evangelical Responsibility in Contemporary Theology,* and *Christian Personal Ethics.* Having been Professor of Systematic Theology and Christian Philosophy at Fuller Theological Seminary for a number of years, he left that post to become Editor of *Christianity Today.*

THOMAS D. S. KEY received the B.A. and M.A. degrees from Southern Methodist University, and has been doing further graduate work at Indiana University. He has taught biology in high schools in Indiana and Texas and at Bob Jones University. He is now teaching biology at the high school in Hartford City, Indiana.

IRVING W. KNOBLOCH received the B.A. and M.A. degrees from the University of Buffalo and the Ph.D. degree from Iowa State College. The author of a number of technical publications, he is now Professor of Natural Science at Michigan State University.

DONALD S. ROBERTSON received the B.A. degree from Stanford University, and the Ph.D. degree from the California Institute of Technology. Formerly Chairman of the Science Department at Biola Bible College, he is now Assistant Professor of Genetics at Iowa State University at Ames.

GEORGE K. SCHWEITZER received the B.A. degree from Central College in Missouri, the M.S. and Ph.D. degrees from the University of Illinois, and the M.A. degree in Religion jointly from Columbia University and Union Theological Seminary. He is the author of over fifty papers dealing with the utilization of radioactive materials in various scientific applications and is the co-author of a textbook, *Radioactive Tracer Techniques.* He holds the positions of Associate Professor of Chemistry at the University of Tennessee in Knoxville, Research Radiochemist with the University of Tennessee-Atomic Energy Commission Agricultural Research Program at Oak Ridge, and Radiological Warfare Consultant with Tennessee Civil Defense.

JOHN C. SINCLAIR received the B.A. degree from the University of California at Berkeley, and the M.A. degree from the University of California at Los Angeles. Following biochemical research at White Memorial Hospital and photomicrography at Moody Institute of Science, he became pre-doctoral research fellow in the Department of Anatomy at the Medical Center of the University of California at Los Angeles.

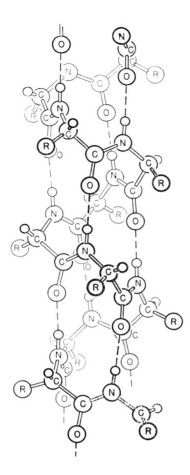

Figure 1: Drawing of a short segment of a helical arrangement of a protein chain. In this model, the atoms are represented by balls, the co-valent bonds by sticks, and the hydrogen bonds by dotted lines. Each amino acid contributes two carbon atoms and one nitrogen atom to the polypeptide chain, leaving its individual side chain group sticking out (in a real protein, all the "R" groups would not be identical). The sequence of the R groups and the coiling of the chain determine the biological properties of the molecule. The enzymes, catalysts necessary for life processes, are huge protein molecules of this type. Reproduced by permission from *The Configuration of Polypeptide Chains in Proteins* by Robert B. Corey and Linus Pauling (Milan: Lombard Institute of Science and Letters, 1955).

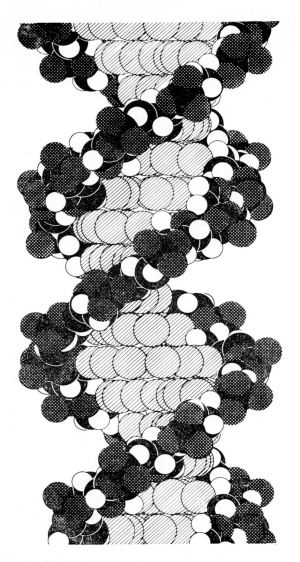

Figure 2: Model of DNA. Atoms are represented as spheres accurately scaled to size in this type of model. The two desoxyribosephosphate chains are wound in a double helix with the space between them filled up by pairs of complementary bases in shelflike layers. The entire molecule would be hundreds or thousands of times as long as the short segment shown here. The order of stacking of the base pairs is believed to be the "code" carrying genetic information in the chromosomes. Reproduced by permission of R. Langridge, H. R. Wilson, M. H. F. Wilkins, and L. D. Hamilton, *Journal of Biophysical and Biochemical Cytology*, III (1957), 767; *Scope,* V (1957), 1.

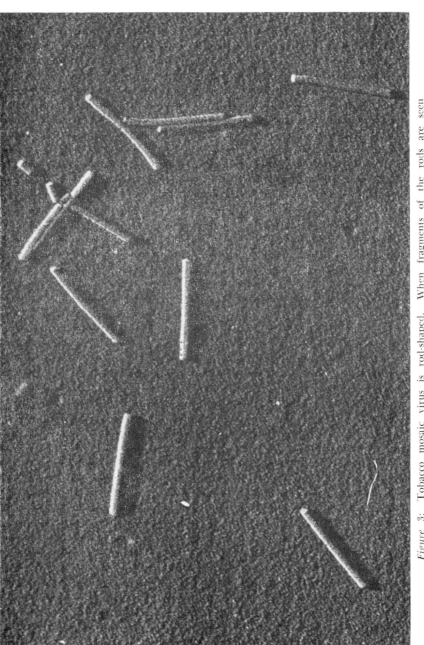

Figure 3: Tobacco mosaic virus is rod-shaped. When fragments of the rods are seen end-on, they are hexagonal. This electron micrograph, which enlarges the virus particles some 93,000 diameters, was made by Robley C. Williams of the University of California. Reproduced by permission of Dr. Williams.

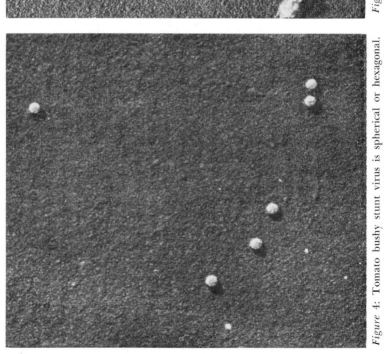

Figure 5: Bacterial virus of the T-4 strain has a tail. This micrograph by Robley C. Williams and Dean Fraser enlarges the particles 65,000 times. Reproduced by permission of Dr. Williams.

Figure 4: Tomato bushy stunt virus is spherical or hexagonal. This micrograph by Robley C. Williams enlarges the particles some 85,000 diameters. Reproduced by permission of Dr. Williams.

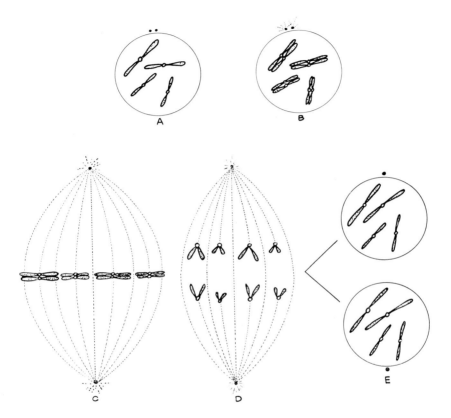

Figure 6: A diagrammatic representation of the behavior of
the chromosomes during simple cell division (mitosis). (A)
Cell showing two pairs of chromosomes. (B) Each chromosome duplicates itself. (C-E) The duplicated chromosomes
separate from each other into daughter cells, producing two
cells with the identical chromosomal constitution as the original cell (A).

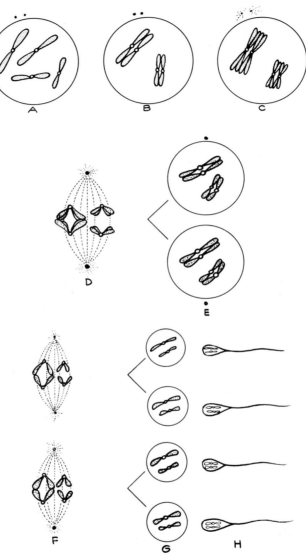

Figure 7: A diagrammatic representation of the behavior of the chromosomes during the two divisions of meiosis in the formation of germ cells of a male animal. (A) Cell showing two pairs of chromosomes. (B) Like chromosomes pair. (C) Each chromosome splits. (D-E) Split chromosomes separate from each other into two cells (end of first meiotic division). (F-G) Each of the cells produced by the first division undergoes a second division in which half chromosomes separate into different cells, producing the four products of meiosis, each of which has half the number of chromosomes as the original cell (end of second meiotic division). (H) Each of the four products develops into a sperm cell.

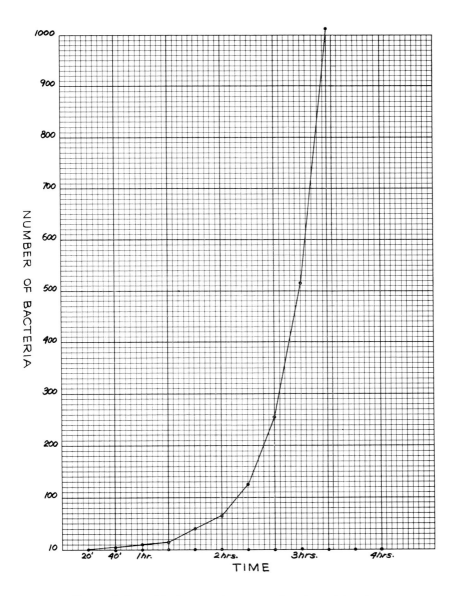

Figure 8: Logarithmic growth curve of a bacterial culture dividing every twenty minutes. In three hours and twenty minutes one bacterium has multiplied to over one thousand.

Figure 9: A fertile mule and one of her offspring, Department of Animal Husbandry, A. and M. College of Texas. See *Journal of Heredity,* XIX:9 (Sept. 1928).

Figure 10: A fertile genus hybrid. The parents were *Triticum monococcum* and *Aegilops uniaristata*. The diploid F_1 is sterile but the amphidiploid (4n) is fertile. Reproduced by permission of *Journal of Heredity*.

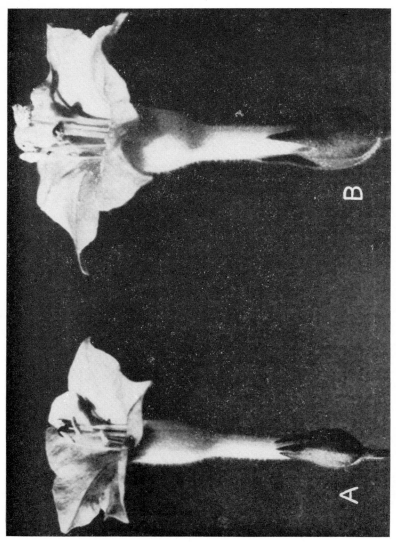

Figure 11: Effect of polyploidy on hybridization. *A* blossom is from an untreated hybrid *Nicotiana glutinosa* x *N. sylvestris* (24 chromosomes). *B* blossom is from a fertile plant of the same hybrid as *A* (48 chromosomes). Doubling has induced fertility, increased length and thickness of filaments and thickness of style, corolla tube and flower stalk. Reproduced by

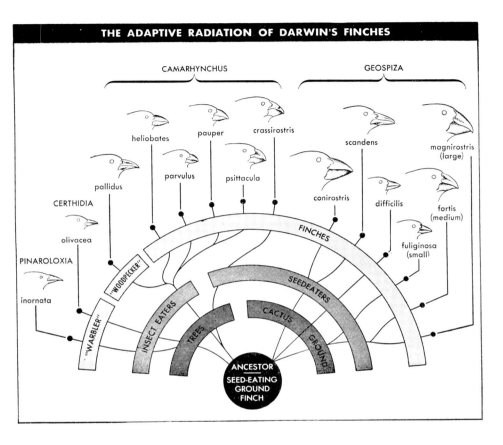

Figure 12: The adaptive radiation of Darwin's finches. From *Life: An Introduction to Biology* by George G. Simpson, Colin S. Pittendrigh and Lewis H. Tiffany, copyright, © 1957, by Harcourt, Brace and Company, Inc. (Based, with permission, on the figures and data of Lack, D., *Darwin's Finches*, Cambridge University Press, Cambridge, 1947).

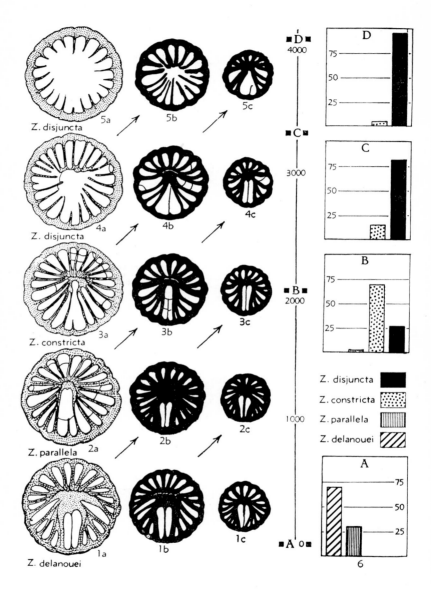

Figure 13: Evolution of a group of Mississippian zaphrenthids. Analysis of collections made from four zones (A, B, C, D) in Lower Carboniferous rocks in Scotland shows evolutionary changes of the coral named Zaphrentoides delanouei during the time represented by the accumulation of approximately 4,000 ft. of strata. The black figures represent immature growth stages, shown in cross-section. Reproduced by permission from *Invertebrate Fossils* by Moore, Lalicker and Fischer. Copyright 1952 by McGraw-Hill Book Co., Inc.

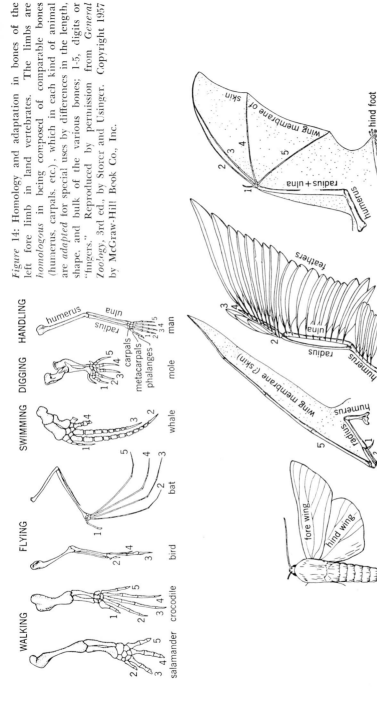

Figure 14: Homology and adaptation in bones of the left fore limb in land vertebrates. The limbs are *homologous* in being composed of comparable bones (humerus, carpals, etc.), which in each kind of animal are *adapted* for special uses by differences in the length, shape, and bulk of the various bones; 1–5, digits or "fingers." Reproduced by permission from *General Zoology,* 3rd ed., by Storer and Usinger. Copyright 1957 by McGraw-Hill Book Co., Inc.

WALKING   FLYING   SWIMMING   DIGGING   HANDLING

humerus
ulna
radius
carpals
metacarpals
phalanges

salamander   crocodile   bird   bat   whale   mole   man

Figure 15: Analogy between wings of insects (no internal skeleton) and of vertebrates (with skeleton) — of like function but different origins. Homology in the wing bones of vertebrates, all derived from the common pattern of fore limb in land vertebrates, but variously modified. Pterodactyl (extinct reptile) with elongate 5th finger; bird with 1st and 5th lacking, 3rd and 4th partly used; bat with 2nd to 5th fingers elongate. Reproduced by permission from *General Zoology,* 3rd ed., by Storer and Usinger. Copyright 1957 by McGraw-Hill Book Co., Inc.

INSECT   PTERODACTYL   BIRD   BAT

fore wing
hind wing

wing membrane (? skin)
humerus
radius

humerus
radius
ulna
feathers

wing membrane of skin
radius + ulna
humerus
hind foot

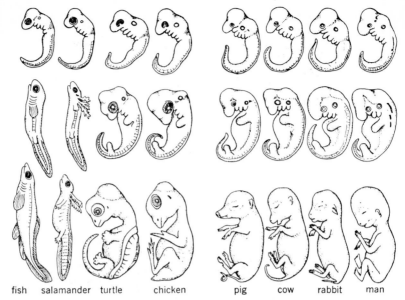

fish   salamander turtle   chicken   pig   cow   rabbit   man

Figure 16: Series of vertebrate embryos in three successive and comparable stages of development. *Top*: All are much alike in the earliest stage. *Middle*: Differentiation is evident, but the four mammals (at right) are quite similar. *Bottom*: Later the distinctive characteristics of each become evident. Reproduced by permission from *General Zoology*, 3rd ed., by Storer and Usinger. Copyright 1957 by McGraw-Hill Book Co., Inc.

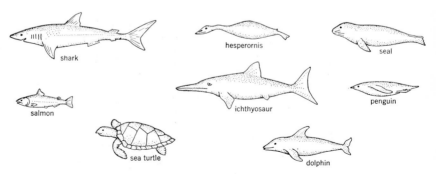

Figure 17: Oceanic vertebrates, sharks to mammals, showing adaptive convergence for swimming — bodies streamlined and fins or limbs paddle-like. Reproduced by permission from *General Zoology*, 3rd ed., by Storer and Usinger. Copyright 1957 by McGraw-Hill Book Co., Inc.

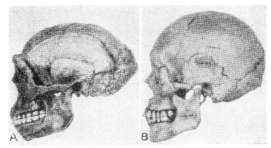

Figure 18: (A) Sinanthropus pekinensis — reconstructed; (B) modern northern Chinese. Lateral views. Reproduced by permission from *Apes, Giants and Man* by Franz Weidenreich. Copyright 1946 by The University of Chicago Press.

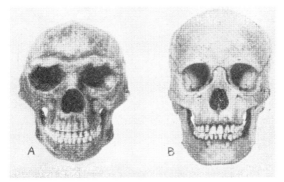

Figure 19: The two skulls of Figure 18 in front view. Reproduced by permission from *Apes, Giants and Man* by Franz Weidenreich. Copyright 1946 by The Univ. of Chicago Press.

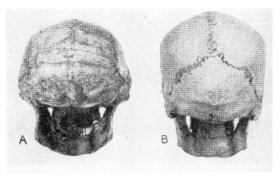

Figure 20. The two skulls of Figure 18 in occipital view. Reproduced by permission from *Apes, Giants and Man* by Franz Weidenreich. Copyright 1946 by The Univ. of Chicago Press.

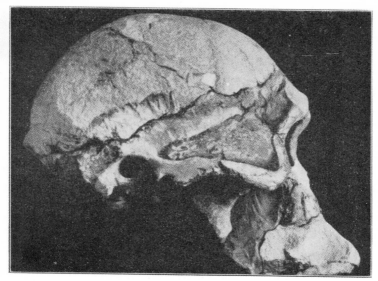

Figure 21: Lateral view of an Australopithecine skull (from a photograph by Dr. R. Broom). Reproduced by permission of Trustees of British Museum from *History of the Primates* by W. E. LeGros Clark.

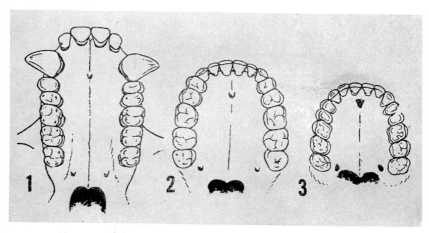

Figure 22: Australopithecine tooth pattern (2) shows distinct human (3), not ape (1), form. Reproduced by permission from *Christian Life Magazine*, May 1956.